DUQUESNE STUDIES

Philosophical Series

2

THE PHILOSOPHY OF NATURE

DUQUESNE STUDIES

Philosophical Series

2

THE PHILOSOPHY OF NATURE

by

ANDREW G. VAN MELSEN, D.SC.

SECOND EDITION
THIRD IMPRESSION

DUQUESNE UNIVERSITY, Pittsburgh 19, Pa.
EDITIONS E. NAUWELAERTS, LOUVAIN
1959

DUQUESNE STUDIES

Philosophical Series

Andrew G. van Melsen, D.Sc., D.Ed., and Henry J. Koren, C.S.Sp., S.T.D., Editors.

Volume One—Andrew G. van Melsen, From Atomos to Atom. Pp. XII and 240. Price: paper $3.50, cloth $4.25. Published also in Dutch, German, Spanish, and Italian.

Volume Two—Andrew G. van Melsen, The Philosophy of Nature. Pp. XII and 263. Third impression. Price: paper $3.75, cloth $4.50. Published also in Dutch. Italian edition in preparation.

Volume Three—P. Henry van Laer, Philosophico-Scientific Problems. Pp. X and 168. Price: paper $2.50, cloth $3.25. Out of print. A few copies have been reserved for libraries that may wish to order the complete set of the philosophical series.

Volume Four—Cajetan's The Analogy of Names and The Concept of Being. Pp. X and 93. Price: paper $1.50, cloth $2.25. Out of print. A few copies have been reserved for libraries that may wish to order the complete set of the philosophical series.

Volume Five—Louis de Raeymaeker and Others, Truth and Freedom. Pp. VII and 132. Price: cloth $3.00. The paper edition is out of print. Published also in French.

Volume Six—P. Henry van Laer, The Philosophy of Science. Part One: Science in General. Pp. XVII and 164. Price: paper $3.00, cloth $3.75.

Volume Seven—Stephan Strasser, The Soul in Metaphysical and Empirical Psychology. Pp. X and 275. Price: paper $4.25, cloth $5.00. Published also in Dutch, French, and German.

Volume Eight—Albert Dondeyne, Contemporary Thought and Christian Faith. Pp. XI and 211. Price: paper $5.00, cloth $5.75. Published also in French.

Volume Nine—Maxwell J. Charlesworth, Philosophy and Linguistic Analysis. Pp. XIII and 234. Price: paper $4.75, cloth $5.50.

Printed in the United States of America by
The Ad Press, Ltd., *New York, N. Y.*

CONTENTS

CHAPTER THREE—The Proper Relationship Between
Science and the Philosophy of Nature

PREFACE TO THE FIRST EDITION

This book is an answer to an invitation. When Duquesne University invited the author to lecture on the philosophy of nature during the academic year 1951-1952, this invitation was accompanied by the suggestion that the content of the lectures be given such permanent form that it could be used as a textbook.

The peculiar difficulty in writing a textbook of the philosophy of nature is, however, that this branch of philosophy is so highly controversial a matter that there is even no agreement on its status. The existence of this controversy and the consequent confusion as to what philosophy of nature is may explain and justify the structure of this study which has two rather distinct parts. The first (Chapters I-III) discusses the status of the philosophy of nature and its relationship to science. The subject-matter of this part, therefore, is not nature, but human *knowledge* of nature. In this part much attention is also paid to the history of the relationship between science and the philosophy of nature. A good understanding of the past will be of great help in avoiding many traditional misunderstandings about the philosophy of nature and its relationship to science, misunderstandings which prevent an unprejudiced view of the problems of the philosophy of nature. The second part (Chapters IV-VIII) deals with the specific problems of the philosophy of nature. Emphasis is laid upon those problems which either pre-eminently demonstrate the method of the philosophy of nature or are able to mark clearly its difference from the scientific method. For this latter reason some scientific problems are discussed which are supposed to have a bearing upon philosophy, but which actually have not. Yet their discussion in a book on the philosophy of nature is useful because it clarifies the difference in approach of science and the philosophy of nature. As to the problems of the philosophy of nature, the discussion in this book is limited to the basic problems of matter as matter. Specific problems of animated matter are therefore not considered.

The author wishes to thank several persons who contributed to the achievement of the text. Dr. Henry J. Koren, C. S. Sp., and Mr. Vincent F. Lackner, members of the Philosophy Department of Duquesne University, were kind enough to read the whole text. Many of their suggestions were gratefully accepted. Dr. James M. Purcell, head of the English Department, has spent many hours with the author in order to overcome the difficulties connected with writing in a foreign language. Without his help this work could not have been published. However, I do not wish him to be held responsible for any imperfections of style and language which still remain in this study. Thanks are due also to Mrs. Margaret S. Lackner and Dr. Henry J. Koren, who have helped in the reading and correction of the proofs in order to expedite the publication of this work.

Andrew G. van Melsen

Nijmegen, September 12, 1952.

PREFACE TO THE SECOND EDITION

In this second edition several small corrections and additions have been made throughout the whole text. Only at some places (Ch. I, 1; Ch. II, 3; Ch. IV, 6 and Ch. V, 5) are the additions of a somewhat more substantial nature.

A. G. v. M.

Nijmegen, February 25, 1954.

CHAPTER ONE

PRELIMINARY CHARACTERIZATION OF THE PHILOSOPHY OF NATURE

1. INTRODUCTION

Why the Problems of the Philosophy of Nature Need an Introduction

It is usual to begin a book on a certain subject matter with a short description or definition of that particular subject. Such a description or definition can sometimes be very short because of the fact that the problems involved do not need a long introduction. They are clear enough and reveal their nature to everyone who takes the trouble to go into them. A textbook of chemistry, for example, does not need to give a well-considered definition of chemistry, nor a careful description of its aim and means. The best way to get an initial idea of chemistry is just to look at some very simple experiments in close connection with our daily experience and to listen carefully to their explanation. There is scarcely any reason at all to define chemistry beforehand. It is much easier to make clear what chemistry is by citing one of its typical problems than to try to do it by means of a definition which attempts to define the place of chemistry among the different arts and sciences. It seems that the human mind is more attuned to a certain practical approach than to theoretical considerations. As a result we learn the scientific methods used in chemistry most easily if we start to practice them.

What is true in respect to chemistry applies *to a certain extent* to all fields of human knowledge; practice is always the best teacher. For a very good reason, however, this general rule was restricted by adding "to a certain extent." For sometimes the problems are not so easy to discover. Sometimes, a long theoretical introduction is necessary to dispose our minds even to see the problems. This is especially true if the problems involved do not have their origin in a simple extension of our immediate daily experience. The latter is the case not only in chemistry, in physics, in biology, in astronomy and in mathematics, but also in history, in the study of languages, in sociology, in economics, etc. Everybody has a certain experience of chemical, physical, biological, and astronomological phenomena, of mathematical proportions, of historical events. Everyone knows

1

something about social and economic relations, about spoken and written language. The scientific and scholarly study of the different problems in these fields, therefore, can be a continuation of that with which we are already familiar. It was indicated above, however, that not all problems have their origin in such an extension of our immediate daily experience. If that is the case, then the right point of view toward certain problems requires a theoretical introduction. The philosophy of nature is one of those subject matters whose problems are not so easy to discover. That is the first reason why we must define the kind of problems we have to deal with in the philosophy of nature. Before we can examine them we must know where to look for them.

Many Reject the Philosophy of Nature Entirely

That the problems of the philosophy of nature are not so easy to discover may be confirmed by the fact that there are many modern philosophers and scientists who either doubt that there is room nowadays for a philosophy of nature or who flatly deny its right to exist. And they have, at first sight, a very plausible reason for doing so. The history of science seems to teach that the real understanding of the facts of nature began when philosophical methods were abandoned, and scientists changed over to the methods now used in chemistry and physics. This change took place in the 17th century. It is, indeed, a simple historical fact that the old philosophical method never did yield as many results as did the chemical and physical methods after the 17th century.

Consequently, the obvious conclusion from this state of affairs seems to be that the only proper methods for dealing with the phenomena of nature are scientific ones. The philosophy of nature may perhaps give a certain satisfaction to philosophically minded persons who like to dwell in the past, but it has no significance for the present time. Its only real value is that it prepared the way for better methods. It has had a certain merit as *Wissenschaft am Anfang,* science in the beginning. This opinion implies that from the very moment new methods were discovered the philosophy of nature had no role to play in the development of human thought.

The historical argument against the very existence of the philosophy of nature has no conclusive force, as will be seen later on. But it at least has the merit of bringing to light a danger: namely, that an uncritical attempt to build up a philosophy of nature might result in a revival of an old-fashioned scientific system. The only way to avoid this danger is to investigate exactly what problems the philosophy of nature deals with, and to show that no other branch of human knowledge can take care of them. So before starting with the philosophy of nature, it is necessary to justify its very existence and determine its character.

This is all the more necessary because even those philosophers who still accept philosophy of nature do not agree about the character of it. And the disagreement is really a fundamental one, as the following survey of current opinions will show.

Different Conceptions of the Philosophy of Nature

The different positive attitudes towards the philosophy of nature can be classified under four headings: synthesis of the results of science, philosophical reflection upon science, analysis of the methods of science, and the philosophical approach to nature.

1. *Synthesis of the Results of Science.* Some thinkers see room for a philosophy of nature as a synthesis of the results of science. Science must first purify our experience, then a "philosophical" reflection upon the general results of science is necessary to get a more synthesized view of the material world than that provided by the separate sciences. Science itself, due to its analytical way of working, is incapable of such a synthesis.

It should be clear that when this attitude towards the philosophy of nature is taken, no *essential* difference between the philosophy of nature and science can be spoken of. As a matter of fact, most of the leading scientists who are interested in philosophy, such as A. Einstein, N. Bohr, L. de Broglie, W. Heisenberg, and J. Jeans, see the synthesizing task of the philosophy of nature only as a preliminary task. They see the philosophy of nature as the speculative part of science. It opens up new perspectives at the frontiers of science. Where science itself is not yet capable of saying anything exact and definitive by way of synthesis, philosophy can stimulate thinking. In due time, however, science will progress and take over the task of the philosophy of nature.

It scarcely needs to be explained that this view of the philosophy of nature does not much differ from the view which considers the philosophy of nature as *Wissenschaft am Anfang.*

2. *Philosophical Reflection upon Science.* Closely related to the foregoing opinion is another which considers the philosophy of nature as a *philosophical* reflection upon the results of science. Both opinions have in common the view that the starting-point for the philosophy of nature should be found in the concrete results of science. The difference is that the opinion under consideration thinks it possible to use these results in a philosophical context. The reflection upon the results of science must be a real philosophical and not a scientific reflection. The results of science are not only synthesized, but considered in a philosophical light. The title of the well-known work of the German philosopher B. Bavink expresses clearly this attitude towards the philosophy of nature: *"Ergebnisse und Probleme der Naturwissenschaften. Eine Einführing in die heutige Naturphilosophie."*

3. *Analysis of the Methods of Science.* A third opinion describes the task of the philosophy of nature as a reflection not upon the *results* but upon the *methods* of science. These methods are open to an analysis which falls outside the scope of science itself. This analysis can be either a *philosophical* or a *logical* analysis.

The logical analysis of the methods of science plays an important role in the philosophical discussions about the quantum theory. The philosophical work of such thinkers as J. L. Destouches, P. Destouches-Février, M. Strauss, H. Reichenbach, J. von Neumann, G. Birkhoff, and E. W. Beth consists essentially in a logical analysis of the methods, language and ways of reasoning used in science. Logic in this context is to be understood as formal logic in the sense of modern symbolic logic.

It cannot be doubted that the identification of the philosophy of nature with the logical analysis of the methods of science is strongly influenced by the neo-positivistic attitude towards philosophy which considers logical analysis as the only form of philosophy which is acceptable. It scarcely needs to be mentioned that this view of the philosophy of nature also does not differ much from a complete rejection of the philosophy of nature. As a matter of fact, most of the logical positivists prefer the name "philosophy of science" to that of "philosophy of nature," and justly so. For the real subject matter of their logical analysis is not *nature,* but *science.* That they retain the term "philosophy" is due to the fact that logic is always considered a part of philosophy.

If logical analysis, however, is not taken in the sense of formal logic, but in that of the transcendental logic of Kant, then the logical analysis of science becomes a *philosophical* problem. For then the problem consists in the search for the *a priori-forms* which are of necessity used in science. At the present time few philosophers will hold the rigid *a priori* point of view of Kant. The majority of the natural philosophers who think more or less in the line of Kant will prefer to establish only *a posteriori* which forms of thought are *de facto* used in science. Representatives of this conception of the philosophy of nature are E. Cassirer, H. Margenau, E. Meyerson, and A. S. Eddington.

4. *Philosophical Approach to Nature.* The fourth category of thinkers who in one way or another accept the idea of a philosophy of nature maintain in opposition to the above mentioned viewpoints that the philosophy of nature ought to be, and also can be, an original approach to the phenomena of nature. The philosophy of nature is, in their opinion, not at all antiquated and superseded by science. They claim that science can study only certain aspects of material phenomena because of the very method of science, whereas other aspects cannot be studied by science but belong to the philosophy of nature. This point of view is common among Thomistic thinkers, although many of them have trouble in indicating the precise character of the philosophy of nature, in defining the limits of both science and the philosophy of nature, and in establishing the mutual relations between them.

At the end of this survey of the different opinions about the philosophy of nature it should be stressed that the division in four headings is very schematic. There are, of course, many intermediate forms. Moreover, not all opinions are mutually exclusive. A philosophical reflection upon the methods of science can, for instance, result in establishing an autonomous philosophy of nature, as will be seen later.

The Very Existence of the Philosophy of Nature Is a Problem

The confusion that exists as to the position of the philosophy of nature stresses once again the necessity of first finding out what the philosophy of nature really is and what its methods are to be. In other words, before we can deal with the problems of the philosophy of nature, we must first deal with the problem of its very existence. Is this existence justified, and if so, what is the true character of the philosophy of nature? We cannot begin by just mentioning some of its problems, because, first of all, we must make sure whether or not there exist such things as genuine problems in the philosophy of nature. And secondly, if they exist we must know where to look for them. If the philosophy of nature is either a philosophical reflection upon, or a logical analysis of science, then we ought to begin with a survey of modern science and try to find there the starting points for a philosophy of nature.

If, however, the philosophy of nature is an original approach to the phenomena of nature, then our first task ought to be to search for such aspects of our experience of material phenomena as will enable us to build up a philosophy of nature.

The lack of unanimity on a definition of the philosophy of nature compels us to try to find out which view is the right one. Fortunately, it is not necessary to examine all the different attitudes exhaustively. For they can be classified first of all according to their different ways of answering the question: is an autonomous philosophy of nature possible? We find only one positive answer to that question and four negative ones (Of the latter, one denies the whole idea of philosophy of nature, and three can see the philosophy of nature only as dependent upon science). Therefore, we can confine ourselves, for the present, to the most important problem, which is whether it is or is not true that there is a possibility for an original and autonomous philosophical approach to the phenomena of nature.

This problem has two parts: first, to investigate whether or not there are certain problems about the material world which cannot be solved or even discussed by the methods of science because they are entirely beyond the possibilities of the scientific method; and, secondly, to investigate whether or not these problems can be discussed in a coherent way by methods different from those used in science but in accordance with those used in philosophy. Both questions will deal with the necessary requirements for an autonomous philosophy of nature.

It will be understood that whereas the first part of the problem can be rather adequately answered within the limits of a preliminary chapter, the second part will of necessity surpass such limits. Only the whole book can provide the answer to the second question. Yet the question must be discussed in this introductory chapter at least to such an extent as is necessary to justify the attempt to build up an autonomous philosophy of nature.

The first part of our task requires a careful analysis of the methods science is of necessity using. Do these methods indicate that science cannot answer all questions which can be asked with respect to the nature of the material world? This fundamental question will be discussed in the following section.

2. THE INSUFFICIENCY OF SCIENCE

All Science Is Based Upon Presuppositions

The title of this section can give rise to a misunderstanding which should be avoided from the very beginning. The term "insufficiency of science" does not refer to the obvious fact that science has not yet solved all the problems within its own field. There is reason enough to speak in this connection of a certain *de facto* insufficiency in all scientific theories. For, notwithstanding the really tremendous development of science and its amazing successes, every scientist will agree that there is more left to be done than has already been achieved. The title does refer to an insufficiency in principle, a fundamental lack of possibilities, to solve, or even to discuss, certain problems which deal with the material world.

The Inductive Method Presupposes Something About the Nature of *Matter*. Let us first make clear what kind of problems these are. The best way to do this is to examine the basic method of all sciences, that is, the inductive method. The use of this method, without any doubt a method fundamental to all the experimental sciences, presupposes that the basic behavior of matter is always the same under the same circumstances. Otherwise experiments to discover what factor is responsible for a certain phenomenon would be without any sense at all.

If we wish to determine, for example, which specific factor in the air supports combustion, then we perform several experiments under a great variety of circumstances. Let us say, for instance, that we take several pieces of burning wood and see what happens when we put them in, respectively, normal air, pure oxygen, pure notrogen, pure carbon dioxide. The result is a normal combustion process in the first experiment, a quicker and more brilliant one in the second, and no combustion at all in the last two. Our conclusion is that oxygen is responsible for the combustion. The chemical aspect of the conclusion, however, is not what is of primary importance at the moment. From our viewpoint another thing is of greater importance, namely, the fact that our conclusion can be drawn only under the presupposition that a piece of wood will always burn under certain circumstances. In other words, we presuppose that the four pieces of wood used in these four experiments have the same nature, the same way of reacting, notwithstanding that they are four different individual pieces of wood. The very moment we doubt this, the whole experiment becomes pure nonsense. The different behaviours of the four pieces could be ascribed to their distinct individualities. Therefore, in drawing the conclusion we did, we took for granted that any piece of wood can be used for studying the nature of wood.

Someone may be inclined to doubt whether the assumption that our four pieces of wood have the same nature really is a *presupposition*. Are we not bound to make sure that they are really four pieces of material of the same kind? The answer is that, without any doubt, it is the task of the experimenter to make sure that what are supposed to be four pieces of wood are really four pieces of wood. However, in doing this the experimenter must of necessity always presuppose something, and that something is precisely what we are after.

The Presupposition Is Necessary. Let us go a little bit deeper into the problem in order to see more clearly what the point is. This is not too difficult. For if we ask by what means a scientist can be sure that he has four samples of the same material in his hand, the only answer is: by induction! He will determine several relevant properties of the different pieces and conclude that they are of the same kind. By using the inductive method, however, he is assuming the correctness and conclusive force of the inductive method, and in consequence also the basic presupposition of any induction, namely that things of the same nature react in the same way under the same circumstances. As a result, the conclusion of our scientist goes far beyond what he actually checked. This can easily be proved.

The only thing the scientist checks is whether his different pieces have *some* properties in common, and these he considers the relevant properties of wood. He knows that if these properties are present he is justified in using the individual pieces as representing wood in his experiment. And he is really justified in doing so if matter has that basic feature we have been discussing: there are things of the same kind in matter, and such things react always in the same way under the same circumstances. This presupposition gives the scientist the right to consider the checking of some properties as sufficient proof of their being all pieces of *wood*.

The importance of this presupposition can be shown in still another way. *Without this basic presumption the scientist could not even use his scientific knowledge.* For let us suppose for a moment that our scientist is a very critical man, who is not satisfied by the outwardly visible properties of wood, and that he goes to the trouble of a chemical analysis. If, however, he looks in his chemical tables in order to check whether a certain product of his analysis has the properties of a certain kind of material, he is already using our presupposition. For he never finds *individual* data listed in his table, but always *specific* data. All data are expressed according to general statements: *carbon* is identified by this set of properties, *hydrogen* by that set, etc. The particular individual cabon that he discovers in the analysis of a piece of wood is not in the table; in the table only carbon as carbon is spoken of. The scientist is unquestioningly convinced that what is said in his table about carbon applies to all individual carbon. All individual carbon will behave in exactly the same specific manner.

The result of this short philosophical analysis can be put this way: it is certainly the task of the scientist as scientist to investigate whether certain objects are really things of the same kind. By the very use of his means of investigation, however, he implicitly of necessity pre-supposes that there are things of the same kind, and that they react in the same way. Only because of this presupposition is it correct to use different individual samples for the same purpose. They represent the same specific nature, although they are different individuals.

The presupposition can, therefore, be formulated in still another way: science presupposes that different individual material things and events can be classified according to certain species. Or, to use a short expression: Material things have a *species-individual structure*. As individuals they are representing a species. This basic presupposition is not discussed or proved in science; it is just a pre-supposition, so to speak, incarnated in the basic methods of science.

Science Cannot Discuss Its Presuppositions

The very fact that a presupposition of science is incarnated in the basic methods of science is the reason why science is not able to discuss the problems involved in this presupposition. For every scientific discussion has to use the basic methods of science, and these basic methods imply the presupposition.

It can be argued, however, that science does not need such a discussion, because the very success of the use of the inductive method in building up science can be considered as sufficient proof of the correctness of the implicit presupposition of the method. This argument perhaps goes in the right direction, but that is not important to notice now. For our purpose it is far more important that the argument, whatever its value may be, brings us outside the scope of science. For it presupposes in its turn that success is a proof for correctness or truth, and it is easy to see that no scientific proof can be given to support this new presupposition. On the contrary, every scientific proof presupposes a conviction such as our new presupposition expresses. We consider an hypothesis true if it succeeds in predicting certain phenomena. So success is the reason why we grant conclusive force to a scientific proof and the presupposition about the conclusive force of success itself must originate in something other than science.

It can be shown, from still another angle, that the reason *science* presupposes the species-individual structure can never be derived from the success science obtains by this presupposition. For science does not have any choice about whether or not to accept the presupposition of the species-individual structure. It must accept it because, otherwise, any classification, induction, and gathering of experience in certain laws would be entirely impossible. For there would be an infinite series of experiences without any possibility of connecting one experience with another. Each individual experience would be isolated because it would have nothing in common with other experiences. Each individual experience would have a content entirely different from the content of another experience.

Consequently the presupposition of the species-individual structure must originate in a kind of *pre*-scientific knowledge, a knowledge already at the disposal of the human mind before science started. The origin is not difficult to find: that things have a species-individual structure is taught by common experience.

So the presuppositions of science are nothing but the presence of certain fundamental data of common experience within the field of science. To say the same thing in another way: it is due to such data as are derived from *pre*-scientific experience that science is possible at all.

The Difference Between Fundamental and Other Presuppositions

To avoid misunderstandings about the kind of presuppositions under discussion, it is necessary to stress the fact that the above mentioned presuppositions are really presuppositions to science as science. They are not presuppositions to some *particular* scientific theory or experiment. Such more restricted presuppositions are, of course, also frequent in science; they are, however, of an entirely different type. To make this clear it may be sufficient to give some examples. In biological studies it is assumed that the fundamental laws of chemistry and physics apply also to biology.

Biology itself does not study chemical and physical laws; it merely uses them on the supposition that they are true. If now such a supposition is proved wrong or only partly correct, as sometimes happens, the only result would be modification of the law involved. What is destroyed in such a case is only a certain elaborated scientific law or theory. The possibility of proposing and using scientific theories is not destroyed. The wrong law can be replaced by a better one.

The distinction between the suppositions of particular scientific theories and the presuppositions to science as science, is, therefore, fundamental. The only type which is important in the present discussion are the *pre*-scientific presuppositions. They are those which are entirely beyond the means of investigation that science has at its disposal. For it is precisely due to such *pre*-scientific presuppositions that scientific methods have any meaning at all. The very moment science becomes doubtful about these presuppositions and, in order to investigate them, suspends all methods which presuppose them, every scientific method, both theoretical and experimental, will be suspended too. The scientist as scientist will then be without any means of investigation.

Conclusion

From the foregoing discussion our conclusion must be that there are very interesting problems concerning the structure of the material world that are beyond the reach of scientific investigation. This does not mean that science neglects entirely these aspects of the structure of the material world, for science presupposes these aspects every time it uses certain basic methods of investigation. Science is, however, for this very reason, not able to discuss them. It is precisely this inability which constitutes the fundamental insufficiency of science.

3. THE POSSIBILITY OF A PHILOSOPHY OF NATURE

Primary and Primitive Pre-Scientific Knowledge

Just because the scientist as scientist cannot handle all the problems connected with the material world, it does not follow that human reason and human experience are entirely unable to do so.   Science borrows its presuppositions from pre-scientific, common experience. Common experience must, therefore, have a certain grasp on the presuppositions of science. And what perhaps is yet more important, those presuppositions are not only known; they are, as the foregoing analysis has proved, also open to discussion.

The nature and the possibilities of this discussion must, however, be determined more closely. Can such a discussion really lead to the building up of a coherent system of knowledge about nature, different from that which science has built?   In order to answer that question, it is helpful to consider for a moment the pre-scientific experience mentioned above in connection with the origin of the presuppositions of science.   What kind of pre-scientific knowledge is here involved?   Not all pre-scientific knowledge is of the same type and, consequently, not all pre-scientific knowledge has the same relationship to science, as will become clear when the role pre-scientific knowledge plays in the building up of science is examined.

Science Starts with Pre-Scientific Knowledge. All science starts as a matter of course with pre-scientific knowledge, not only in the particular way we already pointed out when discussing the presuppositions of science, but also in a very general one.   This can easily be shown by an examination both of the historical development of science and of the way a modern student gets acquainted with a certain amount of science.   The start has been and always has to be an elaboration and critical examination of data of daily experience, such as the phenomena of melting, freezing, combustion, oxydation, etc.   The student of the past differs from the student of the present only in that the student of the present is guided immediately towards the correct classifications and explanations, thus avoiding the misconceptions of former ages.   The modern student's mind is directed away from certain, at first sight very obvious, ways of looking upon the phenomena, because those ways have been proved to lead to nothing.   Thus science accepts the data of daily experience, but not without purifying the way daily experience classifies and describes them. Scientific knowledge of the same data of daily experience is, therefore, far better than pre-scientific knowledge. It would be senseless, indeed, to attempt to build up a system of daily experience without the corrections, purifications and elaborations of modern science.

It may be remarked here that one of the main reasons why so many scientists object to a philosophy of nature is exactly that they suppose that a philosophy of nature is just such an attempt. If that supposition were true, then their criticism would be correct. There cannot be any serious doubt about that. The problem is, however, whether all pre-scientific experience is of the same kind and whether the relationship between scientific and pre-scientific knowledge is always of the nature just pointed out. That is the crucial question with respect to the possibility of a philosophy of nature.

Different Kinds of Pre-Scientific Knowledge. In speaking of pre-scientific knowledge a difference should be made between a primary fundamental pre-scientific knowledge and a primitive one. The latter is that which is involved in supplying the different data of daily experience to science as the first material to investigate. Primary pre-scientific knowledge, however, reveals to us such fundamental data of matter as, for example, the species-individual structure.

Making a distinction between the two types of pre-scientific knowledge does not mean that there are really two different and independent realms of knowledge, existing in a kind of juxtaposition, each supplying us with its own data. This sort of difference exists for example, between the daily experience of a farmer and that of a sailor. Either experience covers, for the greater part, different phenomena, and supplies, therefore, different data. Likewise, in the experience of each of us different realms of experience bearing upon different parts of the material world can be distinguished. And such parts exist beside one another, as do the different data of experience, although there are naturally many interrelationships. The difference between primary and primitive experience is, however, of another type; it is a structural difference in one and the same experience. What has been called primary pre-scientific knowledge is that part of our experience which has to do with the basic pattern of the material world, whereas primitive knowledge fills this pattern with a certain specific content.

As a result of the cooperation between primitive experience and primary pre-scientic knowledge, the data of our daily experience have the same basic structure regardless of their specific content. Take, for example, the knowledge we have in our daily experience of wood, of iron, of melting, of falling stones, of rain, of snow, etc. In that knowledge two aspects can be distinguished. First, the typical features of iron differ from those of wood, and, secondly, the concept "wood" covers different pieces of wood. This second aspect does not reveal much about the distinctive character of wood as such, because such aspect applies as well to iron, rain, snow, etc. It reveals only that all types of material things have in common specific properties that are present in different individuals. "Wood" does not refer to one individually existing thing known as wood, nor does "iron" refer to such an individually existing thing known as iron. The one concept refers to a certain specific nature present in many separately existing things. The very fact that this is always true of material things reveals a fundamental structure in all material things, the structure which was designated above as the species-individual structure.

The interesting point now is that scientific knowledge in its elaboration and correction of the data of our pre-scientific knowledge does not affect the aspect of the underlying general pattern of the material world; whereas it does affect the aspect of the specific content. The specific content is continuously in a process of purification and elaboration due to the development of science; as a result the scientific concepts of, for example, rain or snow are more adapted to giving a systematic view of what is going on in nature than the primitive concepts are. The reason why science purifies and elaborates the concepts of daily experience is in order to draw attention to such features as seem more essential in making possible a systematic explanation rather than to other, perhaps more obvious, ones. Such a concept as that of combustion, for example, has for the chemist a different specific content than it has in daily life. The presence of flame, essential in the primitive concept of combustion, is no longer essential in the scientific concept of combustion. And why not? Because the chemist has discovered that another characteristic, namely, "combining with oxygen," is much better suited to give a systematic description of combustion than is the presence of flame. As will be seen later on, it is not an easy task to discover what features are really relevant for such a systematical explanation of a certain group of phenomena. It took a long time before chemistry became aware of the fact that, among the great amount of data involved in the chemical process, the aspect of weight was of the greatest importance. This fact could be known only after the success of an explanation of chemical phenomena on the basis of the relevance of the weight-factor had been proved. So we do not know *a priori* what is really primitive in the concepts of daily experience, and that what we take for essential and relevant may be only accidental. There is an exception, however, and this exception, as we saw, refers to that aspect of our daily experience which reveals to us the basic structure of the material world. Science adopts this part of our daily experience completely and without any restriction because its fundamental methods are built entirely upon the presupposition of this basic structure.

The Object of the Philosophy of Nature

The field of investigation open for the philosophy of nature, as distinct from that open to science, can easily be indicated as a result of the foregoing analysis of pre-scientific experience. The philosophy of nature is concerned with the basic structure of matter and all material phenomena as such. It finds its starting-point, as does science, in common experience, but each investigates a different aspect of daily experience. The philosophy of nature is interested in the primary and fundamental aspect of this experience, whereas science, taking this aspect for granted, focuses attention on the more detailed aspects of daily experience. These latter aspects, as the results of science prove, have obviously a primitive character.

Science and the Philosophy of Nature Are Mutually Independent

From the sharp distinction existing between science and the philosophy of nature, it will be understood that the respective methods of consideration do not have much bearing upon each other. The specific results of science do not contribute to the philosophy of nature because those results are obtained by methods which already presuppose the starting-points for the philosophy of nature. Consequently, the results of science do not throw any *new* light on these starting-points. No more can the results of the philosophy of nature be of any direct value for science. For the philosophy of nature is concerned with such features of matter as science, by using methods built entirely upon the presupposition that matter has those features, has already reckoned with.

The Importance of the Philosophy of Nature for Science

It is necessary for a good understanding of the relation between science and the philosophy of nature to stress, first of all, their relative mutual independence, as was done above. It would be wrong, however, if it should be left at that. There is more to say about the relationship between science and the philosophy of nature. Since this can be done better in a later chapter of this study, only a short remark about the importance of the philosophy of nature for science will be made here. The philosophy of nature may have no direct value for the specific results of science, but this does not mean that it has no importance at all for science. From the point of view of the human knowledge of nature as a whole, it remains unsatisfactory that science takes only a certain part of it into consideration. Scientific knowledge leaves some basic things in the dark. It is really fundamentally incomplete. This incompleteness is not always obvious by reason of the fact that every scientist completes, often without being aware of it, his scientific knowledge by viewing it in a kind of philosophical perspective. That perspective contains among other things a vague idea of the fundamental structure of matter. That is the reason why most scientists do not realize the incompleteness of their scientific knowledge. They supply a philosophical background, but in an unreflected and, therefore, from a critical viewpoint, very unsatisfactory way.

How true this latter statement is becomes clear the very moment we ask a scientist whether he can justify the philosophical part of his thinking in as critical a manner as he can the scientific part. Most scientists have a kind of world picture,[1] wherein scientific knowledge and philosophical consideration go together in a very confused way. Such a world picture seems to be the result only of scientific theories, but is, as a matter of fact, the outcome of a combination of those theories with certain philosophical theses. The importance of the scientific theories of reality is evaluated in the light of philosophical theses. The scientist has, whether he is aware of it or not, a certain philosophical outlook toward his science and toward the object of his science.

Although it is true that philosophy is of no direct use for science, philosophy can be very important for a critical examination of the always present philosophical perspective in which the scientist sees his scientific knowledge. It depends upon the nature of this perspective

---

[1] German writers call it *"Das Weltbild der Physik."*

whether the philosopher will correct or only justify this perspective. For the philosophical perspective of the scientist is not necessarily wrong by being more unconscious than conscious. Even if the task of philosophical reflection is only justification, then this task is not unimportant, because the very fact that there is always a philosophical perspective proves that the human mind is not satisfied by partial knowledge only. There is a real desire in the human mind to investigate its object in all its aspects and that is exactly what gives the philosophy of nature its specific task alongside science.

Epistemological Complications

The above elaboration of the task of the philosophy of nature presents a difficulty which must be dealt with. Is not the task of the philosophy of nature, properly speaking, the task of philosophy in general, and more especially, of epistemology? Does not the fact, for example, that science has to work in all its methods and even in its language on a species-individual schema, reveal a basic structure of the human mind and its methods of expression rather than a basic structure of the world? A similar question grows out of our assertion that the scientist has always a certain philosophical outlook toward his science. Is not that problem also rather an epistemological than an ontological one?[2] A separate section of our study will be devoted to that question.

4. SOME EPISTEMOLOGICAL CONSIDERATIONS

The Importance of Epistemology for the Philosophy of Nature

The answer to the difficulty mentioned at the end of the last section must be that the problems concerning the presuppositions of science, and the philosophical perspective in which the scientist sees his science, belong as well to the philosophy of nature as to epistemology. A complete philosophical investigation of our problems ought, therefore, to make clear, first of all, what the possible role of the structure of the human mind could be in the presuppositions of science.

---

[2]The terms "epistemological" and "ontological" are in this connection used in a general way. The term "epistemological" indicates that the problem involved is concerned with the way we know. The object to be considered is not what is known but *how* it is known, i.e., how it is present in our mind. If a problem is said to be of an ontological nature, then our attention is entirely focused upon what is known, i.e. we are interested in reality, independent of our way of knowing.

It will be understood that the answer to this question will greatly depend on the fundamental philosophical viewpoint of the philosopher involved. A follower of Kant will ascribe more to the structure of the human mind than a philosopher who belongs to a realistic school of thought will be inclined to do. The latter, acknowledging that there is a certain influence of the structure of the human mind upon the way our concepts are formed, will nevertheless maintain that there must be something of a species-individual structure in nature itself. A positivistic thinker, on the other hand, will acknowledge that science has to make certain presuppositions, but at the same time he will deny the possibility of saying more about it than that it is just a kind of scientific belief, unexplainable but justified by the success of science.

As a consequence of the different epistemological viewpoints above briefly indicated, the attitude towards the philosophy of nature is different too. The positivistic epistemology, for example, leaves no room for a philosophy of nature because of the simple fact that it leaves no room for a philosophy at all. Thus the implicit view science has of the basic structure of matter can never furnish a starting-point for an autonomous philosophical consideration.

The Kantian epistemology, on the other hand, sets a high value on philosophical considerations, but denies their *ontological* value. The presuppositions of science, according to Kant, do not reveal a basic structure of matter; they reveal only a structure of the human mind. The examination of them, therefore, does not lead to a philosophy of nature, which should be an ontology of the material being. The examination of the presuppositions of science remains entirely in the field of epistemology, since such presuppositions are due to the structure of the human mind.

From the above it follows that a philosophy of nature can be built only upon a realistic epistemology.

The logical procedure seems to be, therefore, to start with an epistemological investigation as to whether a philosophy of nature is possible. The justification of building up a philosophy of nature seems entirely dependent upon the answer to the epistemological question of whether a realistic standpoint is correct or not. It is clear, however, that such an epistemological justification demands a study of its own. So in this book only a few remarks can be made about the underlying epistemological conviction that supports it. This is unsatisfactory, of course, but only to a certain extent, for all things are very closely interwoven in philosophy.   It is, for example, an historical fact, that such a philosopher as Kant came to his epistemological conviction, among other things, out of the serious difficulties he encountered in his philosophy of nature.   Thus the philosophy of nature can in its turn have a great influence on epistemology. A good understanding of the problems of the philosophy of nature can support certain epistemological convictions, whereas insurmountable difficulties in the philosophy of nature can indicate that there is something wrong with the underlying epistemological principles.

The Importance of the Philosophy of Nature for Epistemology

The dependence of epistemology on the philosophy of nature seems to be strange, especially after what has been said at the beginning of this section.   Yet, in a way it is not so strange.   We must not forget that epistemology as such can be only a *reflecting* upon human knowledge.   Human knowledge of a more immediate kind must, therefore, be already present as material before epistemology can start a critical examination of it.   A fruitful and honest reflection requires, however, that epistemology consider human knowledge in all its essential aspects and possibilities.   Epistemology has not the right to confine itself to the consideration of scientific knowledge in a narrow sense.   It must also take into account the underlying pre-scientific knowledge, which is as important as scientific knowledge in building up a complete human knowledge.   Many modern epistemological approaches are one-sided, because they do not pay sufficient attention to the always present philosophical element in all human knowledge.

The modern attitude is understandable in view of the historical development of philosophy and science.   It seems that science has entirely replaced the philosophy of nature in modern thinking and, as a consequence of that, epistemology seems to be justified in taking as its subject matter only the way the human mind works in scientific investigations.   For a more purified and more mature form of human knowledge can be supposed to offer better material as a subject for reflection than the primitive old philosophy.

There is something true in this idea. The development of human knowledge in the different sciences in the course of history has shown the possibilities of the human mind and is, therefore, of great value to epistemology.   It is wrong, however, to deny philosophical knowledge a place among modern forms of human knowledge worthy of epistemological attention. This denial is based upon the supposition that the only importance of the old philosophy of nature was to be a first and rather primitive attempt to give a scientific explanation of the phenomena of common experience. The old philosophy of nature was more than that, as will be shown in the next chapter. It fulfilled, as a matter of fact, two tasks. First of all, it answered real philosophical questions and, secondly, it tried to give scientific explanations. It has already been seen in this section that science can fulfill only one of these tasks. It does not study in a systematic way what above have been called the primary aspects of human experience. Its only function is to purify, to correct, and to elaborate the primitive part of common experience. An epistemology which considers science alone as elaborated human knowledge, therefore, mutilates human knowledge. It ought to take into account the philosophy of nature as well, because the attempt to build up a philosophy of nature based upon the primary part of common experience is as important a wellspring for epistemology as is science. Science and the philosophy of nature each has a specific function in the elaboration of common experience. To exclude from the very beginning a philosophy of nature in the name of epistemological convictions is choosing the wrong sequence; it is putting the reflection before that which we have to reflect upon.

Conclusion. As a conclusion to the foregoing discussion, it may be said that there is no reason to worry too much about not being able to make a thorough examination of the different problems of epistemology. Epistemology is much more in need of the philosophy of nature than the philosophy of nature is of epistemology. There are, properly speaking, only two epistemological problems to be discussed before beginning a discussion of the philosophy of nature.

The first is to make clear that that epistemology which is convinced that science has entirely taken over the task of philosophy is wrong. Some consideration has already been given to the matter in the foregoing section, and the same question shall be considered from the historical viewpoint in the following chapter. Thus at this time the discussion of the matter will be rather brief and confined to showing that philosophy is unavoidable and that no positive science can take over its task.

The second is to justify briefly, and in a general way, the realistic epistemology which underlies this philosophy of nature. Such a justification may not solve all problems of epistemology; it shows, however, that it is at least worthwhile to make the attempt to build up a systematic philosophy of nature. That justification will occupy us first.

Justification of a Realistic Attitude

It is necessary to begin with a remark of a general nature about the value of a realistic attitude toward problems of epistemology. It is as follows: Every attempt to deny in principle the possibility of the human mind knowing things as they really are leads to a contradiction. The main thesis of Kant himself offers a very good example of such a contradiction.

This very well known thesis stated that reality in itself (*Das Ding an sich*) is unknowable to us on account of the structure of our mind. Because of this structure all our knowledge lets us know only reality as it appears in our mind according to *a-priori* forms both of sensibility and mind, and not as it is in itself. Well, this statement contains a contradiction between what is said explicitly in the statement and what is obviously the intention in making the statement. The intention in making the statement can be only to give us real and true knowledge about something that really is as the statement says it is. Or to put it another way: The *aim* of the statement is to let us know how things really are and not how they appear. According to Kant, we think we have real knowledge about reality in itself, but we are told that this conviction is wrong. The *content* of the statement, however, tells us that we cannot know how things really are. There we are involved in a flagrant contradiction. If Kant's statement is true, then there can be no reason to pronounce it, because it teaches us nothing about how things really are; and that is the only thing we (and Kant too) are interested in. The only way to avoid the contradiction is to give the statement about the unknowableness of things as they really are a very limited sense, so that it does not affect the fundamental possibility of the human mind to know reality as it is. In that case, however, we are no longer in a non-realistic line of thinking. The basic attitude is now a realistic one.

The contradiction can be approached from still another side. If what the statement says be true, namely, that reality in itself is unknowable for us, how could we know that? How could we know that there is a reality and that this reality is unknowable? It can certainly not be entirely unknowable, otherwise it would not make any sense at all to say *anything* about it. The strong conviction of Kant that his statement made sense deprives his statement at the same time of its purposed content.

The Species-Individual Structure Is an Ontological Structure

If it is true that basically only a realistic attitude is tenable, then it does not follow that there is no influence at all of the structure of our mind on our conception of the material world. Consequently, it is necessary to make sure that the general characteristics which material things have in our primary experience really are characteristic of the things themselves and not of the structure of our mind. So we have to make sure that the species-individual structure which pre-scientific knowledge sees in the material world cannot be due to the structure of our mind. For even if we reject the all-predominant role the structure of the mind plays in Kantian philosophy, then the possibility remains that certain general features in our knowledge originate in this structure. It will be easily understood, however, that this cannot be true as regards the species-individual structure. Whatever may be the part played by our way of thinking or of speaking about the material world, which way seems to suppose a species-individual structure, we would never arrive at a coherent understanding if the material world itself did not really have such a species-individual structure.

It is perhaps better to replace the word "understanding" by the phrase "application of understanding," since not only the understanding of the material world, but also the application of our knowledge is based on a species-individual structure. Not only is the fact that we formulate our theories in general statements important, but also that we apply those general statements without question to individual instances. We apply, for example, the general laws of mechanics to the different individual things we are making. The confidence with which we board a plane is based on our knowledge that the general mechanical laws really apply to this particular device. No general statement would make any sense at all if it could not be applied to individual cases.

What we are interested in is not the general statement, but what the general statement says about the concrete reality with which we live. Any concrete reality is always individual. When we say: "silver is affected by sulfur," we are perfectly aware that silver does not exist in a general way. What exists are different silver things. So what we say in our statement has a bearing on reality only in so far as the existing silver things have certain features in common. Otherwise our statement would not have a real sense. It does make sense, however, to formulate our knowledge in general statements, because certain individual things or events also behave according to a certain nature they have in common. Individual things have, evidently, an individuality, which includes a common specific nature. By knowing this specific nature, we know at the same time certain aspects of individual things. The species-individual structure in our knowledge must, therefore, correspond to a species-individual structure in reality.

Philosophy Is Unavoidable.

The Positivistic Attitude. An epistemological justification of a philosophy of nature on a realistic basis has to be concerned not only with a non-realistic attitude, but also with an epistemology which denies the possibility of philosophy as such. This epistemology is known as positivism or empiricism. Although there are different forms of both, they all have in common the claim that the only way open to the human mind to know something of reality is the way of positive empirical science. Consequently, a philosophy of nature, as advocated in this study, does not make any sense.

This phrase "does not make any sense" must be understood in a typically technical meaning. It says that the statements of a philosophy of nature are neither true nor false; they are simply deprived of any meaning at all. The positivist arrives at this conclusion by a twofold consideration. He points out, first of all, that to have meaning supposes that it is possible to describe or, at least indicate, a way of checking truth or falsehood. This principle taken by itself is without any doubt a sound one and can by no means be harmful to philosophy.

The fundamental empiricist standpoint restricts the possibilities of checking truth or falsehood, however, exclusively to concrete sense-experience. This means that the content of each statement should be such that it directly or indirectly can be verified by the result of a certain sense-experience.[3] It is this restriction which is responsible for the positivistic claim that only positive science can give us information about reality. It is this restriction, added to the general principle above mentioned, which makes all philosophy, including the philosophy of nature, meaningless. For the philosophy of nature does start with sense-experience, but takes precisely such aspects of ex-

---

[3]Cf. A. J. Ayer, *Language, Truth and Logic,* London, ²1946, p. 35 ff.

perience as do not form the specific content of a sense-experience.[4]
The species-individual structure of matter, for example, never forms
the specific content of a sense-experience. It is for this very reason
that positive science is unable to check in an experimental way the
existence of such a structure; only specific contents of sense-experience
can be checked by science. And according to the positivistic doctrine,
no discussion of things that cannot be checked by sense-experience
makes sense. Therefore, philosophy is meaningless. There is no
possibility of checking truth or falsehood of the results of its philosophical discussion.

Answer. Our answer to this serious objection to philosophy in
general can take much the same direction as did our criticism of Kant's
thesis. Positivism and empiricism suffer from the same kind of fundamental contradiction. In empiricism the contradiction takes an
almost visible form. Again and again, positivists and empiricists write
philosophical books to make clear their thesis that philosophical statements cannot make any sense at all. But their own books are of a
philosophical nature! According to their own principles, their rejection of philosophy is *meaningless.*

Broadening of the Positivistic Thesis. The fundamental contradiction remains the same when positivists try to extend the category
of meaningful statements in such a way that there is at least room for
philosophical statements of a very special kind. To do this they distinguish between those statements which directly express certain data
of sense-experience and those which say something about the *way* we
express the data of sense-experience. Statements of the latter type
belong to logic, if we take the word "logic" in a broad sense. They
reveal nothing about reality, concerned as they are only with our way
of expressing and combining already known data. The first type of
statement is the basic statement of all sciences, expressing as it does
concrete sense-experience, as for example, "this thing is red."

Either type of statement can be true or false. The ways of knowing
whether they are true or false differ, however. In the case of statements expressing sense-experience, we have to determine if the statement is in accordance with the data of experience, as already explained
above. The truth or falsehood of a logical statement depends on

---

[4]By the specific content of a sense-experience I mean the content which
characterizes a certain observation. For example, the size, shape, color, etc.
of a particular piece of wood. Cf. p. 14.

whether or not it is in accordance with the rules of logic or with the rules of the language which is used to describe the data of experience in a certain field.

There is reason to relate these logical statements to philosophy, because they find their origin in a certain critical reflection on the different methods we have of reasoning and expressing ourselves.

This conception of philosophy, acceptable in positivistic eyes, has quite another aim than that which a realistic philosophy claims to have. The former says nothing about reality, whereas the latter thinks it possible to say something about reality in another way than science does, for it claims that its statements go beyond a pure registration of sense-experience. And exactly for that reason, the positivistic claim that such a philosophy is deprived of any real sense remains entirely valid. The different statements of such a philosophy can perhaps have value as expressing certain emotional reactions towards reality; they are, however, entirely outside the realm of knowledge.

The Same Inconsistency. The broadening of the positivistic thesis does not take away the contradiction always present in this line of thought. For if the question is asked: "To what category belongs the statement that only the two exclusively permitted kinds of statements make sense?", then we again have the contradiction between what is stated explicitly and what is meant to be the aim of the statement. Without doubt the aim of the statement is to say something that makes sense about philosophy or about human knowledge in general. What is said explicitly, however, deprives the whole statement of any sense at all, since the statement says neither anything about certain sense-experiences nor about logical constructions. It states something about the limits of our knowledge and is, therefore, of a more basic nature than are the two permitted categories.

Conclusion. The only way to avoid contradiction is not to restrict human knowledge about reality to the field of immediate sense-experience. Obviously, there is more present in human experience than what can be expressed in statements about data of sense-experiences as such. Otherwise it would not be possible at all to discuss what kind of statements can make sense and which cannot. And such a discussion is certainly not without sense. Hence we may say that positivistic attempts to exclude philosophy are based upon too narrow an idea of the possibility of human knowledge, which possibilities are, however, implicitly acknowledged even by the positivists when they discuss the matter.

Thus our conclusion should be that philosophy is inescapable, because the very attempt to escape philosophy proves to be itself a philosophical attempt. Consequently, there is no reason to fear a verdict forbidding, in the name of epistemology, philosophical speculation as though it were meaningless. No epistemology can justify such a verdict without getting involved in contradictions.

The conclusion that human knowledge about reality is not, *a priori*, limited to positive empirical science is of special importance with respect to the problems which occupy us. For it has been seen that no positive empirical science can solve these problems, because such a science deals explicitly only with the specific content of sense-data. The systematization of the primary part of our experience is beyond the possibilities of a positive science. Positive science presupposes implicitly the data of our primary experience, but it cannot discuss them. It is for that very reason that a philosophy of nature is needed.

Philosophical Knowledge Has More Than Relative Value

On account of the importance of the problem, it is necessary to discuss still another attempt to deny human knowledge the capacity to say something more fundamental about reality than sense-experience is able to do. This attempted denial includes, as a matter of course, the denial that philosophy can make sense since philosophy claims to be a systematic reflection on precisely this fundamental part of human knowledge.

Sometimes it is argued that the kind of philosophy one chooses depends upon one's temperament or character. This implies that the choice is not open to intellectual justification. Or to put it another way, it says that our fundamental philosophical convictions have only a relative, not an absolute, value. The same contradiction met in the former statements also deprives these of their intended meaning, however prudent, however humble, or however attractive they may appear at first sight.

If, for example, the statement that one's philosophy depends on one's temperament should be meant to reveal the reason why people do not agree upon philosophical questions, then it must be asked: Does or does not this statement depend upon the temperament of the man who made it? That question reveals the obvious contradiction between the aim of the statement and its content. The aim of the statement was to indicate a really existent connection between the temperament or character of a person and his philosophical convictions and to explain by this connection why people differ in their philosophical convictions. It is clear, however, that this statement makes sense only if we accept the principle that human knowledge is able to say something fundamental, something that in the last resort judges of the value of all human knowledge, because it says something fundamental about the relation between what *is* and what we *know,* between reality as such and knowledge as such.

The same applies to the other statement that philosophical convictions have only a relative value. This statement is really meant as an *absolute* judgment about the value of different philosophical convictions. Again there exists the same contradiction between what is explicitly stated and what is implicitly meant by making the statement. If those statements were not uttered as expressions of what is held to be true, they do not have any value at all. And it does not help if somebody should weaken such a statement by saying, for example, "Our fundamental philosophical convictions probably have only a relative value". The contradiction remains between the meaning of the fundamental philosophical statement, namely, that a certain statement is probably true, and the content of that certain statement which denies the possibility that such a statement can be true at all.

It is really impossible to attribute an exclusive relative value to human knowledge without depriving human knowledge of all meaning whatsoever.

Conclusion

Looking back upon the different attempts made to eliminate some fundamental features of human knowledge, the conclusion must be that human knowledge is, in principle, realistic; it is not confined to sense-data alone; and it has a certain absoluteness with regard to its possibilities of knowing what is true.

It may be that human knowledge in several of its aspects is due to undergo all kinds of influences, that its judgments are sometimes based upon appearances more than upon reality, that they are more relative than absolute. This does not take away from the fact that, fundamentally and in principle, human knowledge is directed towards reality and absoluteness. Kant may be right in his claim that the structure of our mind makes it impossible for us to have a complete knowledge of reality as it is. This claim can, however, never affect our knowledge in its fundamentals; it can at most only have a bearing upon certain aspects of our knowledge. Likewise, the positivists and empiricists are right in stressing the point that the basis of all our knowledge is sense-experience, but they are wrong in trying to limit all our knowledge merely to the registering and combining of the data of sense-experience. Human knowledge can do more than that.

Finally, the fact that psychologists and sociologists show how strongly our convictions, even fundamental ones, are influenced by our psychological structure and social position, does not make human knowledge relative. It only shows how careful we have to be even as regards our most fundamental convictions. If, however, the ultimate value of human knowledge as such were at stake, then what could be the value of sociological and psychological considerations at all?

So we turn back to the primary data of pre-scientific knowledge, with the strong conviction that no epistemological difficulties can prevent us from a philosophical analysis of them. What has already been said in the beginning of this section may be repeated: a systematic philosophy of nature is of great value for epistemology because it broadens the basis upon which epistemology can be built. It offers epistemology a different type of human knowledge than science does.

5. RECAPITULATION

The foregoing analysis has enabled us to outline both the task and the possibility of the philosophy of nature. The philosophy of nature is a systematic philosophical reflection on the data which primary pre-scientific knowledge of the material world reveals. These data concern the general nature of matter; they reveal something of that which all matter as such has in common. Science, on the other hand, deals with the specific content of experience. This may, for the present, be sufficient to indicate the difference between science and the philosophy of nature. Later on the subject will be discussed in greater detail.

Because the philosophy of nature abstracts from the specific content of our experience and pays attention only to that which all matter has in common, it is possible to build a system of philosophy of nature which is independent of science, because the data of primary pre-scientific knowledge can be known, in principle, with certainty without the help of science. However, the same data can also be found, as has been seen, in the presuppositions of science. For science has incorporated in its basic methods an implicit philosophical outlook on the material world. This opens to us the possibility of checking the authenticity of data, which are supposed to be part of our primary knowledge. And this is a fortunate situation, for it is not always easy to distinguish primary experience from primitive experience. History proves how many times a philosopher has held to be a primary experience what was actually only a primitive one.

Therefore, it shall often become necessary in difficult problems to have recourse to these presuppositions in order to make sure that we are not deceived by our imagination as it is fed by primitive sense-experience. It must be stressed that such an appeal to the presuppositions of science does not in the least imply that the philosophy of nature is based upon the specific results of scientific investigations. For the *results* of science are not taken into account. Only the implicit philosophical *presuppositions* contained in the basic methods of science are considered. The philosopher is entitled to assume that in view of the success of science its basic methods are correct. In this sense it can be said that science can help in the formation of a philosophy of nature, in so far as science offers in its presuppositions verified data of primary experience.

The specific results of science are as such of no direct use for the philosophy of nature, since these specific results are intended only to purify and elaborate in a systematic way the primitive data of our experience. Likewise, the philosophical evaluation of the data of primary experience does not contribute anything to the specific results of science. For this reason the mutual independence of science and the philosophy of nature was insisted upon.

It was pointed out, however, that although it is possible to distinguish sharply between primary and primitive pre-scientific experience, both experiences are a natural whole. This fact makes it difficult always to see clearly the distinction between science and the philosophy of nature. And the distinction was especially difficult in the earlier periods of the systematic study of nature, for then there was hardly any distinction at all. Not until science had become more developed did the distinction of science and the philosophy of nature become sufficiently clear to benefit both.

For a correct understanding of the philosophy of nature it is necessary to have an idea of this development; hence the next chapter shall be devoted to an historical survey of the study of nature, and a more profound discussion of the relationship between both ways of studying nature shall be postponed until Chapter Three. Such a survey will, of course, not be very fruitful from the strictly scientific point of view, because there is no reason to believe that the science of the past has anything of real importance to say to us in the field of science itself. We know all too well that the means of investigation available in the past were too poor to correct primitive experience, a correction which is necessary to obtain scientific results.

The position of the philosophy of nature is, however, entirely different. A fundamental datum of common experience for the building up of a philosophy of nature, such as the species-individual structure, was available to the Greek philosopher as well as to the modern. The same applies to all data of what has been called primary experience. Consequently, reflection upon such data by Greek philosophers can not only be interesting from the historical point of view, but also from the systematic one. As a matter of fact, Greek thinkers have reflected so profoundly and fundamentally upon the problems of the philosophy of nature that, notwithstanding their limited scientific knowledge, their systems have prevailed throughout the centuries. One of the reasons for their successful thinking in the philosophy of nature was perhaps that their scientific knowledge was so limited. That did not give them much chance to develop satisfactory scientific theories, and it made them concentrate more upon philosophical problems, where the data to build up a coherent system were available.

Limited scientific knowledge has, on the other hand, also many disadvantages. We find within the philosophy of nature several wrong but very plausible scientific theories which because of their plausibility were considered to be based upon primary data. Precisely this has contributed to the confusion about the real character of the philosophy of nature, as the next chapter will show.

Suggested Readings

A. J. Ayer, *Language, Truth and Logic*, London,[2] 1947.

P. Henry van Laer, *Philosophico-Scientific Problems*, Pittsburgh, 1953, Chapter III (vol. III of Duquesne Studies, *Philosophical Series*).

Henry Margenau, *The Nature of Physical Reality*, New York, 1950, Chapters I-V.

Arthur Eddington, *The Philosophy of Physical Science*, Cambridge, 1939, Chapters I-II.

The following studies in Dagobert D. Runes (editor), *Twentieth Century Philosophy*, New York, 1947:

Victor F. Lenzen, *Philosophy of Science*, pp. 107-129.

Everett W. Hall, *Metaphysics*, pp. 145-195.

Herbert Feigl, *Logical Empiricism*, pp. 371-417.

CHAPTER TWO

A SURVEY OF THE HISTORY OF THE STUDY OF NATURE

1. THE PREPARATION OF THE GREAT SYSTEMS OF THE PHILOSOPHY OF NATURE

It is a well-known fact that the Greeks are the teachers of both modern science and philosophy, as they are in so many other fields too. That is why our historical survey of the study of nature begins with a discussion of the doctrine of some important Greek thinkers.

For reasons already pointed out in our first chapter, there is a great difference in the actual value of these doctrines with respect to the different fields of human thought. Grecian scientific thinking began only a development which, after centuries of vain efforts, finally led to modern science. The stimulating value of Grecian science is, therefore, much higher than the actual one. With respect to philosophy, however, the situation is different. No student of philosophy can neglect the Grecian philosophers without being deprived of thoughts of everlasting value.

This state of affairs means that attention should be focused, first of all, on the philosophy of nature of the Grecian thinkers, and only obliquely on their science.

The main thinkers to be concerned with are Democritus and Aristotle, because their systems of the philosophy of nature have more than any other influenced the minds of later centuries right up to the present day. The right understanding of both these thinkers requires, however, a short preceding discussion of two other philosophers, Parmenides and Heraclitus (about 500 B. C.), whose speculations stimulated greatly both Democritus and Aristotle.

Heraclitus

Heraclitus was struck by the continual change of material things. Consequently, it seemed to him that change should be considered as the main feature of matter. The essence of material being was change, a continuous becoming. To be is to change. Primary matter, the original, elementary matter from which all other matter originated by way of differentiation, must, therefore, be something which pre-eminently possesses the typical feature of all matter, namely change-ableness. For that reason Heraclitus looked upon fire as the primary matter. Fire is never the same; it is forever composed of different burning matter.

Thus the essence of fire was continuous change.

There was still another reason why fire seemed so well suited to be chosen as primary matter. Heraclitus knew very well that sense-experience not only taught continual change, but also permanency. Many things remain the same. This is, however, only appearance according to Heraclitus, and in order to explain a seeming per-manency of something that in reality is constantly changing he refers to fire. Fire seems to remain always the same, even though we know that it is subject to continuous change.

There is undoubtedly something primitive in the reasoning of Heraclitus. What else could we expect so soon after the start of Grecian thinking? However, even in this early and primitive doc-trine, it is possible to discern a clear and systematic attempt to focus attention on certain essential problems and to solve these problems according to definite principles. For example, the obvious coherence of the world asked for a common origin, a primary matter. Heraclitus' choice of primary matter was not arbitrarily made. Primary matter must possess exactly those features which Heraclitus considered as typical for matter, namely, continual change with the appearance of permanency. It is interesting to note how philosophical and scientific considerations go together in Heraclitus' reasoning. His primary matter has some characteristics of that which we nowadays call a chemical element. Primary matter is the element from which all other things are made. It has, however, another function, too, namely, to exemplify the true essence of all matter.

Parmenides

The theory of Parmenides was directly opposite to that of Hera-clitus. According to Parmenides, no change is possible at all. What seems to be a change can be only an illusion of sense-experience.

It is of importance to follow very closely the trend of thought which led Parmenides to this startling conclusion, because no Greek phi-losopher can be well understood without sufficient knowledge of the arguments which forced Parmenides to this conclusion. Although most of the philosophers after him rejected Parmenides' conclusion, they did so only after a thorough consideration and discussion of his arguments. All agreed that some parts of it were irrefutable.

The Principle of Intelligibility. Parmenides starts his argumentation with a statement of a very general nature. Perfectly aware of the unexpected result of his reasoning, a result entirely contrary to the testimony of the senses, he tries to make sure, first of all, what the competence of the human mind is. "Only that can really exist which can also be thought."

On account of this principle, Parmenides is sometimes called the first metaphysician, and justly so. For he makes a statement about all being as being. He tries to formulate a principle that implicitly underlies all human reasoning about reality. And this is one of the specific tasks of metaphysics.

The importance of this principle, often referred to as "the principle of intelligibility," is obvious. If our speculations and our reasoning about reality are to have any sense at all, then they must have a reference to reality. It has already been pointed out in the foregoing section that the denial of this reference to reality takes away all meaning whatsoever from our intellectual activity. Although some philosophers try to deny the pretention of the human mind to know what reality is, their very denial contradicts that they really believe what they are saying. It is very difficult, however, to formulate the principle of intelligibility in such a way as not to produce serious misunderstanding.[1] The above formulation could suggest that we are allowed to accept something as really existing only when we have a complete understanding of it. Therefore, any difficulty in understanding something should be a reason for rejecting its very existence. The intention of Parmenides is, however, different. He intends only to say that when our reasoning shows us that something is impossible, it is impossible in reality and not only in our mind. At least, that is the interpretation he uses in his argument denying the existence of real change.

After consideration of the competence of the human mind, Parmenides makes some statements which at first sight seem very trivial, but which nevertheless refer to truths that may be easily overlooked. They are that "only being exists" and "non-being does not exist." The reason Parmenides mentions them is that we use the term "non-being" as easily as the term "being." We form sentences wherein "non-being" as well as "being" can be a subject. So we may be inclined to think that both terms have the same kind of reference to reality. "Non-

---

[1]Cf. *From Atomos to Atom*, Pittsburgh, 1952, pp. **14 ff.**

being" seems to exist just as "being" exists. So Parmenides warns us never to forget that "non-being" does not exist in reality.

The Possibility of Change. Then Parmenides is ready for his argument against the possibility of change. "Being" must be *one,* because there cannot be anything to divide "being," for the reason that outside "being" nothing exists. And "nothing" or "non-being" does not exist.

Because "being" must be one, there can be no change. For what could change mean? Either a transition from one being to another being or a transition from non-being to being. Either horn of this famous dilemma leads to the same conclusion, namely that change is impossible. The first alternative cannot indicate a real change because being is *one,* so this part of the dilemma amounts to "being" remaining what it is. The second alternative of the dilemma likewise offers no escape, because "non-being" does not exist; therefore it can never be the origin of "being."

It hardly needs to be said that Parmenides' doctrine is philosophic, for it is a doctrine about the generic essence of matter, declaring on rational grounds that matter is unchangeable. At first sight, this doctrine about the unity and immutability of being impresses us as being unreal and the result of sterile reasoning. Yet, closer inspection shows that Parmenides has touched upon something that is of lasting value. In its search for *universal* and *unchangeable* laws, modern science is to a great extent inspired by the same idea as Parmenides. For *universal* laws presuppose a certain *unity* in the material world, whereas *unchangeable* laws cannot be established without the presupposition that something unchangeable must be hidden behind all changes to which matter is subject. Parmenides' doctrine was, of course, still too primitive and not sufficiently qualified to be able to furnish the necessary presuppositions for science, but the first outline is clearly indicated.

Influence of Parmenides. The impression made by Parmenides upon his Grecian contemporaries was profound. He provoked a real crisis in the still young world of Greek thought. It had been only a few centuries before Parmenides that Greek thinkers started to explain in a rational manner the phenomena of nature observed by the senses. Now the result of this effort, culminating in Parmenides, was a categorical denial of such phenomena. Instead of explaining the manifold of changing phenomena, Parmenides declared change impossible, and this destroyed for the time being any possible basis for a rational explanation of these phenomena.

It might be true that Heraclitus came to an opposite conclusion; Parmenides, however, was obviously the sharper thinker. He must be reckoned with first of all. No explanation of any particular phenomenon could be attempted before a solution was found to the difficulties presented by Parmenides. The first task of the philosophers after Parmenides was, therefore, to reconcile the philosophical principles formulated by Parmenides with the obvious facts of sense-experience. This is especially true with Democritus and Aristotle. Both saw the great import of this task. They were convinced that Parmenides' principles and his different arguments were correct up to a certain point. They differed, however, upon where that point was.

2. DEMOCRITUS

Philosophical Aspects of Democritus' Atomic Theory

The best way to understand the atomic theory of Democritus is to see it as an attempt to explain the possibility of change as taught by sense-experience, but to do so in such a way as to preserve as much as possible the central ideas of Parmenides. As a matter of fact, Democritus took over most of the ideas of Parmenides. But there was one important exception, however. He refused to accept the fact that change is nothing but an illusion. Or perhaps it would be better to say that what Parmenides belittled as an illusion was physical reality for Democritus. Thus Democritus' point of departure was, on one hand, Parmenides' conclusion that being is unchangeable, and on the other hand, the reality of change. How could these two points be reconciled?

In order to understand Democritus' line of reasoning, it must be recalled that the reason why Parmenides rejected *all* change was the unintelligibility of change. Democritus asked himself, however, whether *every* change was really unintelligible. Does this unintelligibility apply also to local motion, to change of place, which seems to offer little difficulty? Local motion seems quite intelligible, and for that reason, also possible. The difficulty was, however, that local motion cannot be thought of without at least two kinds of beings: one that moves, and one in which the motion takes place. Parmenides' statement that being was one did not leave much possibility for local motion. In what medium could that one being move? And how could a motion of that one being account for the tremendous variety of change which sense-experience taught us did occur? It was clear to Democritus that he must give the principles of Parmenides a careful consideration in order to find a possibility of modifying them in such a way that local motion could be made intelligible. Could he give some a slightly different meaning without violating their original content too much?

The Atoms and the Void. He started with the principle of the unity of being. According to Democritus, space divides being into several beings, namely, the atoms, which can move within that space and thus effect a change. Thus he gave space the function of dividing the different atoms. In doing this he had to mitigate the absolute antithesis between being and non-being. Parmenides had stated that beyond being there was nothing, but Democritus claimed that in a certain way *nothing* existed, too.

Taken literally this sounds very startling, and would even appear to be a glaring contradiction in terms, since *nothing* by definition is that which is *not*. Democritus, however, did not mean it literally. *Nothing,* for him, means the void; and *being* means the full, i.e. that which is full of atoms. Thus Democritus' solution practically amounts to a surrender of the absolute uniformity of all being, because for him *to be* means either *to be atom* or *to be void*. This distinction between two kinds of "being" is, properly speaking, more important and more fundamental than the division into atoms, because atoms are all of the same nature.

Democritus and the Principles of Parmenides. At first sight, the deviation from the principles of Parmenides by the theory of Democritus seems to be very great. Closer inspection, however, gives a different picture. First of all, Democritus maintained the principle of intelligibility. He accepted local motion only because he thought it intelligible. All other changes he continued to reject on account of their alleged unintelligibility. So the atoms were, according to Democritus, not subject to any internal change. They could not be divided (hence the name *atom,* which literally means "indivisible"); nor could two atoms fuse into a new one. Thus the only possible change consisted in local motion by which the atoms could combine into an aggregation, or disengage from such an aggregation. The atoms themselves remained, however, intrinsically unchanged during such combinations or separations. By stressing this point, Democritus remained true to the principle of Parmenides, which stated that being was unchangeable. The atoms could not really change.

Democritus maintained still another principle of Parmenides. The unity of being was also preserved to a certain extent by the assumption that all atoms were of the same kind, of the same intrinsic nature. The only difference consisted in their size and figure, which varied infinitely and continuously, in order to exclude any possibility of an atom having a nature of its own. And why quantitative differences only? Because these alone met the requirements of intelligibility. Democritus never forgot the basic principle of Parmenides that being must be intelligible. He was convinced that quantitative differences, subject as they were to mathematical considerations, remained within the realm of that which was intelligible. Qualitative differences were not intelligible and therefore impossible.

The idea which pervades the whole of Democritus' theory, that the intelligibility of matter has to be sought in quantitative relationships, was not new. It was already clearly expressed by Pythagoras and shortly after Democritus, Plato was to support it strongly.

Thus Democritus succeeded, by giving a priority to the principle of intelligibility, in preserving to a certain extent the other principles of Parmenides and at the same time in accounting for the obvious facts of sense-experience. The infinite variety of things could be explained by the different shapes and sizes of the atoms which constituted them, and by the different positions of these atoms. The observable changes of a thing were based upon a change in the position of its atoms, upon the loss of some of them, or upon their union with other atoms.

Philosophical Character of the Atomic Theory. It should be clear from this relationship between the principles of Parmenides and the atomic theory of Democritus, that the latter must be looked upon as a *philosophical* theory. It is meant, first of all, to explain how change and the variety of beings can be possible in the light of the requirements of intelligibility. Hence its absolute character. Democritus did not conceive his theory as a hypothesis for explaining certain particular physical or chemical phenomena. Its principal aim is to outline the general nature of matter, both in accordance with what a general experience teaches us about matter, namely its mutability, and with what reason compels us to accept.

This mainly philosophical character does not imply that the whole theory is entirely useless for specific physical explanations. What has been said previously about Greek thinking should be remembered.

The sharp distinction we can make nowadays between science and
the philosophy of nature does not apply to the first attempts at
explaining the phenomena of nature. These first attempts had a
double character, but the prevailing feature was philosophical.
Although philosophical problems dominated the thinking of the
Greeks, including Democritus, this does not imply that the atomic
theory did not include certain physical aspects as well.

Physical Aspects of the Atomic Theory of Democritus

After showing that change is possible, Democritus tries to explain
several physical phenomena as, for example, evaporation and melting.
Evaporation consists in the loosening of atomic connections. Therefore, vapor will occupy more space than the liquid did before its evaporation. Melting is likewise reduced to a shift in position of the atoms.

Next Democritus endeavors to indicate what density is. Matter
has a high density if it contains many atoms and relatively little void.
He points out that dense matter will be difficult to divide, because
matter can only be divided where there is a void. All those ideas can
be found in any modern elementary treatise about the different states
of aggregations.

The same is true of Democritus' idea of motion. He considered
motion as an original property of atoms. Like the atoms themselves, motion is eternal and incorruptible. It is clear that this idea of
atomic motion contains in germ the later Law of the Conservation of
Motion, so extremely fruitful in mechanics. Of course, we should
beware of exaggeration, for every thing was still vague and there was
no possibility of experimental control, since Democritus did not draw
any definite conclusion which could be checked by experiments. That,
however, was not yet possible at his time. Moreover, it was not
important at all to him, because his theory was not meant to be a
physical theory based upon experiments. The trend of thought was
philosophic; that formed the backbone of his theory.

3. ARISTOTLE

Rejection of Democritus' Atomism

Aristotle was not satisfied by Democritus' atomism, because it did
not sufficiently explain the existence of specifically different beings
with their intrinsic changes, both taught by sense-experience. He was
of the opinion that Democritus went only halfway. The atomic theory

certainly opened the possibility of explaining some, but not all, changes which occur in nature. Nor did it account for all variety. Briefly, Democritus did not take the data of sense-experience seriously enough. Aristotle admired in his predecessor the attempt to bridge the gap between what sense-experience taught and what was found by rational analysis. But what was the use of such an attempt if it was not based upon the full content of what sense-experience taught? The result could only be that certain fundamental data of sense-experience still had to be denied, as Democritus had been forced to do. For he denied the existence of intrinsic changes and specifically different beings.

On the other hand, Aristotle was not the man to brush aside Parmenides' speculations with this simple appeal to sense-experience. Not even for an instant did he lose sight of Parmenides' fundamental principle that all being must be intelligible. Such an attitude against the power of reason could hardly be expected from the founder of scientific logic.

So the first task imposed upon Aristotle was a careful and critical re-examination of the speculations and reasonings which had led Parmenides to reject multiplicity and change. Democritus had already re-examined them; but Aristotle knew that he had to go deeper into the problems than Democritus had done, for the results of Democritus did not explain enough.

Analysis of Parmenides' Concept of Being

Substantial and Accidental Being. Aristotle formulates his main objection against the analysis of Parmenides in the following words: "False is Parmenides' reasoning because he takes being in only one sense while it really has several meanings."[2] There is, for example, a real difference between substantial and accidental being, between, on one hand, things which have in themselves their own *to be,* as men and animals, and, on the other hand, that which we call properties of things, as their size, shape, color, etc. The *to be* of a man is just as real as the *to be* of his size; of both we may truthfully say that they are, but *to be* in both cases does not mean exactly the same thing. *To be* refers in the first instance to something which exists in itself, which is a substance; in the other it refers to something which is *in* another and *of* another. Size does not exist separate from that which

---

[2]*Physics* I, 3, 186 a 24-25.

has size. Speaking without distinction of *being* and *to be* is dangerous, according to Aristotle; the univocity of the term *being* applied to all that is can be the cause of a serious misunderstanding, namely, that all beings are exactly the same as to their status of being.

It will be well to point out that in making the distinction in *being* Aristotle does not intend to say that there are several different *beings*, i.e. disconnected beings such as are the atoms of Democritus. He certainly does not deny multiplicity of beings; but that problem is not in his mind when he speaks about the different meanings of *being*. He intends to show only that Parmenides' concept of *to be* has in itself several meanings which refer to different aspects of concrete reality. Those several meanings are not entirely different, however. There is a very good reason to use just the one concept: *to be*. But we must be aware that this one concept has a certain internal structure, referring as it does to the different ways in which concrete reality shows us the realization of *"to be."* Therefore, Aristotle's conclusion is that Parmenides' reasoning is inconsistent because it is based upon a concept of *being* which does not agree with reality. Before considering this conclusion of Aristotle more closely, another distinction of his must be mentioned.

Being-in-Act and Being-in-Potency. If we ask, for example, whether an acorn is an oak or not, then the answer can be either yes or no. Either answer is to a certain extent equally right and equally wrong. It is correct to say that an acorn is not an oak, for an acorn is not a tree. On the other hand, the simple denial that an acorn is an oak does not tell the whole truth. Such a negative answer could also be given to the question, is a stone an oak? Both negative statements have, however, not the same denial value. An acorn has a certain capacity or potency to become a tree, which a stone does not have. It makes sense, therefore, to say that an acorn is an oak, although this answer is also not entirely satisfactory. Hence the mere contrasting of *being* with *non-being* is insufficient to cover the situation.

For this reason Aristotle distinguishes between *being-in-capacity* or *being-in-potency* and *being-in-perfection* or *being-in-act*. Thus if we say that an acorn is an oak, our statement is correct provided we understand it as an oak-in-potency; but it is false if we mean it is an oak-in-act. Hence *capacity-for-being* is neither simply *non-being,* nor simply *being.* It is a *being-in-potency,* distinct on one hand from absolute *non-being* and, on the other hand, from *being-in-act*.

Analysis of Change

With the distinction of *being-in-potency* and *being-in-act* in mind, Aristotle gives an analysis of change which, according to him, makes change intelligible. As will be recalled, Parmenides' dilemma was intended to show that change is unintelligible and therefore impossible. One alternative of the dilemma was: from *non-being* no *being* can come; and the other: what *is* already, cannot *come to be*.

Aristotle wholly concedes the first alternative if non-being is understood as that which *is* not under any respect. But a thing can very well come *to be* from something which *is not yet* in some respect. From an acorn an oak can come *to be*. This is no coming *to be* from absolute *non-being* nor a remaining-what-it-is of some existing thing. The latter is excluded by the second alternative of the dilemma. Hence, for Aristotle, *coming to be,* is the transition from *being-in-potency* to *being-in-act,* from potency to act.[3] In this manner he thought it possible to solve the difficulties of *coming to be* and change by an analysis of the concept *being.*

Difference Between Substantial and Accidental Change. All changes are not the same. It has already been seen how Aristotle distinguishes between substantial and accidental being. To this distinction corresponds the distinction between substantial and accidental change. In a substantial change the thing as a thing changes; it is no longer what it used to be. In an accidental change the thing remains what it is, only some accident changes.

An example of the first kind of change is the death of an animal. After its death the animal *is* no longer. What remains is something entirely different—let us say, an accumulation of chemical compounds. Now for an example of accidental change. If an animal changes in size, it does not change as an animal. It remains the same animal it was before the change. Only an accident is changed. Aristotle examines both changes very carefully. He is not satisfied with the general statement that change is a transition from potency to act, but endeavors to indicate exactly what happens in both changes. Let us follow him closely in his analysis of both changes.

Accidental Change. Let us begin with an example of an accidental change, namely the formation of a statue from clay. This is an accidental change, for the clay remains clay. Three things are to be distinguished: namely, the initial state (before the change), the final state

---

[3]*Metaphysics* XII, 2; 1069 b 15-16.

(after the change), and that which undergoes the change, the subject. The initial state in this case is the rough shape of clay; the final state is the form of the statue; and the subject is the clay itself. The rough clay contains the potency to become a statue. Hence the elementary condition of all change, the transition from *being-in-potency* to *being-in-act* is fulfilled. Now in every change there must be something which changes, something which forms the link between the initial and the final state. Otherwise there would be no question of change, but of annihilation followed by creation. The link in our case is the clay. This material substance has remained the same, so that no substantial change has occurred.

This statement, however, can easily be misunderstood. In order to avoid misunderstanding it should be kept in mind that this "permanent" thing itself also has changed. The form which was there before the change, the rough form, was not something merely glued to the clay; it was a determination of that substance, the determination of its external shape. Even when only a change of external shape takes place, this nevertheless implies a change of some determination of the substance in question, and thus indirectly a change of the substance itself. This can be expressed by saying that remaining entirely itself, remaining what it *is,* the clay has changed.

This point must be insisted upon. Aristotle would be misunderstood if too much insistence were made upon taking substance as a thing to which another thing, i.e., an accident, is externally connected without any internal bond. Not even accidental change takes place without affecting the substance.

To give another example, the aging of a man is a change which affects his whole being, yet he remains the *same* man. Thus in Aristotle's conception, a substance is not something rigid which either remains rigidly the same (in accidental change) or is totally destroyed (in so-called substantial change). On the contrary, it is some determinate, fundamental structure which can be further determined in many ways, and needs to be further determined.

Substantial Change. After having made a careful observation of nature, Aristotle considered himself bound to conclude that not only accidental changes occur in nature, but also changes by which the nature of things changes entirely, so-called substantial changes. Plants and animals can transform food into their own substance, elements enter into composition to form new substances, and these in turn decompose or form new compounds. In order to make these substantial changes intelligible also Aristotle had to accept something which would form the link between the initial state and the final state in these processes. Now the substance itself cannot be this link because the substance disappears. When an animal dies, it ceases to exist as an animal; hence that which remains must be something else. This *something else* is the common principle of all material being, so-called prime or primary matter (*materia prima*).

Doctrine of Matter and Form

The concept of *primary matter* is one of the most subtle concepts of Aristotle's philosophy. To show what he means by it the example of clay may be used again. Clay was the matter which underwent change, a change of external form or shape. In order to see the similarity between primary matter and ordinary matter, such as clay, something just mentioned in connection with the concept of substance is of importance. The clay does not exist without its external form. It is always determined by *some external form*. Neither does primary matter exist all by itself. It exists always under some *form*. This form, however, should not be understood as an external form, but as a *form of being,* i.e. as a determining factor which makes primary matter *be,* for instance, copper, gold, water, marble, or a living being. Thus there is never any primary matter all by itself, but always primary matter which is determined to a certain matter by some *form of being*. Primary matter is never complete. i.e. a being which is in itself; it is a principle of being, as Aristotle expresses it. Primary matter by itself is nothing but the material potency to several forms of being. Only by one of the *forms of being* is it determined to be a real material thing, to be matter in the ordinary sense of the word.

Matter and Form Are Difficult Concepts. Few Aristotelian concepts have been so mishandled by later generations as the concepts of *primary matter* and *form of being*. Later on we will explain why these concepts are so easily misunderstood. For the present, it must be stressed that only a profound study of the philosophic setting of the problems which gave rise to these concepts can provide a correct understanding of them. These problems originated from the endeavor to make substantial change intelligible. When any kind of matter can be changed into any other, there must be some common element in all material things. This common element cannot be any being which exists in itself, for otherwise the change would not be a substantial change. Neither can it be a component part which can be separated and continue to exist by itself. For otherwise the component part would be a permanent substance, so that there would be no substantial change. Hence Aristotle's conclusion: primary matter is pure being-in-potency, a capacity for material being which is really present in all material being, but only insofar as actualized in this or that material being. This actualization he calls *form of being* or *substantial form (forma substantialis)*. Just as in the case of primary matter, substantial form of a purely material being is not a component part which can exist separately, but is only a principle of being, namely the determining principle.

Although our modern concept of matter is, without doubt, related to the Aristotelian concept of primary matter, the modern term is not equivalent in meaning. When we speak about matter-in-general we do not mean any determined matter, yet we always think of something which exists as such. Perhaps we can best express it by saying that matter-in-general is primary matter with a kind of *neutral* form.

Protons and Electrons Are Not Primary Matter. From the above it should be clear that we misunderstand Aristotle if we consider protons and electrons as primary matter. Aristotle would have answered immediately to such an interpretation: "No, I do not mean that. By primary matter I mean precisely that *principle of being* which equally makes these two elementary forms of material being *matter,* that principle of being which makes it possible for them to react in such a way that both cease to be what they were at first."

The Function of Primary Matter. It is because of the common principle, primary matter, that material beings can change into one another and form compounds or, in general, undergo essential change. Whether such a change takes place very easily or not depends on the form of being in which primary matter exists, or rather the form of being which determines primary matter. For instance, in a chemical element primary matter is determined by the form of being of the element in such a way that primary matter is in immediate potency to those compounds into which the element in question enters easily. Its primary matter is, so to speak, ripe for the compound. Hence very little will have to happen to make this primary matter change the form of being of the element for that of the compound.

Likewise, we can reason that the element can again be separated from the compound.[4] It was said above that primary matter is in

---

[4]*Metaphysics* XII, 2; 1069 b 26-34.

potency to become all matter, but that whether primary matter changes easily or not from one form to another depends on the relationship between these forms. To clarify this assertion let us look again at the analogous example of the external form. Just as less change is needed to make an ellipse from a circle than from any other form, so also is less change needed to make a compound disintegrate into its component elements than into other elements, although the possibility of change into other elements is admitted in principle.

The Non-Simplicity of Material Beings. According to Aristotle, every material being is composed of *primary matter* and *form of being,* but this again should not be misunderstood. They are not physical components; they cannot be separated in such a way that we can lay hold of them one by one with our hands or in a reaction tube. They are not simple substances in the sense in which chemistry speaks of elements. According to Aristotle, even chemical elements fall under this law of "composition," but this composition is not chemical or physical. The composition of primary matter and form of being is one which Aristotle considers necessary in order to make the reaction of one chemical element upon another possible, because even in this change there must be something which remains, and something which changes.

Hence Aristotle considers all material beings as non-simple, composed beings, because a really simple being, i.e. a being which in no respect is "composed," cannot be subject to change. The possibility of change presupposes a certain non-simplicity, for otherwise it is not possible to account for both aspects which are present in change—the aspect of a certain permanence and the aspect of something which is really new. There is a certain inner tension in all material things in virtue of which they are subject to essential and radical change.

Hylomorphism is a Philosophic Theory

The purpose of Aristotle's matter-form doctrine, usually referred to as hylomorphism,[5] was, as we have seen, to make change as such intelligible. The theory is not able to explain the particular features of a particular change. A question as to why iron does rust and gold does not can never be answered by the hylomorphistic doctrine in a specific way. Hylomorphism deals only with the general nature

---

[5]*Hylomorphism* is composed of the Greek term for matter, *hyle* and that for form, *morphè*.

of matter, with that which characterizes matter as matter. Hylomorphism does explain the existence of specific differences within matter, for the existence thereof belongs to the general nature of matter. Hylomorphism does not, however, go into the specific consideration of these specific differences. The difference between iron and wood and that between rusting of iron and putrefaction of wood is not dealt with in specific terms. Iron and wood are considered only insofar as they represent specific kinds of matter. Rusting and putrefaction are looked upon only as instances of substantial changes. The discussion of the precise difference between these two kinds of chemical processes lies outside the scope of hylomorphism.

Not outside this scope, however, is such a problem as the species-individual structure, which has been mentioned in the first chapter as a typical problem of the philosophy of nature. This problem can be satisfactorily dealt with by hylomorphism. Later on this will be discussed more fully. For the present it may be shown that hylomorphism is able to explain the existence of many individuals of one species.

Because all material things are composed of matter and form, it is theoretically possible that two material things have the same form and yet are separately existing beings. These two beings can therefore be of exactly the same kind; they can have all formal properties in common; and they can be entirely identical except for their being separated individuals. This possibility is explained by the fact that the same substantial and accidental forms are realized, so to speak, in different primary matter.

Recapitulation of Aristotle's Philosophy of Nature

Before discussing some of the more scientific parts of Aristotle's system, let us briefly recapitulate the main points of that part of his system which can truly be said to belong to the philosophy of nature.

According to Aristotle, we must distinguish between substance and accidents in every material thing. The former gives the material thing its *to be in itself,* a *determinate to be in itself,* such as to be man, horse, iron, copper, etc. This substance is further determined by all kinds of accidents, which cannot be absent, but which to a certain extent can vary without a change in the substance itself. Such a variation is called an accidental change. Examples of accidents are quantity, external shape, and color.

The material substance itself is composed of *primary matter* and *form of being*. The former makes the thing an individual *material* thing, the latter makes it a *determinate* kind of material thing. This "inner" composition of the essence of every material thing makes possible so-called substantial change, i.e. a change in the nature of the thing.

Critical Remarks

A few critical remarks may be added to the above exposition of the main concepts of Aristotle's philosophy of nature. Hylomorphism finds its strongest support in two categories of things, living beings and man-made things. With living beings, especially higher animals, it is fairly clear what individual substance means, namely, the concrete existing being considered under the aspect of its existing in itself and not in something else. With non-living things however, it is not so clear what substance means. Does it mean, for example, an individual piece of copper or the essence of copper? Aristotle certainly felt this difficulty and for that reason he made a certain distinction between the primary substance, the concrete individual beings, and the secondary substance, the essence of such a being. But the objection remains that, especially with non-living things, the concrete individual substance means little. There is not much individuality in a piece of copper. As a result, speaking of the substance of copper we think more of the essence (the secondary substance) than of the concrete individuality. It is not without interest, however, to note that with man-made things (artefacts) such as houses, ships, bridges etc. the idea of the concrete individual substance gains importance. We think of a house as of one individual thing, although Aristotle would remark that strictly speaking, a house is not one substance but an aggregate. It has no substantial form but only an artificial, i.e., a quasi-substantial form. It is clear, however, that the terminology of matter and form, as a matter of fact, has been derived from such examples. The transition from the external to the internal form (from shape to the form of being), which takes place in the doctrine of hylomorphism, is much easier to make in thinking of the transition from the external form to the internal *construction principle* of an artefact than in thinking of the transition from an external form to a substantial form in the strict sense. The construction principle has something of an internal form given to the material elements of the artefact. The use of the term "substantial form" or "form of being" is based on a further analogous extension of the concept of the internal form of an artefact.

The Science of Aristotle

It is of course not possible to give here a complete survey of the scientific conceptions of Aristotle; the exposition will, therefore, be limited to one example with the intention of focussing the attention more on the way in which Aristotle deals with a scientific subject than on the concrete content.

Doctrine of Elements and Compounds. It has been mentioned that Aristotle also knew elements in the chemical sense, i.e. chemically simple substances. This chemical simplicity, however, does not imply that as material beings they are not subject to the composition which characterizes all material things: namely, the composition of primary matter and substantial form. When Aristotle mentions chemical elements, he is on another track. He has other problems in mind than those which he solved with his doctrine of hylomorphism. Speaking of chemical elements, Aristotle deals no longer with matter in general; he attempts now to give a specific explanation of some material phenomena also, albeit that this specific explanation is given in a very general way.

Aristotle accepts as chemical elements the same four which were generally accepted by his contemporaries and immediate predecessors. Probably they were proposed for the first time by Empedocles; they are: fire, air, water, and earth. Aristotle, however, did not consider his duty done by copying them from Empedocles. In the second and third chapters of the second book on *Generation and Corruption,* he endeavors to give a comprehensive derivation of these elements.

Aristotle is deeply convinced that this derivation is based upon experience, but he is also convinced that reason is able to see the necessity for these four elements being just these particular four. Let us follow Aristotle in his derivation.

The problem is to discover the elements. Elements now must be, because of their very definition, the substances with the most primordial forms. Primordial forms are in their turn characterized by the most elementary opposite properties. Since the sense of touch is the primary sense (Aristotle seeks to prove this by a kind of comparative animal psychology[6]), we must seek the elementary properties

---

[6]These arguments may be found in the second chapter of the second book *On the Soul.*

among the qualities which are objects of the sense of touch. In this search we must pay attention to the pairs of opposite primordial properties which are the foundation of the others. These primordial properties are cold and warm, dry and wet. The possible combinations in pairs of these properties are:

Warm—cold	Cold—dry (earth)
Warm—dry (fire)	Cold—wet (water)
Warm—wet (air)	Dry—wet

The first and the last pairs cannot be found in any material being because they are contraries, so that only four pairs remain. Now, observes Aristotle, these four combinations of properties are usually found in material beings which seem to be non-composed and therefore are considered to be the elements.

Even without any profound analysis, it is clear that the derivation of this theory of elements is not on the same level with the preceding speculations about change. The latter were concerned with change in general. They appealed to only one fundamental fact of observation, namely, that changes do occur in nature, and are of two kinds: changes in which things remain what they are, and changes in which things do not remain what they are. In the derivation of his theory of elements, Aristotle appeals to a far more detailed experience which is composed not only of a systematic classification of all material properties, but among other things, also of certain hypotheses about their mutual dependence. The difference is evident. Whether Aristotle's arguments are considered convincing or not, it is clear that his speculation about change is based upon far more solid data of experience than the derivation of his theory of elements. Yet it cannot be denied that Aristotle's doctrine of elements also makes sense. Modern science still makes use of a division of matter which more or less corresponds with Aristotle's doctrine of elements, namely, the division in the three states of aggregation, and also the state of incandescence still plays an important role in modern physics. It is clear, however, that the theory of Aristotle needs an experimental verification which Aristotle does not give and could not give, as will be seen later. Instead of an experimental verification Aristotle gives something else. He attempts to integrate the doctrine of elements in the whole of his cosmological doctrine; so we find his doctrine of elements connected on the one hand, with his philosophy of nature and, on the other, with his astronomy.   Both connections will be briefly considered.

Theory of Chemical Compounds. Aristotle's speculation about chemical compounds is interesting.   Now that we are acquainted with his doctrine of change, it will not surprise us to hear that for Aristotle chemical composition implies more than a commingling of intrinsically immutable components.   He rejects explicitly the theory formulated by Democritus.   Chemical composition is the *"coming to be one* of the *changed* reagents."[7] A new substance possessing a new specific form of being comes into existence.   The sum total of its properties is not simply the sum total of the properties possessed by its component parts.   Hence the components did not enter the new whole without changing.   In entering they underwent an internal change through which they became conditioned for this whole.   The nature of the change which the components must undergo is, of course, determined by the nature of the whole.   This implies that components which are able to unite into a given whole have a nature which is intrinsically capable of being united into this whole.   Through external influences this *capacity* becomes an actuality, i.e. the whole comes to be from the components.

Accordingly, there must be some relationship between the properties of the components, as these properties existed before the union, and the properties of the whole.   It must be possible to find in the whole something of the properties which the components possessed separately.   Aristotle explains this by saying that the components continue to exist virtually in the compound.   Later in the course of history this will give rise to the famous controversy whether elements continue to exist in compounds or not.

Aristotle's theory of chemical composition is really nothing but a development of his theory of change.   Primarily it amounts to this: that he considers chemical composition to be substantial change.   The elements, for instance, which enter into composition with each other do not remain what they are, but become a compound.   Every part of a compound is compound.   The elements can no longer be indicated anywhere, although it is true that the compound remains always potentially the elements of which it is composed.   This shows clearly how Aristotle's conception differs from that of Democritus.   While Aristotle requires for a chemical composition that the reagents act

---

[7] *De Gen. et Corr.* I, 10; 328 b 22.

upon each other and thus undergo an internal change, Democritus is satisfied with an external change in configuration of the atoms, which leaves the atoms unchanged in themselves.

The Integration of the Theory of Elements Into Astronomy. According to Aristotle, the four elements are not only characterized by the above-mentioned combinations of qualities, but also by tendencies to certain motions. The elements earth and water are "heavy," i.e. they have a natural tendency to move downwards, whereas the elements air and fire have a natural tendency to move upwards. Both motions are rectilinear. Aristotle explains these tendencies with the structure of the cosmos, the centre of which is the earth. The *"locus naturalis,"* the natural place, of the element earth is, therefore, located in the center of the cosmos. Round the sphere of the element earth the concentric spheres of the other elements, water, air and fire, are located in the indicated sequence. If an element is not hindered in its natural motion it will strive for its natural place, i.e. for the sphere to which it belongs. For this reason, air and fire move upwards, and earth and water downwards.

Apart from the four "sublunary" elements there exists a fifth element, a *"quinta essentia,"* of which the celestial bodies are made. This element is of an entirely different nature—it is not subject to change, and its natural motion is not rectilinear but circular. This circular motion is eternal and uniform and therefore of a more perfect nature than the motions of the sublunary elements, a fact which forms a suitable occasion for Aristotle to connect several philosophical speculations with this particular type of motion.

The Principal Character of Aristotle's System

The manner in which Aristotle integrates his doctrine of elements both into his hylomorphism and into his astronomy is a good example of a general characteristic of his system. His manner of dealing with a subject is always synthetic; each phenomenon is seen in connection with the whole of his philosophy. Whatever Aristotle's starting-point may be, he will always return to general philosophical considerations. So it is noteworthy that Aristotle's chemical treatise starts with a study of the specific properties of the different elements, but he returns gradually to his general doctrine of change.

This is a typical feature of all physical and chemical works of Aristotle. The desire to give detailed and specific explanations is undoubtedly present; but it is as if forces stronger than himself always brought him back to general philosophical problems. In the next section, the nature of these forces will be discussed, for a good understanding of this feature of Aristotle's work can explain much of the course which the history of the study of nature has taken.

For the present, it will suffice to note that scientific and philosophical considerations are very closely connected in Aristotle's study of nature. The dominating note of that study is philosophic. Aristotle tries, first of all, to remove the antinomy between the experience of intrinsic change and its alleged impossibility before the court of reason which Parmenides and Democritus had been unable to explain away. Aristotle thought that he could solve this difficulty by his analysis of the concept *being* and by his theory that matter is intrinsically composed of a material and a formal principle, and that this composition makes change an essential characteristic of matter. This doctrine of matter and form will dominate all other explanations of Aristotle, even in matters belonging to physical science. All explanations of particular phenomena are seen in the light of this fundamental philosophical doctrine. Sometimes Aristotle even seems to forget his intention of explaining some particular phenomena—he seems too absorbed in philosophical problems.

4. THE EXPLANATION OF ARISTOTLE'S UNCHALLENGED AUTHORITY DURING TWENTY CENTURIES

Introduction

The impression produced by Aristotle's system upon later centuries has been tremendous. For twenty centuries he has been the guide of the intellectual and scientific world. Studying the phenomena of nature has amounted to studying the works of Aristotle. The long duration of Aristotle's practically unchallenged authority proves that it was not the result of rather accidental circumstances. This is confirmed by the fact that Aristotle's authority is limited not just to one circle of culture. He was considered an almost absolutely reliable teacher in the study of nature and in philosophy not only in the circles of the Hellenistic philosophers, but also in the Arabian world and in mediaeval Western Europe. The commentaries on Aristotle's works are consequently countless; some of them do not have any importance of their own; some are very interesting on account of the development of thought which they express.

Since this book is not a historical one, it is not our task to follow step by step Aristotle's influence throughout the Hellenistic, Arabian and Mediaeval periods.[8] The aim of this section is only to understand why Aristotle's influence could be so great. It has already been said that the cause could not be only accidental circumstances. The main cause should be found, first of all, in certain essential qualities of Aristotle's work which were bound to impress everyone who became acquainted with this work. This does not exclude, of course, the fact that sometimes circumstances could be favorable. This was, for example, undoubtedly the case with the circumstances in which Western Europe found itself in the 12th century when it discovered Aristotle.

These circumstances were such that the discovery of Aristotle during the 12th and 13th centuries was a real revelation to Western Europe. Western Europe had not had much chance for an intellectual life of its own during the centuries immediately following the fall of the Roman empire. Only after Charlemagne did something start that might be called an intellectual culture, especially in the field of theology and philosophy. Philosophy, however, at that time was not considered as an autonomous and separate branch of knowledge. Due to the influence of the Fathers of the Church, especially of St. Augustine, philosophy was looked upon as entirely dependent upon theology. Properly speaking, there was no philosophy; there were only philosophical problems.

Outside the field of theology, relatively very little progress was made before the 13th century. Hence it will be understood what the acquaintance with the works of Aristotle, made by means of his Arabian commentators Avicenna and Averroës, meant for the Western World which was intellectually poor but eager to learn. Great theologians and philosophers, like Albert the Great and Thomas Aquinas, saw the importance of the system of Aristotle.

They were immediately aware that the knowledge gathered in his works and enlarged by the Arabian commentators in many aspects meant a tremendous enrichment of the knowledge of the Western world. Most important was, however, the fact that, they saw in the system of Aristotle the proof that it was possible to build up a philosophy independent of theology, i.e. a philosophy based not upon the Divine Revelation, but upon the natural powers of the human intellect. Thanks chiefly to the work of Albert and Thomas, Aristotle became

---

[8]The interested reader may be referred to *From Atomos to Atom*, Ch. II.

accepted by the Western world in less than one century as the teacher both in all kinds of scientific subjects and in philosophy. He was referred to as *"the philosopher."* This supremacy of Aristotelian thought in all fields of knowledge (even in the philosophical terms used in theology, but naturally, not in matters of theology itself) lasted till the 17th century, when it began to decline and then came rather suddenly to an end.

Problems to Be Considered

Several problems arise with respect to this great influence of Aristotle. The first series of problems to be examined concerns the historical fact that Aristotle could be for twenty centuries the uncontradicted authority not only in philosophy but also in science, notwithstanding the fact that his science was almost entirely wrong.

The second series of problems deals with the events of the 17th century, the century in which the authority of Aristotle was fully destroyed, not only in science, but also in philosophy. The events of that century will be the subject matter of our next division.

As to the first question, the authority of Aristotle, the discussion will be limited chiefly to the position of Aristotle in the Western world, because that period, embracing about four centuries, is the most important one. It immediately precedes the century of the birth of the new science, which superseded the science of Aristotle.

In order to understand the great influence of Aristotle in the Middle Ages it is not sufficient to point out the great *philosophical* qualities of Aristotle's work; for these qualities can never be sufficient to explain his great authority also in the field of *science*.

It should be asked, therefore, why was the whole system of Aristotle, containing both science and philosophy, judged, first of all, according to its philosophical merits and not according to its scientific mistakes? The problem is especially urgent because most of the scientific mistakes were not of such a kind that they could be discovered only by means of the modern tools of experimental observation. For most of them very simple experimental tests would have been sufficient. Galileo and his contemporaries, as a matter of fact, performed only very simple experiments to discover correct mechanical laws.

Thus, it seems that the fact that Aristotle's followers in twenty centuries did not discover the mistakes in his scientific conceptions might be ascribed to a certain lack of interest in scientific problems. It could be that their attention was too much focused on philosophy.

So our first problem in this section will be: was this focusing of attention on the philosophy in the work of Aristotle really due to a lack of interest in scientific questions, or could other factors be responsible for it? It will be seen that the answer has to be that the first attempt to understand nature could not be scientific, but had to be chiefly philosophical. This important point must be thoroughly examined because a good understanding of the reasons why the first explanation of the phenomena of daily experience was bound to be philosophical makes much of the history of science understandable. It also explains the second problem to be considered: namely, why certain erroneous scientific theories could last so long, without their error being discovered.

Scientific Laws Are Not So Obvious

To us who are in possession of, for example, a set of relatively simple fundamental chemical laws, it may sometimes seem strange that it was not till the end of the 18th century that they were discovered. We cannot understand why thinkers in former ages did not concentrate upon the discovery of laws so easy to establish and based upon the simplest facts, instead of toying with philosophical problems that were scientifically fruitless.

The answer must be that somehow this is not strange at all. It *seems* strange only because we do not have the right understanding of the difficulties involved in the discovery of fundamental chemical laws. We are often inclined to ascribe an obviousness to those laws which they do not have at all.

It is easy to understand the reason for this mistake. We learned the principles of chemistry by means of some very simple school experiments revealing certain facts which seemed to indicate certain obvious laws. Let us take an example. One of those experiments shows that 7 grams of iron combine with 4 grams of sulphur to form 11 grams of ironsulfide. Similar facts concerning other reactions of chemical elements suggest that chemical compounds are always composed out of certain fixed amounts of elements, a regularity that is known as the law of Proust. It seems so easy that we feel anybody could discover such a law, if he only took the trouble to perform some simple experiments in order to learn the facts.

What we forget, however, is that those facts are not just simple facts. We are sometimes very careless in using certain terms and one of them is the term "fact." If that experiment which is described above, namely, that 7 gm. of iron and 4 gm. of sulphur combine to form 11 gm. of iron sulfide were really nothing but a factual description of what happened, then our verdict that former generations neglected facts would be correct. But it is not exclusively a *factual* description. A factual description would be entirely different from the statement: 7 gm. of iron and 4 gm. of sulphur combine to form 11 gm. of iron-sulfide. Although it is impossible to give a really factual description, let us try, nevertheless, to indicate what it would be.

A Factual Description. In a very abbreviated form, it would run something like this: Mr. So and So at 10:30 E. S. T., October 10, 1951, took a certain quantity of a grey powder, known as iron, which quantity was at said time in equilibrium with three pieces of copper, marked respectively 5, 1 and 1. At 10:35 E. S. T. he took a certain quantity of a yellow powder, known as sulphur, which quantity was in equilibrium with two pieces of copper, both marked with the number 2. The volume of the grey powder was 6 cm.³ That of the yellow powder was, however, 4 cm.³ Both powders were mixed in a copper mortar for 2 minutes. The origin of the yellow powder was unknown, the grey powder was obtained by grinding a piece of iron, formerly used as a magnet.

At exactly 10:40 E. S. T. the mixture was placed in a test tube of Pyrex glass of the following form (description of form follows), then heated by a Bunsen burner (description of the Bunsen burner follows). During the experiment the sun was shining, the temperature was 20° C., and the pressure of the air was 75 cm.

Let us not continue our description, which is here very, very incomplete. For instance, we know nothing about the room in which the experiment was performed; our knowledge about the origin of both sulphur and iron is very deficient; and what do we know of what actually happened in the universe during the time that the experiment was performed? But let what has been said be enough. Many a reader will already be inclined to ask, "What is the use of all this nonsense? We do not have to know the volume, the temperature, the time, the stand of the sun, and the name and particularities of Mr. So and So. The only facts which matter are the weight and the kind of stuff involved." The objection is to a certain extent just.

Selective Description We chemists of the 20th century know that only weight and kind of matter are important in describing chemical reactions, but our knowledge is not the result of considering facts, and only facts. That exactly is the point at issue. Our knowledge is a result of certain chemical theories, from which we have learned what factors are important, and what are not. For that reason we do not need to worry about describing countless concrete details which in reality are present in an experiment; we mention only weight and kind of matter. We make a careful selection as a result of our pre-knowledge. But do not think it normal that only weight is important. There are other experiments where time is very important, and the mentioning of weight would be considered plain nonsense.

A doctor, for example, would be very surprised if we should tell him that our temperature was 37° C., whereas our weight was 180 pounds at the moment we took the temperature. He would be more interested in whether we were giving him our morning or evening temperature. In many experiments the *volume* is very important, whereas there are others in which we have to pay special attention to the *shape* (e.g. in optics). Add to this the experiments with divining-rods, where the person of the experimenter is not unimportant; and it should be clear, that there cannot be given *a priori* reasons, why the various abovementioned so-called irrelevant details are really irrelevant. They can be known as irrelevant only after the discovery of certain laws which draw attention to those factors which are proved to be relevant for the phenomena involved. Without knowing these laws a factual description would be endless. We can, of course, for practical purposes give an abbreviated description of phenomena of nature and of certain experiments. But what guarantee do we have that this abbreviated description stresses the important details, if we do not know the theory?

The obvious answer to this question seems to be that we can use the inductive method to find out what is relevant and what is not. However, the inductive method can be used only if we already have a certain theoretical understanding of the problem involved. Otherwise, the details are so manifold that our induction would simply not come to an end.

The Necessarily Philosophic Character of Aristotle's System

In view of the difficulties connected with the discovery of even simple scientific laws, we should not be surprised that such a man as

Aristotle was convinced that the only possible way for an intellectual approach to the phenomena of nature was a philosophical one. Faced, for example, with a phenomenon such as the reaction of iron with sulphur, he thought it impossible to account in a rational way for the *specific* features of such a change. There were too many details involved and there was no way to abstract the relevant from the irrelevant ones. Each chemical reaction had its own specific features without much connection with the specific features of other reactions. Each chemical substance was characterized by a set of properties which a prescientific induction showed to be rather constant.

Consequently, Aristotle considered the knowledge of the specific way in which the different chemical substances react a matter of experience, of practical knowledge *(technè)*. He could know *how* such reaction took place, but not *why* it took place as it did. Thus the knowledge of the specific properties of matter was not subject matter for a systematic science *(epistèmè)* based upon an insight into the essence of things. It was only practical knowledge.

Aristotle was aware, however, that some approach to the phenomena of nature, other than the purely practical one, was possible, an approach that was entirely intellectual. It was possible to consider a factual change, with its many specific details, exclusively under the aspect of being a change. In this method of consideration all specific details become irrelevant. In the intellectual analysis of change as change, it does not matter whether iron and sulphur are combining to form iron sulphide or to form something else. It is not even important that it is particularly iron and sulphur, with their typical properties, which are reacting. The only important factor is that there are processes in which a certain substance loses its nature. In other words, considering a certain chemical reaction under the aspect of change, the mind is able to abstract the irrelevant from the relevant factors. This being so, we can understand why the natural science of Aristotle was chiefly a philosophy of nature based upon some fundamental and general features of matter, such as mutability and species-individual structure.

We do not have the right to blame him for building up only a philosophy of nature, and not a science in the modern sense of this term. For Aristotle was perfectly right in his opinion that the philosophy of nature was the only possibility for *him*. Another question is, however, whether he was also right in his assumption that it was really the only possibility for mankind. History has proved

Aristotle wrong; but could he be blamed for not seeing a possibility which certainly could not be realized in his time?

The Mixed Character of Aristotle's System

Meanwhile, there are still some other aspects of Aristotle's system to consider. For it is only partly true to say that Aristotle's system was exclusively philosophic. As a matter of fact, he endeavored also to give the foundations for different sciences like mechanics, physics, astronomy, chemistry, and biology. These very attempts of Aristotle seem to contradict the above assertion about the necessarily philosophic character of Aristotle's system. However, they do not. For, although it was justifiable to make such a sharp distinction between philosophy and science, and between the philosophical and the scientific approach, as was done in the preceding paragraphs, it must be stressed that this distinction is a result of a *post factum* analysis. That means it is the result of an analysis made after an historical development of science and philosophy, which has clearly shown the sharp distinction which exists between a philosophical and a scientific approach. Aristotle did not know that distinction. He knew only one intellectual approach to the phenomena of nature. This approach can be classified as chiefly philosophic, if modern standards are used, but that classification is only partly correct.

Consequently, it would really be a misconception of our foregoing analysis if it were understood to imply that Aristotle deliberately pushed away scientific explanations as being not possible for him, and paid attention only to philosophical problems because they were accessible to him. Aristotle searched for intellectual explanations *tout court,* but his situation was such that these explanations were bound to be chiefly philosophical for the reasons given above.

Philosophical Handling of Scientific Problems. Sometimes, however, Aristotle also saw possibilities of explanations which we now consider scientific, but which he saw as being of the same kind as his philosophic explanations (for example, his theory of the four elements). And now the real trouble starts. The fact that Aristotle's method was, first of all, philosophic influenced strongly his handling of physical problems. Not being aware of the difference, he was convinced that a careful consideration of the facts of common experience would reveal the essential scientific features of the phenomena being studied. He thought it possible to abstract the relevant factors from the irrelevant ones by a careful intellectual analysis only, based upon insight into the essence of things. The possibility of such an abstraction and analysis was for Aristotle the decisive criterion for determining the possibility of an intellectual approach. Usually this criterion guided him into philosophical problems, but sometimes, by mistake, into scientific ones. The success of this method of abstraction with respect to philosophical problems (and these formed the greater part of the problems he was dealing with), strengthened Aristotle's conviction that his method was correct wherever it could be applied. And the method is correct indeed as long as philosophical problems are involved. The very fact that philosophical problems deal with the primary aspects of experience makes it possible to abstract the relevant primary aspects from all that is irrelevant. For all *specific* content of experience is then irrelevant. The species-individual structure of matter can be discussed without any reference to the properties of the different species of matter. Being wood or being iron as such is irrelevant for the problem of the species-individual structure. The method of Aristotle leads, however, to erroneous conceptions in scientific problems.

In order to show this, let us reflect once again upon the experiment discussed above. We found that the description of the reaction of iron with sulphur is based upon a theoretical selection of certain characteristics while many others, perhaps even more obvious than the selected ones, are entirely left out of consideration. The important point now is that the reason why certain aspects are chosen to characterize this reaction is not based upon an intellectual abstraction alone. Such an abstraction can never make clear why only weight and kind of substance are relevant. This can be done only by means of theoretical considerations which themselves are based upon a long and varied experience, a point which will be discussed in a moment.

Aristotle, not in possession of elaborated scientific theories, was bound to make mistakes, not in the observation of certain facts, but in the description of them, and consequently in the theoretical evaluation of them. He saw, for example, some bodies fall and other bodies rise, just as we do. So he concluded that some bodies are heavy and others are light, and thus he considered this distinction a fundamental one. Some bodies have the property of heaviness, whereas light bodies have the opposite property, lightness. For us it is easy to see where he made his mistake. He overlooked in his statement, "some bodies rise," just one detail: namely, that the rising occurs in a certain medium, air. By omitting this particular circumstance in his description, he made an abstraction which afterwards proved not to be permissible. But now could he know that exactly this detail was responsible for the difference between heavy and light bodies?

One could say it would have been better if Aristotle had entirely refrained from any attempt at explaining the phenomena of falling and rising bodies, or, having proposed his explanation, not to make it in such a positive way. This last would undoubtedly have been better (the attempt at explanation is, of course, praiseworthy). But how could Aristotle have known that he was in a field where the philosophical method could not be used? He could have known it, had he been aware of the distinction between philosophic and scientific problems. But he was not. He did realize that he was not able to apply his method to all kinds of problems, as his distinction between *epistèmè* and *technè* proves.

This distinction, however, is not exactly the same as that made nowadays between philosophy and science. It refers rather to the difference between the presence and the absence of the possibility of complete intellectual knowledge. For example, the specific way in which the numerous chemical substances respectively react could, according to Aristotle, not be accounted for in an intellectual way. It was just a matter of plain practical knowledge, of *technè*. The enormous amount of detail in the phenomena made an abstraction of essential features impossible. In the case of falling and rising bodies such an abstraction did seem possible. Sense-experience seemed to show the essential difference as clearly as it revealed, for example, the species-individual structure and the mutability of matter.

So notwithstanding the fact that Aristotle's natural science is basically philosophical, we should not be suprised to come across different scientific topics in his works. Aristotle's genius was great enough to let him concentrate on that part of intellectual knowledge that was already available. No genius, however, can be entirely free from mistake. Sometimes he took under consideration problems which were not philosophical at all, and for which his method was not suited.

The Development of Science in the Past Had to Be Slow

The reason so much attention has been given to explaining the fundamental mistakes of Aristotle is not to excuse him. He does not need that. For although he was on the wrong track in physics and chemistry, this alone can hardly minimize his significance. In physics and chemistry the basic method is trial and error. Successors could learn from Aristotle's mistakes. The curious fact is, however, that for twenty centuries he remained an undisputed scientific authority in such different cultures as the Hellenistic, the Arabic and the Mediaeval. That must be explained.

The reason Aristotle's scientific authority could last so long is to be sought in the fact that the weak points of his system—his physical and chemical theories—could only become obvious after a necessarily very slow development of practical knowledge.

Two points are of importance in this connection. First, the intellectual approach to nature had to be philosophical, as long as practical knowledge (*technè*) could not substitute a more specific scientific approach to its own specific problems. Thus Aristotle's successors were still working under the same conditions as Aristotle. They too had to focus attention upon philosophical problems. So they were willing to accept Aristotle's elaborately systematized and cogently expressed philosophic theories. For the time being, there was no other attitude possible. This philosophic attitude carried with it the natural tendency to accept the methodically false scientific theories. For although these theories might be methodically wrong from a modern scientific viewpoint, they fitted quite naturally into the dominating philosophical attitude. The only possible way of becoming aware of the difference between philosophical and scientific methods lay precisely in the development of a specific scientific approach. But—and that is the second point—that development necessarily took a long time. Let us see why this is so.

The Gap Between Theory and Practical Knowledge. It has been mentioned that, generally speaking, the data of experience are too manifold for the student of them to know *a priori* which details are relevant for a scientific theory and which are not. This was precisely the reason, why, for the time being, the intellectual approach to material phenomena had to confine itself to a general philosophical theory of change as change. Thus a certain theory about these phenomena did exist. The practical knowledge of the engineer, the chemist, the physican, etc., was seen in a certain theoretical light, but these theoretical considerations had no immediate bearing upon the knowledge of the phenomena in their particularity. Consequently, those theoretical considerations did give a certain satisfaction to the human mind, which is never satisfied by a practical knowledge only;

but they could not be of any use for the development and extension of that practical knowledge. There was a fundamental gap between the theoretical, intellectual approach and the knowledge of the different facts in their particularity. Hylomorphism was without any doubt a very interesting explanation of the possibility of change, but it did not offer any useful explanation as to why iron oxidizes and gold does not. This inability to explain chemical phenomena was hardly considered an intellectual deficiency, because they seemed so far beyond the possibility of intellectual understanding.

It must be understood that, without theoretical guidance, the development of practical knowledge is very slow. Every new fact has to be found by the trial and error method, and the countless number of details give opportunity enough for following a wrong track. So for several centuries there was hardly any development of practical knowledge. Gradually, however, chiefly due to the needs of daily life, the amount of practical knowledge grew, and with that growth appeared the possibility of certain limited theories for a certain realm of phenomena. Growing practical knowledge, especially the greater variety of that knowledge, made induction more effective. The available variety of experience suggested the relevance of some features and the irrelevancy of others. As a result, some lines of theory became apparent as time went by. They stimulated certain experiments, and the outcome of these experiments made it possible to improve the theoretical approach. This in its turn led to new experiments.

So we find, for example, centuries before the modern foundations of chemistry were laid by Lavoisier and Dalton, certain theoretical conceptions of oxidation and reduction. True, these conceptions were perhaps more wrong than right; but a beginning was made, and that is what matters. The same can be said with respect to the mechanical laws proposed by Galileo, Newton and Huygens. We already find in the 14th century some very good mechanical ideas; but it still took a long time before the experimental data were sufficiently large to show clearly what value those ideas had for the understanding of mechanical phenomena.

A Vicious Circle. The development of science could not be otherwise than slow because the whole process had some of the characteristics of a vicious circle. Correct theories could be proposed only after sufficiently varied experimental data, and especially the correct understanding of those data, were available so as to reveal those features which were of importance and those which were irrelevant. Such an understanding is possible, however, only after the development of correct theories. This state of affairs accounts for the very peculiar way scientific knowledge and its natural result, technical mastery of nature, developed.

A graph reproducing this development would have the following features: first a long, practically horizontal, line, in which only a very slow rise can be noticed. In view of the whole development of science up to the present time, there would be, roughly speaking, almost no difference in the rise of the line between the 4th century B. C. and the 15th A. D. After the 15th century the line begins to show an upward trend; then it begins to rise with great rapidity until the 19th century, when its rise is simply astonishing. From the 19th century onward the line will seem to be more vertical than horizontal.

The start of science, with no theoretical guidance, was indeed very difficult. Once the correct theoretical approach was found, experimental knowledge of matter could develop with tremendous speed. No comparison is suitable, but the development of scientific knowledge can be illustrated in much the same way as the solution of a jig-saw-puzzle proceeds. Without knowing something of the ultimate picture to be reproduced by the different pieces, we find it very difficult to get started. We have to try every piece individually. Every piece can seemingly be correct in any position. After a beginning is made and the features of the picture became visible, the progress is much more rapid. We then know in advance where to place the separate pieces.

The same is true of the picture of nature as given by our scientific theories. Mankind had some pieces in hand without knowing how to evaluate them. How could he characterize the phenomena of melting and freezing? How describe a falling stone and rising smoke in such a way that a coherent picture of all natural phenomena could be obtained? The steady extension of the different phenomena, however, very gradually gave a clearer idea of which phenomena were to be classified as being of the same kind. Only countless mistakes could show the right way, and that took time. But after the right way was found, progress could be rapid.

There are, of course, some exceptions to the general rule outlined above. When we consult the history of science, we find already in the Greek period some branches of science which had reached a very high standard, such as logic (Aristotle), mathematics (Euclid), astronomy (Ptolemy). Yet these exceptions do not contradict what is said above. For the reason why these sciences could be successful from the very beginning lies precisely in the fact that in these sciences it was possible to abstract the relevant from the irrelevant factors. The possibility of this abstraction is clear enough in formal sciences, such as logic and mathematics, but it also existed to a certain degree in astronomy. For the most striking feature of astronomical phenomena is, of course, the aspect of motion. The celestial bodies perform regular periodic motions. The mind cannot fail to focus attention on the mathematical forms of the motions. The same holds to a certain extent true with respect to the motions on earth, although here things are more complicated. We have already seen how with respect to the phenomena of rising and falling the neglect of just one small detail, the medium (air) in which the phenomena take place, caused serious misunderstandings. Yet a beginning of theoretical (mathematical) understanding was possible, which after having been improved in the Middle Ages could develop into classical mechanics. So it is not accidental that the first serious attempt to build up modern science was based upon the phenomena of fall and throw. The application of mathematics to the described paths had something of an obvious invitation. Consequently when it was said above that the development of empirical science had some of the characteristics of a vicious circle, then this thesis needs correction in so far as there were some branches of science in which the correct distinction between the relevant and irrelevant factors was not too difficult. Some theories could find a starting-point and stimulate further investigation. But on the whole the start of science had to be slow.

The Position of Aristotle in the Middle Ages

The foregoing considerations enable us to understand better the curious position of Aristotle in the Middle Ages. We understand better why in the Middle Ages the attention was still focussed on his philosophy, and why mediaeval scholars did not abandon his wrong scientific theories, although some of them were aware of several of his scientific mistakes. Apart from the above-mentioned general reasons, which made the mediaeval mind easily susceptible to the Aristotelian approach to the phenomena of nature, there were some other reasons of a more special kind which must also be considered.

Characterization of the Mediaeval Scholar. Mediaeval scholars were, by tradition and interest, theologians. Thus they were accustomed to a system of knowledge, in which the fundamental principles were certain, founded as they were on Divine Revelation. The first aim of their scholarly activity was, therefore, to draw conclusions from these principles. The truth of the principles themselves was not open to question. An acquaintance with Aristotle broadened immensely the field of their knowledge, but it offered no reason for altering their attitude towards the aim of their own scholarly activity. Certainly, the fundamental principles of philosophy and natural science were to be obtained by another way than by that of theology. They were to be found in an intellectual reflection on the data of sense-experience. The natural powers of the human reason in combination with the sense-experience were all that were necessary to arrive at philosophic and scientific truth. A special Divine Revelation was not needed. That was the reason why a pagan such as Aristotle could be trusted in philosophy and science.

The difference recognized as existing between the origin of the fundamental principles of theology and that of profane knowledge did not, however, alter the student's attitude toward scholarly activities. The impression made by the Aristotelian system, enlarged and enriched by Arabian commentators, was such that this system seemed right, at least in its fundamental principles. Although the mediaeval scholars were, in principle, convinced that profane knowledge ought not to be based on authority but on experience, they did not doubt that Aristotle had found the fundamental principles of science. As a practical result of this conviction, the task of the scholar was no longer the *discovery* of these principles. They had already been discovered. His task was to draw conclusions from these known principles. This explains the great value which the mediaeval scholar attributed to logic. It was the science of drawing conclusions, the main scientific tool.

Aristotle and Theology. Aristotle's authority was still more confirmed by the careful and original analysis which Thomas Aquinas and other mediaeval theologians made of his system. This analysis was necessary, because there were some points, especially in the commentaries of Arabian philosophers (such as Averroës and Avicenna), which were in flagrant opposition to revealed truth. So it had to be discovered whether this was the result of false principles or of false interpretations.

A clear and direct analysis of the philosophical principles of Aristotle, unmixed with Arabian influence, convinced the majority of theologians under guidance of St. Thomas that Aristotle's principles were correct. The philosophy of Aristotle could even be used for a rational treatment of such truths as the existence of God, the immortality of the soul, the free will of man. Although these so-called *prae-ambula fidei* were natural truths, they were considered a necessary basis for Christian faith. This agreement between the conclusions of Aristotelian philosophy and the data of theology, insofar as the latter was concerned with truths available to the human reason, tremendously increased the authority of Aristotle.

Furthermore, the systematic study of theology requires sharp definitions of many philosophical concepts. Aristotelian philosophy turned out to be extremely suitable for providing theology with just such well-defined concepts. Mediaeval theology could no longer be thought of without concepts borrowed from Aristotelian philosophy. Not that Aristotle became an authority in theology itself; the distinction made by Christian philosophers between theology and philosophy was clear enough to prevent this. But the use which theologians could make of Aristotelian philosophy seemed to prove that Aristotle could be considered a trustworthy guide in non-theological truths.

This state of affairs had a natural effect upon the manner in which mediaeval thinkers looked upon profane science. It confirmed the belief that the fundamental principles of profane science had already been found and that scientific study was tantamount to drawing careful deductions from these principles. This attitude of mediaeval thought should never be lost sight of when judging the course of events from the 13th to the 17th century.

The mediaeval attitude towards science is partly the result of the predominant position held by theology, partly of the chiefly philosophical character of Aristotle's system; for philosophical principles can be found without an extensive experience. This attitude, therefore, did not harm mediaeval philosophy too much; but it was ruinous, of course, insofar as natural science was concerned.

It has been explained why this misconception of science could not be easily corrected. The scientific approach, in the modern sense, was not yet possible. The center of gravity of mediaeval science was bound to lie for a considerable time in the field of theology and philosophy.

First Signs of a New Orientation. Yet, the first signs of a new orientation soon began to appear. The Arabian followers of Aristotle supplied the Western world not just with philosophy but also with a great deal of practical knowledge in various fields. Thus not only did philosophy prosper in the Middle Ages; but technical knowledge (*technè,* as Aristotle called it) flourished as well. The latter remained for the time being under the patronage of Aristotelian philosophy. What this patronage really meant, we have seen above. It gave a certain intellectual satisfaction to the human mind because it provided the possibility of uniting an intellectual approach with technical knowledge of certain phenomena. It did not, however, provide a theoretical guidance for the discovery of new facts. The best to be said is that this intellectual approach stimulated, in a general sense, the idea that there was a rational order in nature and that human reason could discover that order. This created an atmosphere favorable for the birth of a natural science.

New facts, however, could be discovered only by the trial and error method. The interest roused by contact with the Arabs tremendously stimulated the search for new data. Little by little some lines of theory became apparent, as explained above. Some theories came into existence which may be called the immediate predecessors of our scientific theories.

The Main Interest of the Mediaeval Scientist. The new theories were sometimes contrary to certain Aristotelian scientific conceptions. The authority of Aristotle was, however, so strongly established that, almost automatically, attempts were made to reconcile those new theories with the rest of Aristotle's work, or at least to give them a place within the frame-work of his system.[9]

In order to understand this behavior of mediaeval scholars it should be stressed that the mediaeval mind was above all accustomed to an all-embracing theological and philosophical synthesis. Such a synthesis was given by Aristotle and by Christian theology built with the help of Aristotelian concepts. The mediaeval mind was far more interested in knowing that human beings were creatures, and in evaluating that basic truth, than in a more specific physiological knowledge of the human body. It was far more interested in determining the difference between human beings and material things with respect to their respective status in creation than in knowing why a particular chemical compound had such and such properties. Briefly, all available knowledge was viewed, first of all, in the light of the most fundamental principles. So hylomorphism was looked upon not only as a philosophical theory which could explain change, but it also suited another purpose, for it stressed the corruptibility of all matter. Thus it

---

[9]Cf. E. J. Dijksterhuis, *Die Mechanisierung des Weltbildes,* Berlin, 1954, Ch. II, section 146; Ch. III, section 55.

drew attention to the contingency of matter and, therefore, to its being created.

Nobody can deny that there is something attractive in such a scientific conception, so different from the modern.

No Other Scientific Attitude Was Possible in the Middle Ages. A fair appreciation and judgment of the difference between the modern and the mediaeval conceptions demands, however, that we never forget that the only intellectual approach available to the Middle Ages was the one just described. The mediaeval lack of scientific theories, limited to particular fields of knowledge, was not exclusively the result of a better understanding of the real values of life. This may have been a factor, but it was certainly not the only one. Equally important is the fact that there was simply no other intellectual attitude possible at that time.

By the same token, the fact that the intellectual activity of our time centers much more around the positive sciences should not be ascribed exclusively to a wordly-mindedness which is no longer interested in a philosophical and Christian outlook in life. There are nowadays intellectual possibilites of understanding material phenomena that were not available in the Middle Ages. The utilization of these possibilites was quite normal. That this utilization brought with it a rejection of much that was good in the mediaeval synthesis is deplorable. But it was not a result of the new possibilities themselves. It was the result of an almost total lack of understanding of these new scientific possibilites on the part of the 17th century followers of the great mediaeval theologians and philosophers. This, however, will be the subject matter of the next section.

Conclusion. To return to the Middle Ages, and to the question asked about them, it was, properly speaking, not so much a lack of interest as a lack of scientific possibilites in such fields as chemistry and physics that naturally resulted in mediaeval thinkers focusing their attention on philosophical and theological problems. This philosophical and theological interest makes it understandable why certain difficulties in the chemical and physical explanations of Aristotle which were discovered in the Middle Ages, did not shake the Ages' confidence in Aristotle. The only result was an attempt to reinterpret Aristotle's doctrine in such a way that the new point of view could be reconciled with the general aspect of that doctrine. More was needed to undermine the authority of Aristotle.

Nevertheless, the coming into existence of new theories, meant to cover only a limited field of phenomena, was the main cause of this undermining. Not so much, however, because this new type of intellectual approach was bound to reveal certain actual mistakes in Aristotle's explanations, but rather because it showed really *new theoretical possibilities* never dreamt of by Aristotle. It showed that Aristotle's intellectual approach was one-sided, and that as a result of that one-sidedness his method for solving scientific problems was wrong. However, it took time to discover that. The first attempts at the formulation of new scientific theories remained entirely inside the realm of the Aristotelian system. The main concepts were still borrowed from Aristotle. This could be clearly shown in an historical study concerning the development of physical corpuscular theories.[10] By the end of the Middle Ages proposed theories of this kind were expressed in accordance with the Aristotelian philosophical concepts of matter and form.

So the first new scientific theories, which were really revolutionary in their nature, could for a long time remain without their true significance being realized. They seemed to be an extension of the Aristotelian system, but they were in reality part of an entirely new approach.

5. THE SEVENTEENTH CENTURY

The True Character of "The New Science"

In the last section it was pointed out why the new scientific approach, from its inception, could not be discerned as entirely different from that of Aristotle, as an entirely new approach to the phenomena of nature. Even the 17th century, the century in which Aristotle's authority definitely came to an end, did not discern the new approach as a *new* approach. For the thing that happened during the seventeenth century, as continuation and achievement of that which had already started in the preceding centuries, was not that several Aristotelian scientific theories were definitely proved wrong and were replaced by better ones, that also was important, but was that an *a-philosophic, i.e. a positive, science* was discovered.

Although it can be said that philosophers and scientists as Galileo, Descartes, Newton, Boyle, Huygens, Leibnitz, and several others were aware of the possibilities revealed by their new science, they were certainly not fully aware of the theoretical import of their new science,

---

[10]Cf. *From Atomos to Atom,* pp. 115 ff.

and especially not of the essential difference between this new science and that of Aristotle. They thought of their new science as a successor to the Aristotelian. They did not consider their new science as an entirely new approach to the phenomena of nature, an approach with a new aim. In their eyes the aim of the new science was, generally speaking, the same as that of Aristotle. The difference was only that the new science was more in agreement with the facts, and that its methods were better able to cope with problems than were the methods of Aristotle. Yet, what really happened was a changing over from a primarily philosophical system to a primarily a-philosophical system.

The increase of data in the field of practical knowledge, which increase opened up the possibility of developing specific theories meant to bind certain groups of data together, had become so large that the time was ripe to put the pieces together. The different limited theories could be united into a large one which would explain several groups of data. So the new mechanics, developed by such men as Galileo and Newton, could account not only for astronomical phenomena, but also for those of gravitation and other kinetic phenomena. And it was likely that the explanation of different physical and chemical properties of matter could be tackled by means of the same mechanical principles which were proving so tremendously fruitful in the field of mechanics.

Thus there came into existence a really new method for building up an all-embracing system of explanation, a way entirely different from the philosophical one. The basis upon which the new science was built was not philosophic reflection on the general features of matter as matter. The new science was built upon the specific behavior of the different kinds of matter. If there were general principles involved in the new science, they were none the less aimed at the explanation of *specific* behavior. The general principles of mechanics, for example, were such that they could explain the specific behavior of both "heavy" and "light" bodies.

Instead of the all-embracing philosophy which forms the backbone of the Aristotelian system, the new science was characterized, on the one hand, by a mathematical method of description which gave the new science its unity and, on the other hand, by the requirement that each consequence of the new science ought to be confirmed by experience. As has been mentioned several times, the importance of these two characteristics of science was not discovered for the first time in the 17th century. Both had been known for a long time—the mathematical aspect of science was stressed by Pythagoras, Plato and the

Platonists of the 15th century; the empirical aspect by Aristotle, Averroës and the Nominalists. But there had not been an effective possibility to materialize these characteristics at an early stage of human knowledge. Briefly, the new science was not a result of a new "philosophy" of science, it was the result of a long development which had to be slow.

The Reason Why the Character of the New Science Was Not Properly Understood

That the 17th century did not fully understand the importance of what really took place can easily be explained. However true it may be that Aristotle's system was chiefly philosophic, this does not change at all the fact that he himself did not make a clear distinction between philosophy and science. And there are actually many scientific theories scattered all over his different philosophic works. Aristotle's system seemed to give an answer to all kinds of problems, both philosophic and scientific.

The strong connection between philosophic and scientific explanation was not easily destroyed by the birth of the new science. People were too accustomed to seeing scientific explanations within the perspective of an all-embracing philosophical outlook. Therefore, from the moment the Aristotelian system appeared not to be satisfactory, scientists looked for another philosophical system within which their scientific explanations could be fitted. The need for such a philosophical system to replace that of Aristotle caused a whole series of systems of philosophical atomism to flourish.

Revival of Atomism as Philosophical Background of the New Science. There was a revival, for instance, of the old doctrine of Democritus: the system of Gassendi is an example of this; whereas Descartes, on the other hand, proposed a more or less original atomic theory. The differences were, philosophically speaking, rather important, but the prominent thinkers of the 17th century did not pay much attention to it. Their main interest was directed towards scientific problems. Boyle, for example, mentioned in his scientific works the atomic theory of both Descartes and Gassendi as fundamental to his system of thought. However, he barely mentioned the considerable philosophical differences between them. He focused his attention on the practical use he could make of the general idea of a corpuscular theory. For that reason he modeled his corpuscular theory according to the requirements of his chemical needs without being too anxious to maintain the philosophic principles underlying the atomic theory.

The attitude of Boyle towards the corpuscular theory offers a good illustration of our thesis: first, that a shift of mainly philosophical problems to mainly scientific problems took place; and, secondly, that contemporaries of that shift were not fully aware of its import. Boyle's interest was scientific and not philosophical, but he could see his scientific theories only in the light of an all-embracing philosophical system, namely, a philosophical atomism. Boyle did not, however, reflect upon the philosophical principles of that atomism. The principles were not the real corner-stones of his system. His system itself was mainly based upon scientific arguments. The fact, however, that his scientific theories seemed to be a continuation of a philosophical doctrine had the natural consequence that Boyle was not fully aware of the change in attitude that had occurred towards the phenomena of nature.

Difference Between Aristotle and Boyle. The difference between Aristotle's attitude and that of Boyle can be briefly stated. Aristotle's system was chiefly concerned with philosophical problems. Reflection on them formed the backbone of his system, whereas scientific problems were more or less intruded in a rather incoherent way. Boyle's system, on the other hand, was scientific, but it was seen as a continuation of a philosophic system. Thus both systems seemed to be attempts to give a complete view of the material world. They seemed to be competitive systems of explanations, working in exactly the same field.[11]

The Reason Why Aristotle Was Entirely Abandoned

Since the main interest of thinkers of the 17th century was directed towards scientific problems, there could be for them no serious doubt which of the two competing systems, that of Aristotle or that of the new science, was the better. They compared both systems on the basis of their respective ability to solve scientific problems. And on that basis the overwhelming evidence pointed in the direction of the new science. Still another point deserves our attention in this connection. Strange as it perhaps may seem, it is

---

[11]The titles of the famous works of Newton and Dalton are significant, namely, *Philosophiae Naturalis Principia Mathematica,* and *A New System of Chemical Philosophy.*

an historical fact that the Aristotelians of the 17th century not only did very little to prevent the misunderstanding of the chiefly philosophic nature of their system, but they even contributed considerably to that misunderstanding. But let us do justice to them; they could hardly help it. They were victims of historical circumstances.

Misuse of Philosophical Concepts. In order to understand the historical situation, it should be remembered that the events of the 17th century did not come all of a sudden; they had been prepared in the foregoing centuries. In these centuries the new scientific discoveries had been expressed in terms of the then preponderantly *philosophical* system. And that was not only because of the spirit of the times, which thought first of an all-embracing philosophical outlook of the world, but also because a specific scientific terminology had not yet come into existence. Philosophic terms, however, are not suited to scientific purposes. Terms like matter and form, the main terms of Aristotle's doctrine for explaining the possibility of change and of the existence of several individuals of one kind, are of no use to account for the typical features of a particular change. To say, for example, that gold does not oxidize on account of the *substantial form* of gold is to say nothing, especially when the problem comes up as to why gold does not oxidize, whereas iron does. The natural result of this misapplication of philosophical terminology was that the scientists of the 17th century who had a new set of more or less purely scientific concepts at their disposal, as for example, Boyle, declared the whole concept of substantial form useless. And they were partly right, for philosophical concepts are useless for the problems the scientists were interested in. This, however, was not the only result of the misapplication of philosophic terms. Another was even more important. By using philosophic terms to explain non-philosophic problems, many Aristotelians themselves lost the proper perspective for viewing those philosophical problems for which these terms were originally designed. As a result, they came to speak a language which they themselves no longer understood and which seemed to have no bearing whatsoever upon the real problems of their day—neither upon scientific problems, to which the terms did not apply, nor upon philosophical problems, because attention was not directed toward them. Because of the gradual development of scientific theories and because of the corresponding shift of interest which had already taken place before the 17th century, the Aristotelian "philosophers" with scientific interest were helpless victims of their own terminology.

As a result of this situation, Aristotelian philosophy did not find any effective advocates among those interested in the study of nature. This makes it understandable why an essentially positive, i.e. a-philosophical, science could supersede an essentially philosophical system of thought. They were considered competitors in the same field, not only by the representatives of the new science, but also by the Aristotelians.

Theology and the New Science. The rest of the story can be told quickly. It was not long before Aristotle's system was entirely abandoned. His influence held out longest in theological circles, where the great mediaeval scholastic tradition, in which the Aristotelian-Thomistic school ranked first, even had a second blossoming in the 17th century (famous are John of St. Thomas and Suarez). One century later, however, the Aristotelian-Thomistic tradition disappeared completely from the *globus intellectualis*. Even Catholic theologians followed those philosophic schools of the time which were not outspokenly anti-religious. And these were not many. The fact that theologians stuck longer than any other group of thinkers to Aristotle's philosophy had seriously undermined confidence in theology. Theology seemed to be an antiquated form of explanation which would gradually disappear after the further development of science. Thus modern science came to supersede not only philosophy, but even theology.

Realization of the Difference Between Science and Philosophy

The misinterpretation of the proper character of the new positive science could not, of course, last forever. When science developed, it gradually became clear which problems could be solved by science and which not. Whereas the 17th century knows many thinkers who find their place both in the history of philosophy and in the history of science (Descartes, Leibnitz, Pascal, etc.), in the following centuries their number becomes smaller. Philosophy and science in the future go their separate ways. Although the success of science inspired many philosophers in their attempts to establish a philosophy on as solid a basis as science (Hume, Kant, Comte), they realized, as a rule, the different tasks of science and philosophy. As a result of this new reflection on the original value of philosophy (Hegel), the 19th century realized also the double character of the system of Aristotle, which thanks to the historical interest of the century was studied both in its original Greek and in its many Latin forms. We cannot, of course, discuss here the different systems of philosophy of modern times and their different attitudes towards the problems of the philosophy of nature and its relations with science. Something has been said about it in Chapter I. The discussion will be confined here to the revival of the Aristotelian philosophy in its Thomistic form, because this will give us the best opportunity to further elaborate some of the problems taken up before.

6. THE REVIVAL OF THE ARISTOTELIAN-THOMISTIC PHILOSOPHY

The Causes of the Revival

The revival of the Aristotelian-Thomistic philosophy in the course of the 19th century was certainly not caused by the desire to restore the Aristotelian philosophy of *nature*. There were other reasons. The sense for historical research, which characterized the 19th century, brought scholars and philosophers again in touch with mediaeval philosophy. It soon became clear that this philosophy had not only a historical, but also an actual value far superior to that of the philosophical systems current among theologians in the 19th century. These theologians discovered to their surprise that mediaeval thought was not at all antiquated; they found in St. Thomas and other Aristotelians a systematic exposition of the answers to the problems of their own time. In the 19th century the lack of a really solid philosophical system for theology tremendously favored the return to Thomistic philosophy, and within a few decades Thomism regained its former position in Catholic thought.

The Aristotelian Philosophy of Nature Offered a Serious Difficulty

The revival of Thomistic philosophy encountered one great difficulty. What was to be done with the Aristotelian philosophy of nature which was, as a matter of fact, one of the central parts of Thomistic philosophy? To drop this philosophy of nature would mean a real mutilation of Thomistic thought; whereas to retain it seemed impossible in view of the development of science, whose continuous success was sufficient proof of its truth. To admit that science was right seemed to imply that Aristotle's philosophy of nature was wrong. For the main issue between the new science and the old Aristotelian philosophy had been exactly the problems of the philosophy of nature.

On the other hand, the revived Aristotelian-Thomistic philosophy proved its intrinsic philosophic value in so many fields that it could hardly be assumed that an essential part of it was entirely wrong. So the first task which the revived Thomistic philosophy faced was to examine very closely its traditional philosophy of nature. Was it really true that the whole content of the Aristotelian philosophy of nature had been proved to be wrong by science? Or were only some parts of it wrong, parts which were not essential? The answers to these questions did not appear to be difficult. In the system of Aristotle a distinction must be made between philosophic principles and scientific theories. Only the latter were proved to be wrong.

That this view of Aristotle's system was correct seemed to be confirmed by an analysis of the 19th century science. In this science, as in Aristotelian science, it was possible to distinguish between philosophic principles and strictly scientific theories. Thus an analysis both of science and of the old philosophy of nature resulted in establishing that neither was homogeneous. The old philosophy of nature contained some unquestionably antiquated scientific theories; and science was concerned with certain philosophic principles. These principles were related to the principles of Democritus and were undoubtedly contrary to those of Aristotle. The question was, however, whether the philosophic principles of science were as true as science itself must be supposed to be. Was science really based upon these principles, or was there only an incidental connection between them? That was the problem to be solved.

Science Did Not Actually Confirm Democritus' Philosophy

In order to find out whether or not science was inextricably involved with Democritus' philosophic principles, the 19th century Thomistic philosophers started to make a thorough examination of the state of affairs in science. The result appeared to be very favorable to their position.

The claim, for example, of the current atomic theory of that day, that a chemical compound was nothing but an external association of the atoms of the elements, was by no means confirmed by the facts. On the contrary, the properties of chemical compounds were entirely different from the properties of the composing elements. True, certain properties of a compound, such as, for example, the molecular weight, which could be found by a simple addition of the atomic weights of the elements, seemed to favor Democritus' point of view; but these were exceptions. The whole set of properties which characterized a compound was always new in comparison with the set of properties of the elements. This confirmed the Aristotelian thesis of the existence of substantial change, the cornerstone of hylomorphism. Moreover, according to the doctrine of Democritus, all atoms ought to have the same basic nature; quantitative differences could be permitted, but not qualitative ones. Chemistry, however, ascribed to its elements qualitatively different properties.

So it seemed obvious that chemistry was entirely in accordance with Aristotle when he claimed against Democritus that a chemical reaction of two elements ought to be considered a substantial change and not a mere juxtaposition. Aristotle might have been wrong in the scientific part of his chemical theory; he was not wrong in his philosophical evaluation of the essence of a chemical reaction. He might have been wrong in his choice of elements, but not in his statement that chemical elements had different qualities. Thus there seemed no reason for the Thomistic philosophy of nature to doubt the soundness of its philosophic principles; on the contrary, they had been more strongly confirmed by science.

A Dangerous Situation. Yet, the confirmation of philosophic principles by scientific theories had its drawbacks too. There was something dangerous in the whole situation. For it could not be denied that the spirit which animated science was based upon the conviction that one day it would be possible to explain properties of compounds by properties of elements. The supposed confirmation of the principles of the Aristotelian philosophy of nature by science was due, therefore, more to a lack of development of science than to a fundamental insight on the part of science that compounds differed essentially from the composing elements. What made things still worse, science gradually succeeded in explaining more properties of compounds by means of properties of elements.

Thus it became clear that the possibility of retaining Aristotelian-Thomistic philosophic principles seemed entirely dependent upon the development of science. If science should succeed in its own program, viz. to reduce the properties of compounds from those of elements, then the Thomistic principles of the philosophy of nature could no longer be considered true. Consequently, every new scientific discovery became the subject matter of vehement philosophical discussion as to its bearing upon the supposed principles of the philosophy of nature. This was especially the case when such discovery seemed to indicate that the essential differences between different kinds of matter could be reduced simply to a different way of combining the elementary parts. In proportion as the differences between elements and chemical compounds, which were at first sight very striking, came within the reach of scientific explanation, the position of the Thomistic philosophy of nature became more difficult. This philosophy seemed able to continue its existence only because science had not developed far enough. The successive proofs, for example, which philosophy put forward in order to establish the existence of substantial change, the traditional basis of hylomorphism, had to be withdrawn again and again, as science discovered more and more of the structure of matter.

This was an extremely unpleasant situation for a philosophy which claimed that its principles were more fundamental than those of science. For the actual situation was that science determined whether or not the basis of the philosophical principles was sound.

No Sharp Distinction Between Science and the Philosophy of Nature Was Made

An examination of the discussions between the philosophers and scientists concerning the existence of "substantial change," leads to the conclusion that there had not been much of a change since the 17th century. The philosophy of nature and science were still considered competitors in the same field.[12] The cause of the misconception was also the same: namely, a lack of understanding of the precise difference between philosophic and scientific problems.

Some progress was undoubtedly made, as has been seen. The 19th century Thomistic philosophers were aware of the distinction that should be made between the current scientific theories themselves and their supposed underlying philosophic principles. However, they did not succeed in making this distinction clear. They did not succeed in outlining in an unambiguous way the different functions to be fulfilled respectively by science and by the philosophy of nature. These respective functions have something to do with a mutual completion. But if that completion is understood as a completion on the same level, then the philosophy of nature is bound to retreat steadily before

---

[12]Tongiorgi in his *Institutiones Philosophicae,* ⁵1873, pp. 215 ff., discusses hylomorphism as a scientific theory which is, as compared to the chemical atomic theory, obsolete.

advancing science. Then the philosophy of nature can only discuss in a vague way problems which science will be able to discuss in an exact way, once science has sufficiently developed to cope with these problems.

It should be recalled what has been said in Section 2 of Chapter I, entitled: "The Insufficiency of Science." These words were meant to indicate an insufficiency in principle, not a factual insufficiency. The way Thomists proposed hylomorphism after the revival of Thomistic philosophy gives the impression that they had lost sight of this important difference between insufficiency of fact and insufficiency of principle. At that time it appeared that the defense of hylomorphism was possible only because science had not yet fully succeeded in its own task. And if that were the case it is clear that the completion which the philosophy of nature had to give to science was a completion on the same level as that on which science itself works.

The fact that the histories of science and of the philosophy of nature showed so much confusion proves that the distinction between science and the philosophy of nature is not an easy one to make. This is sufficient reason to study the problem more closely. It may prevent us from drifting into the errors of the past. So the next chapter will be devoted to a careful study of both the difference and the relationship between science and the philosophy of nature.

SUGGESTED READINGS

Aristotle, *Physics* bk. I; *On Generation and Corruption*, bk. II, 1-3.

A. Mansion, *Introduction à la physique Aristotélienne*, 2nd ed., Louvain, 1945.

A. N. Whitehead, *Science and the Modern World*, 11th ed., Cambridge, 1946, Chapters I-V.

Andrew G. van Melsen, *From Atomos to Atom*, Pittsburgh, 1952, Chapters I-III.

Frederick Copleston, *A History of Philosophy*, Westminster, Md., 1950, vol. I.

E. J. Dijksterhuis, *Die Mechanisierung des Weltbildes*, Berlin, 1954.

CHAPTER THREE

THE PROPER RELATIONSHIP BETWEEN SCIENCE AND THE PHILOSOPHY OF NATURE

1. THE REASON FOR THE CONFUSION BETWEEN SCIENCE AND THE PHILOSOPHY OF NATURE

Introduction

History teaches us an important lesson about the relationship between science and the philosophy of nature. It may be that each has its own place in the study of nature, as has been pointed out in the first chapter. It seems, however, that it is very difficult for the human mind to recognize clearly what those particular places are.

Artificiality of Abstraction. In order to understand the difficulty, we must keep in mind the fact that both the philosophy of nature and science are the result of an abstraction, and that an abstraction is to a certain extent always artificial. It has been seen that the philosophy of nature is concerned only with the primary part of common experience, whereas science has exclusively to do with the primitive part of that same experience. Concrete experience itself, however, is one and undivided. We never have a primary experience apart from a primitive one. They are two different aspects of one and the same experience, related to one and the same reality. We are, however, able to consider both aspects separately and to build up two different systems of knowledge, each with its own specific set of problems and its own methods of solving these problems. But there is always a certain artificiality in doing this.

In the human mind is a natural desire for complete knowledge. Consequently, both the scientist and the philosopher have the strong tendency to consider their respective system of abstract knowledge as a knowledge of the whole reality and not of certain aspects only. This tendency is a natural response to the artificiality of abstract scientific knowledge. Therein lies the germ of the confusion between science and the philosophy of nature. Before discussing this point in further detail, an important question should be asked: namely, must the new science, born in the 17th century, be blamed or given credit for its abstract, a-philosophic character?

81

The Importance of the Discovery of Positive Science

In order to evaluate the abstract character of modern science it is necessary to stress the following. This abstract character may be artificial, considered from the point of view of the natural desire of a complete, all-embracing knowledge. It is not artificial, however, with respect to the means of knowledge available to the human mind.

All Concepts Are Abstract. The human mind has to work with concepts, and concepts are always abstract, i.e. each concept refers only to certain aspects of reality and not to all. But not only does a single concept have an abstract character, but even a combination of concepts has this character. Even the entire set of scientific concepts as a whole, arranged in such a manner that they form a scientific system, have an abstract character. True, the different scientific concepts complete each other. With the help of the concept "mass," for example, we know more about a certain object than with the concept "volume" only. Each physical concept added to the description of that object enriches our knowledge of it. The addition of a set of chemical concepts to this description again enlarges the total knowledge we have of that object, but this does not take away from the fact that certain aspects are still unrevealed.

The reader should recall what has been discussed in the first chapter. The *entire* physical and chemical knowledge of an object reveals nothing about those aspects which are discussed in epistemology. If we, with Kant, ask whether or not material reality in itself possesses the properties ascribed to it in natural science, science cannot answer. It has no means for discussing this problem. Its set of concepts does not even touch the problem, because every scientific concept is abstracted in such a way as to avoid the philosophical problem.

The Merit of Positive Science. The great merit of positive science, born in the 17th century, is precisely the discovery of the possibility of discussing scientific problems without first going into a discussion of its philosophical aspects. That is a merit, not because those philosophic problems are unimportant, but because the discussion of those problems does not contribute to the solution of any scientific problem.

This applies both to epistemological and ontological questions. The scientist does not need to consider the philosophical implications of the inductive method in order to use induction in his scientific investigations. There is no scientific purpose served in discussing what should be considered the value of a scientific law. The question as to whether a scientific law is an approximation of an inherent law of nature or only an easy way of describing certain phenomena may be very important from the philosophic point of view, but the answer is of no direct value for science. All epistemological problems are real problems for the human mind and perhaps no scientist can avoid thinking of them; but those problems are entirely outside the field of science.

The situation with regard to ontological problems is the same. Aristotle's theory of hylomorphism, without any doubt, is very important for understanding the general nature of matter, but contributes nothing to science.

The Difference Between Aristotle's Conception of Science and the Modern One. The basic difference between the Aristotelian and modern line of thought is that Aristotle was convinced that before there could even be a beginning of science, science itself must be the subject of philosophical speculation. Before the causes of different phenomena could be examined, the concept "cause" itself had to be discussed. Before a logically built scientific system could be constructed, such questions as what logic is, and why a scientific system must be logical, had to be worked out. As a matter of fact, Aristotle did not go much beyond the discussion of such philosophical problems, and we know the reason why he could not go much further and start science in the modern sense of the term.

When modern science finally did get underway, after many fruitless attempts, it gradually became clear that Aristotle's conviction was wrong. We do not need an elaborate philosophical reflection upon epistemological and ontological problems to start science. The solution of the philosophical problems is not a necessary condition for the construction of a scientific system. The discovery of this truth is perhaps the greatest discovery in the history of science and in the history of human thought in general. It is the discovery of the independence of the scientific approach. The scientific approach is independent of the elaboration of the philosophical implications of that approach.

The Fallacy of Misplaced Concreteness

The autonomy of positive science brings with it a danger, the danger that Whitehead has appropriately called "the fallacy of misplaced concreteness."[1] Because of the autonomy of science, the scientist may be inclined to overlook the abstract character of his science. For science does not exist in itself. It exists only as a knowledge in man. And man has a desire for complete knowledge; he wants to know reality according to all its aspects, in its full concreteness. As a result, the scientist is never content with his abstract scientific knowledge in its abstractness; he always projects his knowledge against a certain philosophical background, as has been seen in the first chapter of this book. Thus scientific knowledge to the scientist loses its abstract character; it seems to be a complete knowledge of the material world. He becomes a victim of "the fallacy of misplaced concreteness."

The result is that the so-called world-picture of the scientist is composed of two elements, a well-thought-out scientific part and a spontaneous and rather primitive philosophical conviction which is usually not well analyzed.

However, the scientist is not the only one who ought to be careful not to fall into the trap of the said fallacy. The philosopher has to watch his step too. For, although the nature of philosophic abstraction is quite different from the nature of that of science (as Section 3 of this Chapter will show), it is nevertheless true that philosophic speculation is also an abstract speculation. And the philosopher likewise has a natural inclination comparable with that of the scientist (since both are human beings); he has the tendency to bring his philosophical abstraction back to a complete reality by combining his philosophical theory with considerations which belong to the field of science. Not being a scientist, however, the philosopher runs the risk of using primitive pre-scientific data to complete his knowledge. As the scientist sees his abstract scientific knowledge in a philosophical perspective, so the philosopher sees the general nature of matter, which he studies, realized in concrete material things. And the way he looks upon concrete material things is determined not only by his philosophy, but also by everyday experience, i.e. primitive, seemingly obvious, convictions about material things.

Thus the philosopher and the scientist are both likely to make the same mistake, namely the mistake of trying to complete their own restricted and abstract way of thought by the use of data borrowed from another system, without, however, being fully aware that they are completing it.

---

[1] A. N. Whitehead, *Science and the Modern World,* 1926, Ch. IV.

Science and the Philosophy of Nature Seem to Be Competitive Theories

In view of the ease with which both the scientist and the philosopher can fall into the same error, is there any reason for being surprised at the perpetual confusion and misunderstanding which the history of science and philosophy shows us? It may be possible to determine carefully the scientific level of abstraction on which science works, safeguarded by the objective methods of science; but the scientist himself is more than a scientist. He is not only the executor of scientific methods and the deviser of scientific theories, he is also a human being, interested in all reality. As a result, he leaves in his final evaluation of the material world the level of abstraction which in science itself is carefully maintained. The fact that he is not always aware that he superimposes the philosophic viewpoint upon scientfic theories makes things only worse and increases the confusion. For he considers his view of the material world to be the outgrowth of his scientfic knowledge, whereas it is, in reality, a combination of science and philosophy. And the scientist is all the more confirmed in his conviction that he is right in his conclusions when he encounters the philosopher of nature who has a different understanding of the material world. If the philosopher were careful to restrict himself to really philosophic theses, then those theses would be a revelation to the scientist. They would make the scientist aware of the philosophic aspects which did not originate in science, but which nevertheless are present in a total view of nature. Often, however, what is called the philosophy of nature is, as has been seen, a mixture of philosophy and science. The natural result is that the scientist, who as scientist is, of course, more attuned to scientific than to philosophic considerations, is convinced that this pseudo-philosophy of nature is nothing but an old-fashioned scientific doctrine built upon primitive experience. So he rejects the whole thing as being inferior to his own system.

On the other hand, the philosopher notices that the science of the scientist contains many philosophic ideas which he considers wrong. The philosopher will never go so far as to reject science entirely— science has proved only too well its right to exist—but he will certainly reject a good many of the scientific conclusions which seem, philosophically speaking, to be wrong.

In this way the philosopher judges what is supposed to be only science, and the scientist what is supposed to be only philosophy. This is possible because science is not purely science, and philosophy not purely philosophy. Both are more or less complete and, therefore,

competitive theories of the material world. This completeness makes
it seem as if one had to choose between them.

Both the Scientist and the Philosopher Are Responsible for the Confusion

It is a matter not devoid of theoretical interest to ask: Who is
mostly to blame for the unfortunate and confusing situation which
exists between science and the philosophy of nature? Both the philosopher and the scientist are to blame, for each is a trespasser. The
question as to the greater guilt is not so easy to answer.

At first sight, we would be inclined to say that the philosopher
should be held more responsible, for it belongs to the very task of
the philosopher to reflect upon what he is doing. Science can be
cultivated in a certain unawareness of the philosophical principles
involved. Science does not require for its own sake philosophic
reflection upon what science is. Philosophy, however, does require
such a reflection. Therefore, the philosopher, when he gets involved
among different levels of abstraction, is more guilty than the scientist.

On the other hand, however, the philosopher lacks the support of
methods which keeps the scientist almost automatically on his own
level of abstraction. If the scientist paid attention to his own methods,
then he would be sure to be warned when he moved outside them.
The same applies to the concepts he uses. The poor philosopher,
however, has to watch carefully every step he takes. His philosophical
concepts are more apt to obscure than to clarify the philosophical level
of abstraction. Recall, for example, the Aristotelian concepts of
primary matter and of substantial form. They refer to the "parts"
of matter. The concept "part" is, however, used in an analogous sense
and should not be understood as "part" where used in the normal
physical sense. An inconsiderate use of the term "part" will, therefore,
become a source of misunderstanding; it requires a continuous intellectual effort to understand the term in the right context. The same
applies to the concept "species-individual structure," of which so
much has been spoken. The philosopher is bound to use a term like
"structure," but again he is not making the normal scientific use of
this term. Philosophical "structure" is not a "structure" in the
physical sense.[2] This possible confusion in terminology makes the
task of the philosopher of nature not at all easy. He is no more to

_____

[2]See the footnote concerning the analogy of philosophical terms and concepts
on p. 141.

blame than the scientist for confusing science and the philosophy of nature.

Conclusion

Two important conclusions can be drawn from what has been said in this section. First, the confusion between science and the philosophy of nature is not accidental, not caused by a special historical situation, such as that of the 17th century. The confusion is closely bound up with the fact that it is difficult for the human mind to stay on just one level of abstraction.

And this leads us to the second conclusion. If we want to avoid the existing confusion, then it is a matter of necessity to clarify ideas dealing with the different levels of abstraction and their respective characteristics. The next sections, therefore, will deal with abstraction in general and with the different possible levels of abstraction.

2. THE NATURE OF ABSTRACTION

General Meaning of Abstraction

In philosophic usage, the concept "abstraction" is more restricted than it is in ordinary language. In ordinary language we call "abstract" every consideration or reasoning which does not take into account the whole and full reality, but which leaves certain details out of consideration. Such an abstract method of consideration is usually the result of a necessity to simplify or schematize the problems considered. Such problems are, originally, too complicated; the only way to cope with them at all is to remodel them in such a way that they are similar to problems which we can handle. The natural consequence of such simplification is, however, that we never can be sure that the outcome of our considerations applies to reality. For what we are considering is not the full reality, but a simplified and schematized reality.

Mechanics offers good examples of such schematizations. If, for instance, the behavior of a gas is calculated, the assumption is made that all molecules are spheres with perfect elasticity, although every scientist knows that this assumption is very likely to be untrue. But this simplifying assumption is a matter of necessity. If we do not neglect the different possible shapes of molecules, then the application of the law of impact becomes too complicated. Of course, we are perfectly aware of the possibility of the results of our calculations not being in agreement with reality, but we take the chance. The result will prove whether or not the simplification was justified.

It must be understood that scientists do not schematize and simplify haphazardly; careful attention must be paid to the extension of the schematization. Only such particulars may be disregarded as are not expected to be of much importance, but which would complicate the calculations in such a way that the solution would either be entirely impossible or unwarrantably difficult. Careful as such schematizations may be, however, they always mean a certain falsification of the physical reality involved. Reality does not have such perfect mathematical form and such idealized physical properties as are assumed in mechanics.

The Meaning of the Term "Abstraction" in Philosophy.

What the philosopher means by abstraction is something different from what the scientist means by schematization or simplification. In abstraction, as in scientific schematization, not the whole and full reality is considered; the difference is this that in abstraction those aspects which are left out of consideration are irrelevant to the solution of the problem under consideration. If I want to determine the dimensions of my desk for example, I do not have to know whether the desk is made of wood or of iron. For the purpose of measuring I have only to consider the shape. It is clear that the shape does not give me a complete knowledge of my desk, but it does give me an adequate knowledge of that in which I am interested. What was left out of consideration did not really matter for my purpose. Thus abstraction gives an *incomplete* but *true* knowledge of what is considered separately, because it can be considered separately without violating reality.

Schematization, on the other hand, always violates reality because it modifies reality. It neglects details which, properly speaking, should not be neglected because they are details of those aspects which are actually under consideration. Thus the similarity between abstraction and schematization is that the result of both is a partial knowledge. The difference is that abstraction gives a *true* partial knowledge, whereas schematization can at best give only an approximately true partial knowledge.

Abstraction and Schematization

It is of interest to note that abstraction is a more fundamental process than schematization. All our intellectual knowledge is abstract, because we always abstract from the individual as such. It may be recalled from the first chapter, for example, that all scientific concepts refer to certain specific features of reality and never to individuality. Even the most complete scientific knowledge of a certain object is composed of a series of universal concepts. Each of these universal concepts can be applied to other individual objects.

An individual piece of iron, for example, is known to me as being iron, as having a certain shape, a certain weight, a certain color, etc., all of these being concepts which are also applicable to objects other than to that particular piece of iron, at least in principle. For even if the color, shape, or weight of an individual piece is unique, then that supposition would mean that this color, shape or weight exists only in that particular piece of iron. But it still remains true that nothing in the concept of this color, shape or weight would prevent the application of the same concept to another object. The very fact that we stress the uniqueness of the color, shape, or weight proves that the uniqueness is something special. The uniqueness has nothing to do with the concept, but with the application of the concept to reality. The concept itself allows us to look for other possible things having the same color, shape, or weight. For the concept of that special color, shape, or weight as concept, has been abstracted from the individuality of the color, shape, or weight as found in that particular piece of iron.

Since now human intellectual knowledge must always use concepts, and since concepts are always abstract, it follows that all our intellectual activities have a certain abstract character. Abstractness is an "omnipresent" characteristic of all human intellectual knowledge.

Schematization Supposes Abstraction. That all human knowledge is abstract carries with it the fact that every schematization is accompanied by an abstraction, whereas the reverse is not necessarily true. In order to see that a schematization is always accompanied by an abstraction is is sufficient to recall what a schematization is. It is a simplification of reality in such a way that some details are so remodeled that certain concepts can be applied to the object under consideration. The mechanical concept of spheres possessing perfect elasticity, for example, can be used only in connection with molecules if we first idealize the molecules a little bit. Thus it is clear that there are two simultaneous processes involved: a schematization of certain objects, and an application of abstract concepts of the schematized objects. For the mechanical concepts we use are abstract concepts; as such they can be applied to any object which has the properties present in these concepts. The fact that we first have to idealize the objects in order to make the application possible in this special case does not mean that the concepts themselves do not have a basic abstract character. On the contrary, this character of abstractness makes the application, in principle, precisely possible. Schematization, therefore, presupposes abstraction.

Abstraction Does Not Suppose Schematization. It had been stated above that the converse is not always true; not every abstraction is based upon a schematization. Nor is every abstraction accompanied by a process of schematization. This thesis is of great importance for the correct understanding of the relationship between philosophy and science. For if no abstraction were possible without schematization, then no true partial knowledge would be possible. And what is still more important, neither positive science nor the philosophy of nature could exist as an autonomous approach to nature. For positive science abstracts from the philosophical aspects, whereas the philosophy of nature abstracts from the scientific ones. The very existence, therefore, of positive science would be endangered if it were not possible to study certain aspects of the material world without paying attention to those aspects which in Chapter I were called the generic aspects of matter. The development which the history of science shows in the birth of a positive science, i.e. a science whose problems can be solved independently of the solution of philosophical problems, is possible only because of the fundamentally abstract character of human knowledge. Likewise, the possibility of proposing a philosophy of nature which is independent of science is based upon that same fundamental fact. There are different levels or different degrees of abstraction, and the mind can examine the material world separately on these different levels of abstraction without violating reality. Of course, the result of such an examination at any special level can never produce a complete knowledge of reality; it can produce, however, a true knowledge. The given limitation on a certain level of abstraction does not necessarily mean a distortion of reality.

3. THE THREE LEVELS OF ABSTRACTION

The Various Expositions of St. Thomas

It is a curious fact that, although positive science is a product of modern times, the possibility of such a science was to a certain extent already anticipated by ancient philosophers, such as Aristotle, and certain mediaeval philosophers, such as Thomas Aquinas. The fact is curious but not unexplainable. For the correct distinction of the different levels of abstraction is a problem of epistemology, and that means of philosophy. And philosophy does not need such a detailed experience for its conclusions as does science. Therefore, a great philosopher could be able to distinguish between the different possibilities of building up systematic knowledge in an age when these possibilities were not yet fully realized.

Thomas Aquinas especially, while following the trend of thought of Aristotle, gives us in a treatise[3] on the different degrees of abstraction a surprisingly clear description of what we today call science, and also of its difference from philosophy. Naturally, the fact that in the Aristotelian system science and philosophy were *de facto* not kept clearly apart caused confusion in the use of St. Thomas' terminology. In particular, the position of the philosophy of nature is not entirely clear on account of the fact that in the Aristotelian system no difference is made between science and the philosophy of nature. Yet, a careful study of the whole treatise of St. Thomas does not leave us in doubt as to the difference between science and the philosophy of nature insofar as their different levels of abstraction are concerned. As a matter of fact, we think St. Thomas' expositions so clear that they serve as a guide through the following analysis of the degrees of abstraction.

St. Thomas propounds several different expositions, each exposition being the result of a different approach. Only two shall be discussed here, but for purpose of a better understanding some data of other expositions shall be added.

First Exposition. In Question V, art. 1, of the commentary on the *De Trinitate* of Boethius, St. Thomas distinguishes the different levels or degrees of abstraction as follows. The first degree of abstraction considers reality with all its attendant material properties. It abstracts of course, from the individuality as such, but it does not abstract from the material properties known by sense-experience.

[The objects in this degree of abstraction are, therefore,] dependent upon matter as to their existence, since they cannot exist

---

[3]*In Boethium de Trinitate.* Quotations in this section are borrowed from the English translation of Sister Rose E. Brennan. B. Herder, St. Louis—London, 1946. All quotations are compared to the critical edition of the *Quaestiones Quinta et Sexta,* recently published by Paul Wyser, Fribourg—Louvain, 1948.

except in matter, and these are distinguished because they depend on matter both really and logically, such as things whose definition posits sensible matter. Hence, they cannot be understood without sensible matter, as, for example, in the definition of man it is necessary to include flesh and bones; and with things of this kind physics, or natural science, is concerned.

[Second degree of abstraction.] But certain other things, although they depend upon matter as to their existence, do not so depend as far as the intellect is concerned; because in a definition of them sensible matter is not included, as in the case of lines and numbers with which mathematics deals.

[Third degree of abstraction.] But there are still other objects of speculation that do not depend upon matter for existence, because they can exist without matter: either they are never found in matter, as God and the angels, or they are sometimes in matter and in other cases not, as substance, quality, potency, act, one, and many, and things of this sort.[4]

The first impression we might get, from this exposition of St. Thomas is that both science and the philosophy of nature belong to the level of the first degree of abstraction. For the philosophy of nature is concerned, as is science, with those objects which cannot exist without matter. Moreover, when St. Thomas speaks of physics, he has in mind the physics of Aristotle, which is chiefly a philosophy of nature. On the other hand, it can be argued that the philosophy of nature uses such concepts as substance, potency, act, quality, which St. Thomas listed under the third degree of abstraction. More light is thrown on this question when we consider another approach of St. Thomas. It can be found in the second article of Question VI.

Second Exposition. St. Thomas makes here a distinction between the beginning and the end of our knowledge. The beginning of any of our cognitions is in sensation.

But the terminus, or goal, of cognition is not uniformly the same; for it is sometimes in sensation [natural science], sometimes in imagination [mathematics], and sometimes in the intellect alone [metaphysics]. When it is case of the properties and accidents of a thing which are demonstrated by sensation, these adequately disclose the nature of the thing, and then the judgment regarding the truth of the thing, which the intellect makes, ought to conform to the things that are known with certainty by the senses concerning it. Of this order are all things of the natural world which are

---

[4]*In Boethium de Trinitate*, Q. V. art. 1. English translation, p. 135.

determined to sensible matter. Hence, in natural science, cognition should be terminated at sense knowledge, since we judge of natural things in accordance with what sense experience demonstrates about them, as III *De Cŏelo et Mundo* declares.[5]

This quotation gives a very accurate description of one of the most striking features of modern science. Modern science not only starts with sense-experience, but also ends with it. For the ultimate confirmation of a scientific judgment is always to be found in observation or experiment. For the value of a scientific theory it is not decisive, whether it gives a beautiful theoretical explanation of the phenomena for whose explanation the theory was devised, nor whether it seems in agreement with certain philosophical or mathematical considerations. What is decisive is whether or not the theory is capable of an experimental confirmation. Thus, in order to convince scientists of the truth of what the scientific atomic theory says about the structure of matter, it is not alone sufficient that this theory explain many chemical phenomena, but also the structure itself must be proved in a more direct experimental way, as is really done in the modern atomic theory.

An Example of a Scientific Theory

An excellent example of the way theories are first conceived in order to explain certain phenomena and are then confirmed is offered to us in the theory of the so-called tetrahedron structure of carbon compounds. Jacob H. van 't Hoff proposed this theory in order to explain isomerism. Isomerism means that compounds composed of the same elements in the same proportions, and having the same molecular weight, can have different properties. Isomerism is especially important in organic chemistry, where the number of isomeric compounds in some instances is very great. This fact is a consequence of the tendency of carbon to form compounds which contain chains of many atoms of carbon. And the number of isomeric compounds increases tremendously in proportion with the number of atoms of carbon. To mention only one instance, in the series of the so-called saturated hydrocarbons, a series of compounds, all of which consist of atoms of carbon and hydrogen exclusively, the following number of isomers can be found: While there is only one compound with the formula CH_4, one with the formula C_2H_6 and one with the formula

---

[5]Q. VI, art. 2, p. 183-184.

C_3H_8, there are two with the formula C_4H_{10} and three with the formula C_5H_{12}. But C_6H_{14} already has five isomers, C_7H_{16} nine, and thereafter the number increases rapidly. For example, $C_{10}H_{22}$ has 72 isomers.

Even a Successful Hypothesis Needs Confirmation. The hypothesis of van 't Hoff, assuming that atoms of carbon are always located in the center of a tetrahedron whereas the other atoms or groups of atoms are located in the four corners, could account for the exact number of isomers. So we have here the situation, mentioned above, that a physical hypothesis can explain in a perfect way the phenomena under consideration. Yet there is something unsatisfactory. For if it is really true that compounds of carbon have the spatial structure which the theory of van 't Hoff attributed to them, then it must be possible to confirm this spatial structure in a more direct way. A spatial structure is something that can be observed, at least in principle. Valuable as the idea of that spatial structure may be for explaining the phenomena of isomerism, still the scientist is not satisfied in merely assuming something that is open to a more direct observation. As a matter of fact, van 't Hoff himself perhaps never dreamed of the possibility of a more direct confirmation of his theory. The practical difficulties connected with the observation of so small a spatial structure seemed too great.

However, such difficulties are accidental; every scientific hypothesis by its very nature as *scientific* hypothesis must be subject to a more or less direct confirmation, i.e. a confirmation by a method especially designed to observe such properties as are proposed in the hypothesis. The confirmation of a spatial structure by phenomena of another nature (isomerism) which can be considered remote effects of that spatial structure is, of course, important, but the theoretical distance is too great to confirm directly the spatial structure. There always remains the possibility that a different hypothesis can explain the same phenomena. The final judgment of a physical hypothesis can only be something that is able to confirm directly what is stated in the hypothesis.

The Importance of Direct Confirmation. In the case of the hypothesis of van 't Hoff, such a confirmation was later given by means of X-rays, which can detect spatial structures far beyond the possibilities of our normal observation. Experiments with X-rays confirmed in a splendid way the hypothesis of van 't Hoff. Naturally, observation of a spatial structure by means of X-rays implies some theoretical considerations. It is never a direct observation. This, however, is not the important point. The important point is that the technique of using X-rays was especially developed to observe and measure spatial structures and nothing but spatial structures. The fact that X-ray analysis shows precisely the same structure as was formerly assumed in order to explain isomerism is, therefore, more than just another confirmation of an hypothesis already confirmed in different ways. It is the direct experimental confirmation of theoretically assumed properties of a theoretically assumed structure.

We have dwelt a considerable time upon this point in order to illustrate the way science works. Science is not satisfied in merely proposing an hypothesis which explains the phenomena involved; it always seeks further for a more or less direct confirmation of what is assumed in the hypothesis. To say it in a different way, the final judgment regarding the truth of a scientific hypothesis or theory is not so much based upon the explanatory value of this hypothesis or theory as upon the more or less direct experimental confirmation of what is proposed in that theory or hypothesis.

Such a confirmation is, of course, only possible when the concepts in which the content of a theory is proposed are concepts of such a nature that the judgments (theses) which contain these concepts can *be subject to an experimental confirmation*. That was, for example, the case with the theory of van 't Hoff. Whether or not spatial structure has certain properties can be decided by certain experiments, devised for the purpose of examining spatial structures.

An Example of a Philosophic Theory

Let us now consider, by way of contrast, a theory in the field of the philosophy of nature, as, for example, Aristotle's hylomorphism. It is clear that the starting-point of this theory also lies in sense-experience. In this respect it does not differ from a scientific theory. If we ask, however, by what means can hylomorphism be confirmed, then its difference from a scientific theory becomes obvious. The final judgment regarding the truth or falsehood of hylomorphism must be based upon intellectual considerations alone: for instance, does this doctrine really explain the possibility of change, and is it the only doctrine which can do so? Does it really explain the species-individual structure of matter? The answer to such questions is decisive for the value of the doctrine. The concepts of primary matter and of substantial form used in hylomorphism are concepts which do not offer any possibility of confirmation by sense-experience. Sense-experience can teach us the existence of change and of a species-individual structure, but it can never confirm in a direct way the content of the intellectual conclusion which Aristotle drew from the existence of change. This marks precisely the difference from a scientific theory. The content of the intellectual conclusion which van 't Hoff drew from the existence of isomerism was itself open to confirmation by sense-experience.

Consequently, according to St. Thomas, we have to consider hylomorphism a doctrine which belongs entirely to the third degree of abstraction, namely, that degree where the terminus of our knowledge lies in the intellect alone.

Seeming Inconsistency Between the Two Expositions of St. Thomas

The clear distinction which St. Thomas makes between the three degrees of abstraction according to the differences in the respective terminus of cognition leaves us no choice with respect to the position of the philosophy of nature. It belongs to the third degree of abstraction. The terminus of cognition is in the intellect alone.

The difficulty is, however, that the first exposition of St. Thomas, based upon the dependence on matter of the objects which the intellect can consider, suggests strongly a different solution. Judged by the criteria of this exposition, the philosophy of nature seemed to belong to the first degree of abstraction, although this was not entirely clear. So it must be asked whether there is really a contradiction between the two expositions of St. Thomas. In order to answer that question, both expositions and their respective criteria of distinction must be more closely examined.

It has already been pointed out how perfectly the second exposition of St. Thomas describes both the character of modern natural science and of modern philosophy. Therefore, regardless of what the interpretation of the first exposition should be with respect to the position of the philosophy of nature, in the light of the development of science and the philosophy of nature there can be hardly any doubt that the second approach of St. Thomas is correct. There is no way of stating more clearly the differences between science, mathematics, and philosophy than the way St. Thomas did when he drew attention to the differences in the terminus of cognition.

The terminus of cognition in science is always sense-experience; whereas it is equally true that the terminus of philosophical judgments lies in the intellect alone. Sense-experience gives us a start in philosophy, but we never get a chance to go back to sense-experience to confirm philosophical judgments resulting from the reflection upon the data of sense-experience.

So far the position of mathematics has not been discussed. So let us consider it briefly and see whether the modern position of mathematics confirms the typical character St. Thomas ascribes to that branch of knowledge.

The Position of Mathematics

St. Thomas refers to the imagination as the terminus of cognition in mathematics. Here, once more, the criterion of St. Thomas is very interesting. For the criterion by which modern mathematics judges its theses is not whether or not they are in agreement with the data of sense-experience, nor whether or not they are to be considered necessarily true by a judgment of the intellect. The only criterion is whether they are in agreement with certain axioms we have imagined ourselves.

Now it is undoubtedly true that St. Thomas did not, first of all, think of the possibility of constructing mathematical systems not in agreement with sense-experience when he spoke of the imagination as the final judge. He had in mind that objects studied by mathematics need to exist only in our imagination. Their actual realization in matter is irrelevant. Neither is actual sense-experience needed to study the properties of mathematical objects. But the fact remains that, by appointing the imagination as the final judge in mathematics, and not "sense-experience" and "intellect alone," St. Thomas has shown a strikingly good understanding of the typical position of mathematics in the field of knowledge. His characterization, based upon the mathematics of his time, was broad enough to allow for the modern development. So our conclusion is once again that, considered from the viewpoint of the development of science, mathematics, and philosophy, St. Thomas' reference to a difference in terminus of cognition in order to characterize the three degrees of abstraction is undoubtedly correct. From this it follows that the philosophy of nature does not belong on the same level of abstraction as science.

Science and the Philosophy of Nature Do Not Belong on the Same Level of Abstraction

It has been shown how strongly St. Thomas' distinction between the three degrees of abstraction, based upon a difference of terminus of cognition, is supported by the modern position of science, mathematics, and philosophy.

Yet, the fact remains that the exposition which St. Thomas gives in Q. 5, art. 1 of *In Boethium de Trinitate* suggests that the philosophy of nature belongs to the first degree of abstraction. For the philosophy of nature deals exclusively with matter. There seems no possibility of avoiding this conclusion. Many Thomists, as a matter of fact, draw this conclusion. By doing this, however, they have great difficulties in explaining the obvious difference between science and the philosophy of nature. Therefore, a discussion of these difficulties may contribute to a better understanding of the position of the philosophy of nature.

Considering science and the philosophy of nature as of the same degree of abstraction is contrary to the factual status these systems hold today. Let us mention only a few points: If the philosophy of nature belongs to the first degree of abstraction, then a very great distinction must be made between metaphysics and the philosophy of nature to account for the fact that they belong to different degrees of abstraction. As a matter of fact, however, the philosopher of nature works with the same kind of concepts as does the metaphysician. The metaphysician and the philosopher of nature fully understand each other because they speak the same language, whereas the scientist and the philosopher of nature speak different languages. It may be that the metaphysician is interested in certain problems with which the philosopher of nature is not immediately concerned as, for instance, the existence of God. But these problems do not require a different mental attitude. The right understanding of that status of being which is typical of matter leads in a natural way to general metaphysical problems.

On the other hand, when the scientist gets interested in philosophical problems, he needs new concepts, a new attitude of mind, and new methods of dealing with those philosophical problems. It is difficult to see why this would be true if science and the philosophy of nature belonged to the same degree of abstraction.

Science Belongs to the First Degree of Abstraction

The difficulties in placing science and the philosophy of nature in the same degree of abstraction causes some Thomistic philosophers to say that science does not belong to what St. Thomas and Aristotle called *scientia,* or *epistèmè,* but that it has more or less the nature of an art, *a technè.* There are several reasons why this is not a very satisfactory solution. For although this solution accounts for the obvious difference between science and the philosophy of nature, it does not explain how it is possible for the problems of metaphysics to be expressed in the same language as those of the philosophy of nature. But that is not the main objection.

The main objection is that saying that science is not *scientia* but *technè* puts science outside the field of theoretical knowledge. It may be that the most striking success of modern science has been in its applications in technical fields, but that successful application itself is the result of theoretical insight. The great development of the arts was possible only after a theoretical insight into the phenomena of nature had been obtained. To call science, therefore, only an art is depriving modern science of precisely that characteristic by which it has been able to guide *technè,* namely its theoretical insights. These theoretical insights into the structure of matter explain clearly the different phenomena of nature and make it, at the same time, possible to master nature for technical purposes.

Furthermore, if modern science stood outside the degrees of abstraction, what could then be the use of the exposition of those degrees? For what is the use of a division of theoretical knowledge according to different degrees of abstraction if one of the most important theoretical sciences of our time should be left out of consideration? Then the only conclusion would be that the division of the three degrees of abstraction is old-fashioned and based upon a misunderstanding of science.

Finally, St. Thomas himself did not hesitate in his discussion of the degrees of abstraction, to introduce prototypes of modern science, already known in his time: namely, astronomy and music. Astronomy and music formed a special problem for him, because they dealt with material phenomena, whereas their method was mathematical. For that very reason St. Thomas called them *"scientiae mediae,"* that is, intermediary sciences which use both the mathematical and the physical degrees of abstraction.

Consequently, to leave modern science out of the discussion of the degrees of abstraction is certainly not in agreement with the intention of St. Thomas. There is no reason to deprive modern science, with its predominant use of mathematics, of that standing which St. Thomas had already given to astronomy. The problem of the mathematical character of modern science will be discussed later on.[6] Right now the purpose is only to make clear that, whatever the status of modern science may be, whether it belongs only to the first degree of abstraction or to both the first and second degrees, it cannot be put outside the field of theoretical knowledge. Its status with respect to the different degrees of abstraction must be considered, and then it will be clear that modern science certainly belongs to the first degree of abstraction. For the present, it can be left undecided whether or not the mathematical influence in modern science is reason enough to speak of a *"scientia media."*

Philosophy of Nature Belongs to the Third Degree of Abstraction

The foregoing discussion should have made clear why there are insurmountable difficulties in placing the philosophy of nature in the first degree of abstraction. This degree is the degree of natural science; and the obvious difference between the philosophy of nature and modern natural science makes it impossible to place both in the same degree of abstraction. Doing this would take away all real value and meaning from the differences between the degrees of abstraction.

There can be no doubt that there really is a difference of degree of abstraction between science and the philosophy of nature. Present-day intellectual activity proves that. Science, mathematics and philosophy represent fundamentally different attitudes of mind towards reality. The mind considers in each of these attitudes fundamentally different aspects of reality. As a result, the concepts of these different *scientiae* have a different relation to sense-experience, and the judgments formed with the help of these concepts are confirmed in three different ways. The truth of physical judgments must be established by sense-experience; mathematical judgments must conform with certain axioms; and philosophical judgments can be proved true or false only by an intellectual analysis which shows the inevitableness of these judgments.

This clear-cut distinction between science, mathematics, and philosophy leaves, as has been repeatedly said, no doubt as to where

---

[6]See Chapter V, Section 1 and Chapter VI, Section 3.

to place the philosophy of nature. It belongs to the third degree of abstraction. This conclusion remains inescapable, even if it should be true that St. Thomas' exposition, based upon the dependence on matter of the objects which the intellect can consider, leads to another conclusion. Meanwhile, it is not St. Thomas who forces his followers, in that exposition, to place the philosophy of nature in the first degree of abstraction. This exposition can easily be understood in such a way that there is no opposition to what is said in Q. VI. The only thing to do is to read carefully St. Thomas' answer to certain objections which can be made against his doctrine.

The Solution of the Seeming Inconsistency

The first objection and answer deal with the question as to whether or not metaphysics should consider matter and motion. Metaphysics is supposed to consider only those objects which do not depend upon matter for their existence. Thus matter and motion seem to lie entirely outside the realm of metaphysical speculation. Hence the following objection:

> According to the Philosopher (I *Poster.*), it pertains to a science to consider not only a subject, but also the parts and possible attributes of that subject: but being is the subject of divine science, as has been said; therefore it pertains to divine science to consider all beings: but matter and motion are certain beings; therefore divine science does not abstract from them.[7]

The answer is:

> A metaphysician considers singular beings, but not according to their proper nature as such and such a being, but according as they participate in the common nature of being. Thus matter and motion are considered by him.[8]

Is this not a precise description of what the philosopher of nature is doing? He is not concerned with the proper nature of such and such a being, its specific nature; but he asks, "In what way are matter and motion *being*?" That means, he examines the general nature of matter and motion as *being;* he analyzes matter and motion not with physical, but with metaphysical concepts. Thus the philosophy of nature can properly be called a special metaphysics, con-

---

[7]Q.V, art. 4, obj. 6, p. 160.
[8]Q.V, art. 4, ad 6, p. 168.

cerned with a certain level of *being,* namely, material *being;* whereas general metaphysics considers *being* in general, and is not restricted to material *being* alone.

It can be argued, however, that if this exegesis of St. Thomas is true, then St. Thomas must also have thought of a certain difference on the level of metaphysics between general metaphysics and the metaphysical consideration of certain parts of reality as *beings.*

That distinction is, as a matter of fact, made by St. Thomas in his answer to objection 6 of Q. V, art. 1.

This objection is:

> The whole ought not to be divided in opposition to any of its parts; but divine science seems to be the whole in respect to physics and mathematics, since the subjects of these latter are parts of divine science [i.e. metaphysics], whose subject is *being,* of which a part is *mobile being,* which natural science considers, and another part quantity, which mathematics studies, as is clear from III *Metaph.;* therefore divine science ought not to be opposed in division to natural science and to mathematics.[9]

The answer is:

> It can be said: Although the subjects of other sciences are parts of *being,* which is the subject of metaphysics, those other sciences ought not to be considered parts of metaphysics.
> Each science considers one phase of *being,* or reality, according to a special mode, which is different from that according to which *being* is viewed by metaphysics. Therefore, properly speaking, the subject of such a science is not a part of the subject of metaphysics, but, according to its own manner of viewing reality, each special science is differentiated from others.
> However, a science can be said to be a phase of the science of metaphysics in this way: if it be concerned with potency or act, or with unity, or with anything of a like nature, because these things require the same mode of consideration as that by which *being* is dealt with in metaphysics.[10]

The answer is clear. Insofar as material being is studied by methods which deal with formal aspects other than those which belong to the subject matter of metaphysics, such a systematic study does not constitute a part of metaphysics. This condition applies fully to science when it studies material being. Science works with other methods and other concepts than metaphysics. The philosophy of

---

[9] Q. V, art. 1, obj. 6, p. 132.
[10] Q. V, art. 1, ad 6, pp. 140-141.

nature, however, studies material being with the same concepts as are used in metaphysics and, therefore, "it can be said to be a phase of the science of metaphysics."

There is a difference between metaphysics in general and the philosophy of nature, but that difference is not a difference in the level of abstraction. Unlike general metaphysics, the philosophy of nature is exclusively concerned with material phenomena, but it studies these phenomena under the aspect of *being*. It asks what kind of *being* matter is. The philosophy of nature studies matter insofar as matter is changeable, insofar as it has a species-individual structure, insofar as it is always both qualitative and quantitative. The philosophy of nature analyzes these characteristic features with the metaphysical concepts of potency and act, of unity and multiplicity, of substance and accident; all these concepts refer to being as such and, therefore, can also be applied to those beings which exist outside matter. Thus its difference from general metaphysics is that the latter is necessarily also interested in those beings which exist without matter. Metaphysics goes further than the philosophy of nature, but it uses the same concepts and the same methods. This means it stays on the same level of abstraction.

4. SCIENCE AND THE PHILOSOPHY OF NATURE

The examination of the character of the philosophy of nature and its degree of abstraction may be concluded by the discussion of some of the consequences which are of special interest, as they illustrate the relationship between science and the philosophy of nature.

The philosophy of nature deals with the essence of material being. It throws, so to speak, metaphysical light upon this essence. It would, however, be a serious misunderstanding to think that only the philosophy of nature concerns itself with the nature or the essence of material being; science does also. This point must be stressed because many text-books of philosophy claim that the distinction between science and philosophy is that the latter has to do with the *essence* of things, whereas the former only is concerned with *phenomena*. Science is assigned the task of finding out certain regularities and relationships between the phenomena and to gather them in laws without penetrating into the essence of things. That latter task is reserved to philosophy. This effort to distinguish between science and philosophy is not only misleading, but is also the reason why so many people are disappointed with philosophy.

An Overestimation of Philosophy. Let us make this point very clear. It may be true—and it is true—that science does not answer all questions about the essence of material phenomena, but it does unquestionably give some answers. The study of chemistry teaches us some of the essential differences, for example, between the nature of salt and that of gold. And because of these essential differences, it is possible to understand to a certain extent the different behavior of salt and gold.

This understanding, however, is not complete. Chemistry and physics leave many points about the nature of salt and gold unsolved. Scientists would like to know more about it, more about the essence of both kinds of matter. They have a strong impression that their understanding of many material properties is due more to the fact that they have succeeded in connecting certain mathematical relations with the structure of chemical substances than that they really understand the nature of those structures. It seems that the essence of such basic physical concepts as mass, energy, and electrical charge, which are used in describing the structure of chemical substances, is unknown, and that the only real knowledge we have is a knowledge of quantitative values connected with those concepts.

This is not the proper place to discuss the importance of a quantitative approach to matter, nor to point out how many qualitative aspects are still considered in modern physics and chemistry. For the present, it is more important to realize that the feeling, just described, is justified; for physical and chemical understanding do not reveal the whole essence of material things. The best we can say is that they reveal only some aspects of that essence. But the scientist who turns to the philosophy of nature in order to find out what is missing in his own science will be quite disappointed. For no philosophy of nature can reveal the essence of energy, mass, electrical charge, etc. If science cannot reveal this essence, then the only conclusion is that we have to resign ourselves to the fact that our knowledge about them is unsatisfactory.

Such concepts as energy, mass, electric charge, etc., are not even open to philosophical discussion, at least not if such concepts are taken in their specific, mutually distinct, physical sense. And if the philosophy of nature tries to discuss them, then the only result is a mixing up of some primitive pre-scientific ideas with some philosophical and scientific concepts, whereby the pre-scientific ideas seem to have the task of linking philosophy and science. Such a mixture, however, may meet the desire for synthesis of some people, but it will certainly not give the scientist a better knowledge of the essence of the physical concepts involved. It only enables us to understand why so many scientists look upon the philosophy of nature as an attempt to solve the problems of the material world by primitive and uncritical means.

Correct Distinction Between the Task of Science and That of the Philosophy of Nature. Yet, there is nothing wrong with saying that the philosophy of nature deals with the essence of material being, if this expression is correctly understood. It does not mean that the philosophy of nature alone deals with the essence of matter. Science does also. Nor does the statement mean that the philosophy of nature can supply on the scientific level the knowledge science lacks regarding the essence of material things. The philosophy of nature can do nothing of that sort, for the very reason that each degree of abstraction gives an essential knowledge, but does so on a different level. Consequently, both science and the philosophy of nature reveal to us something about the essence of matter, but each of them reveals different essential aspects.

In the beginning of this work we distinguished these aspects by pointing out that the philosophy of nature examines those aspects of matter which science presupposes by its very use of general scientific methods, as, for example, by induction. The aspects of matter studied by the philosophy of nature are, therefore, of a very general nature, always present where matter is present. So the task of science can be distinguished to a certain extent from that of the philosophy of nature by saying that science has to do with the more specific features of matter whereas the philosophy of nature deals with the more general. Even then, however, the distinction is misleading, because of the simple fact that the terms "general" and "specific" are supposed to refer to a distinction on the same level. The distinction is, therefore, to be handled with great caution. It is used here only to indicate that the knowledge the philosophy of nature gives us about matter concerns what characterizes *all* matter as matter. Or to put it in different words: the philosophy of nature can speculate only on the generic aspects of the essence of matter and never on the specific aspects which, according to science, distinguish one kind of material being from another.

And to make clear what these generic aspects are, the best thing to do is to point out again what was said in Chapter I. The generic aspects of matter which the philosophy of nature studies are those which science presupposes. The method of dealing with such aspects requires an entirely different approach from that used by science. It requires other concepts and another way of verification. It requires an entirely different attitude of mind. Briefly, we are in a different level of abstraction.

This will be sufficient for the present. After some important problems of the philosophy of nature have been discussed and it has been shown what kind of concepts are used in that discussion, it will be possible to return to what has been said so far about the character of the philosophy of nature and of its degree of abstraction. For not until this task has been accomplished will it be possible to pass final judgment on the question of whether or not the conception of the philosophy of nature developed here is tenable.

SUGGESTED READINGS

St. Thomas Aquinas, *In Boethium de Trinitate, Quaestiones* V and VI. English translation by Sister Rose F. Brennan, St. Louis, 1946. Separately published in English translation under the title *The Division and Method of the Sciences* by A. Maurer, Toronto, 1953.

J. Maritain, *The Philosophy of Nature,* New York, 1951.

Vincent E. Smith, *Philosophical Physics,* New York, 1950, Chapter I.

CHAPTER FOUR

THE ESSENCE OF MATERIAL BEING

1. INTRODUCTION

This chapter will deal with the essence of material being insofar as this essence is the subject matter of the philosophy of nature, and will try to answer the question as to what kind of being matter is.

The following chapters will be devoted to such fundamental characteristics of material being as are important enough to be discussed separately. They are the following: quantity, quality and activity.

One of the greatest difficulties of this chapter will be to determine the correct starting-point and—still more important—the correct view of that starting-point. In the Aristotelian school of thought the traditional starting-point for the discussion of material being is, of course, the fact that matter is subject to substantial change. The simple fact, however, that history proves that substantial change has given rise to many misunderstandings, makes it necessary to examine closely its merits as the starting-point for a philosophy of nature. It will appear that this starting-point has many disadvantages. Therefore another starting-point will be chosen, namely, that of the species-individual structure. And only after this starting-point has given a clear idea of what the essence of matter is, will it be possible to return to the problem of substantial change and the questions related to it.

2. SUBSTANTIAL CHANGE AS A STARTING-POINT FOR THE PHILOSOPHY OF NATURE

Our Problem Differs From That of Aristotle

Aristotle proposed his matter-form theory so as to explain the phenomena of change, and in particular, of substantial change. For him the occurrence of substantial changes was no problem; sense experience demonstrated this occurrence not only clearly, but also in an overwhelming number of instances. Aristotle's problem, therefore, was not whether or not substantial changes occur; his problem was how to *explain* the possibility of substantial change. He asked: what must be the nature of matter so that material things can be subject to

107

substantial changes? Consequently, the starting-point itself of the philosophy of nature did not cause Aristotle any trouble; it seemed safely anchored to a general datum of primary experience, namely, the capacity of matter to undergo substantial change.

The development of science, however, has had, among other things, the effect of explaining away many of the striking differences which seem to exist, at first sight, between one substantial form and another. Many a change, which Aristotle looked upon as a substantial one, seems in the judgment of modern science to be only a rearranging of the same material particles, as for example, the transition of ice into water. True, this in itself does not necessarily have great consequences for the philosophy of nature. For Aristotle did not base his philosophy of nature upon just one particular substantial change; he based it upon the occurrence of substantial changes in general. Therefore, the fact that he mistook some accidental changes for substantial ones does not imply that his whole theory was wrong. This would be the case only if science could explain away all substantial change, i.e. if it could show not only that Aristotle was wrong in his judgment of certain particular changes, but also that the whole idea of substantial change should be abandoned, based as it is upon too primitive a view of matter.

Science and Substantial Change. Now it would certainly be wrong to say that science has forced us to drop the whole idea of substantial change, although it must be said that it at least appears that science has gone in that direction. Most scientists are, therefore, convinced that science will ultimately prove that the whole idea of substantial change is nothing but a primitive concept originated at a time when there was little real understanding of the phenomena of nature. It is clear, as has been pointed out in Chapter II, Section 6, that there is some misunderstanding about the real nature of a substantial change behind this attempt of scientists to explain away all substantial change.

It would, however, be a mistake to blame only scientists for it. Philosophers as well are guilty of the same misunderstanding. To meet this tendency of science to explain away all substantial change, philosophers have used much ingenuity to show that science was claiming more than it could prove when it denied that substantial changes take place. Insofar as philosophers made use of arguments based upon certain scientific considerations intended to prove that the properties of a chemical compound could not be deduced from the properties of the elements, the danger was great that substantial change would come to be considered equivalent to a change that science could not, or could not yet, sufficiently explain.

Philosophers were inclined to think that science could never explain a substantial change, whereas scientists were convinced that in the future it might be possible. The scientists were right. For the discussion was a scientific one, and what science cannot do today it may be able to do tomorrow. Only when a problem is of such a nature that it lies entirely within the field of philosophy does the philosopher have the right to speak categorically. The dispute between scientists and philosophers about the possibility of deducing the properties of a chemical compound from those of its elements was certainly not purely philosophical.

Let us, however, forget for the moment this confusion between scientific and philosophic arguments; this subject will be taken up in the next paragraph. For the moment the only point at issue is the difference between the way in which Aristotle faced the problem of substantial change and the way we do. For Aristotle, the occurrence of substantial change was no problem. For us it is. We are faced with the task of proving the very existence of substantial change. Science has, to put it mildly, changed the way we look upon material phenomena to such an extent that the concept of substantial change which once was so clear seems now too difficult to apply to the concrete phenomena of nature. That in itself is a reason why substantial change can no longer be considered a safe starting-point for the philosophy of nature. It does not seem clearly enough established as an indisputable datum of primary experience. The very fact that it is deemed necessary to prove the existence of substantial change makes this obvious. This is not, however, the only reason. For the development of science has not only made the existence of substantial change a matter to be proved; it has also shown that such a proof can easily lead to a confusion between scientific and philosophic problems.

The Concept of Substantial Change Needs a Profound Examination

The danger that the dispute between scientists and philosophers about the existence of substantial change results in a wrong idea of what substantial change is, is not only theoretical. As a matter of fact, in many disputes it seems that a substantial change is more or less taken for granted to be a change for which science cannot give sufficient explanation. It is a change in which the newly formed substance displays properties not understandable as the sum total of the properties of the substances out of which the new substance was formed. This, however, is certainly not the right conception of substantial change. It is an unfortunate controversy between scientists and philosophers which has made the point of deductibility an issue. If the philosopher enters into that dispute without a clear idea of what the philosophical concept "substantial change" means, he is lost, and gets involved in all kinds of inconsequential considerations. We must first have a more or less elaborate philosophy of nature before its concepts can be compared with those of science.

It should be stressed that such a comparison is a matter of necessity. For both science and the philosophy of nature deal with the essence of matter, each in its own abstract way. Precisely for that reason both methods of considering matter must be used concurrently to achieve a more complete knowledge of the material world.

The only danger is that this combination may be attempted too soon. Then the result is that the more elaborate of the two different approaches dominates and suppresses the development of the other. A fruitful cooperation of philosophy and science requires that both start in such a way as to make a mutually independent development possible.

Who Should Decide What Are Substantial Changes? Choosing substantial change as a starting-point endangers, from the very beginning, the independent and autonomous development of the philosophy of nature. A concrete example will illustrate this. When we say that the properties of rust differ from those of iron in such a way that the transition from iron into rust means a substantial change, then the question arises: who has the greater competence in judging the difference between iron and rust, the philosopher or the scientist? It seems to be the philosopher, because the concept "substantial change" belongs to his vocabulary. But by what means can he judge the differences between iron and rust? Certainly, he can use sense-experience; but is not this sense-experience of a rather primitive kind? Sense-experience alone cannot be trusted. The fate of Aristotelian science clearly taught us that. So it seems that the scientist is the man who has to determine whether or not a certain change is a substantial one. But now the difficulty is that the scientist does not even use the concept of substantial change. He does not look upon natural phenomena in such way as to enable him to speak of substantial changes. Although he is interested in the difference between iron and rust, his classification makes use of other concepts.

Now it is wholly possible that certain scientific classifications can be translated by the philosopher into philosophical terms. Thus it was often said before the development of nuclear physics that what a scientist called a chemical change was, philosophically speaking, a substantial one, whereas a physical change could be looked upon as an accidental one. However, even apart from the development of both physics and chemistry, which has made this difference between a physical and a chemical change a very relative one, the main difficulty is that such cooperation between the philosopher and the scientist requires that the philosopher already know what a substantial change is. That means he must already have a philosophical system at his disposal. Hence the occurrence of substantial change can hardly be a good starting-point for the philosophy of nature. For whether or not substantial change occurs can be decided—according to the line of argument that has been followed here—only with the help of scientific consideration. This explains why the philosophic concept "substantial change" with many philosophers has a more or less physical and chemical content. As a result, they never arrive at the level of the philosophy of nature. For once in the grip of science, there is only one method to follow, the scientific one.

The only way to avoid this danger is for the philosopher to examine profoundly the nature of matter in order to get a clear idea of what a material substance is, and what the possible philosophical meaning of substantial change in matter is. This is tantamount to saying that he must first build a philosophy of nature before he can determine whether or not there are substantial changes in nature, and what changes can rightly be labeled substantial ones.

Substantial Changes Between Living and Non-Living Matter

To avoid the dangers pointed out above, most contemporary Thomistic writers on the philosophy of nature pursue a middle-course. They first try to show that some substantial changes exist beyond any possible doubt, namely, the transitions from non-living into living matter. Having thus safeguarded the existence of substantial change, they build a philosophy of nature upon this foundation and then they examine whether or not other changes in nature are substantial changes. This can be considered a solution of the problem then, but only if two conditions are fulfilled. First, there must be no doubt that the transition from non-living into living matter is a substantial change. Secondly, it must be shown that all matter is subject to such a transition. It seems to me that both points are open to doubt.

No Sufficient Evidence. To begin with the first point, it is true that one is more inclined to consider a transition from non-living into living matter to be a substantial change than to admit that a chemical reaction implies a substantial change. But is there sufficient evidence that the transition from non-living to living matter is a substantial change? Can there be no doubt? It is interesting to note in this connection that a scientist looks upon an atom of a certain type in exactly the same way, regardless of whether it is inside or outside a living body. It is his job to define the properties of an atom in such a way that these properties characterize the atom, regardless of whether or not it is a part of living matter. This attitude of mind of the scientist makes it difficult for him to understand what is meant by "substantial change." According to him, there is no alteration when a carbon atom enters a living body. Before and after that process it has precisely the same fundamental properties. He will concede that he cannot yet entirely explain the behavior of a living body with the help of the chemical properties of its chemical constituents. But his aim is to do so. And that aim is based upon the simple fact that he has already partly succeeded.

The transition from non-living matter into living matter may be more complicated than a chemical reaction in non-living matter; but for science this difference is not essential. As a result, the philosopher is forced to prove that a transition from non-living into living matter is a substantial change. But how can he do that without already having at his disposal an elaborate system of the philosophy of nature in which his philosophical concepts, such as change, and especially substantial change, find their natural place? If he tries to prove his point without such a system, he will soon discover himself engaged in all kinds of biological discussions; and once he enters the field of biology, he is lost, because biology itself never speaks of a substantial change.

It is not necessary to go so far as to say there is no evidence at all that a transition from non-living into living matter is a substantial change, for that is not the point at issue. The point at issue is: is such evidence open to doubt before an adequate philosophy of nature is established?

Does All Non-Living Matter Change Into Living Matter? There is still another point to be considered. The philosopher has to show also that *all* non-living matter is, in principle, subject to a transition into living matter. On this point, he is in an even worse position, for he can in no way avoid the use of certain scientific arguments, which at best can suggest but never prove what he wants to prove[1].

Therefore, I do not think that choosing the transition from non-living into living matter can really avoid the difficulties encountered in finding an indisputable starting-point for a philosophy of nature. The danger of getting the philosophical point of view confused with the scientific one from the very beginning seems too great.

Conclusion

The conclusion to be drawn from the foregoing discussion is not—it may be stressed again—that a philosopher should never discuss from the philosophical point of view phenomena which science also discusses. If there is any meaning at all in the concepts "substance" and "substantial change," and if science gives us a real knowledge of material phenomena, then there must be the possibility of a philosophical evaluation in terms of substance and substantial change of those transitions in matter which science speaks of. A chemical reaction, a physical change, a biological process are all open to discussion by the philosopher. It is the philosopher who has to determine whether or not there is reason to speak of a substantial change, but he can do so only when he has first built up his system of the philosophy of nature. For only then does he know what substantial change means in the realm of matter. Or to put it in the terms of the point at issue in this section: Substantial change is a very important philosophic concept, but it does not furnish a good starting-point for the philosophy of nature.

3. THE REQUIREMENTS FOR A GOOD PHILOSOPHICAL STARTING-POINT

It Must Be a Fact Beyond Any Possible Doubt

The discussion in the last section has brought to light the fact that the occurrence of substantial change cannot be considered a good starting-point for the philosophy of nature. That discussion also out-

---

[1]Cf. Petrus Hoenen, *Cosmologia*, Roma, 4th ed., 1949, p. 268.

lined implicitly and in a negative way what requirements a good starting-point should possess. One has only to examine what was wrong with the starting-point of Aristotle to know, also, explicitly the right course to follow.

The first objection to substantial change was that its occurrence cannot be established as being beyond any possible doubt. Human experience shows changes of different kinds, but we cannot be sure, at first sight, whether or not some of them are substantial. And the aid of scientific experience does not clarify the situation, for pure science does not work with such a concept. Science makes our knowledge more profound and broader, but it does not answer the specific question the philosopher is interested in. And if he insists nevertheless on getting an answer, the only one he gets will be inspired by the traditional bond which in the past tied up science with a kind of mechanistic philosophy. As a consequence he gets a wrong answer from a wrong philosophy, even though the answer is given in the name of science. It seems as if science is trying to explain away all substantial change. It may be true that the recent development of science has loosened the traditional bond between mechanistic philosophy and science, even to such an extent that a philosophic interpretation of certain phenomena in terms of substantial change seems much more appropriate than in terms of a mechanistic philosophy. Such a development, however, can never offer an incontestable starting-point for the philosophy of nature. Nobody can predict the course science will follow in the future.

The first requirement, therefore, that a good starting-point for the philosophy of nature should meet is that it be established beyond any possible doubt. That means that it should be what has been called in Chapter I a fact of our primary experience. Such a fact is really beyond any possible doubt, because it forms the necessary basis of all our further knowledge, even of our scientific knowledge. For the data of our primary experience enter science as presuppositions. These presuppositions contain a kind of implicit philosophical outlook upon matter. By basing our philosophy of nature only upon those data, we can be sure that there is not much chance that we will mistake a primitive datum of our experience for a primary one. Thus we will avoid an error which it is always possible to commit, as the history of philosophy proves. For though it may be true that the human mind can abstract philosophical truth with certainty, this does not imply that we are not liable to make mistakes.

A Starting-Point for the Philosophy of Nature Must Say Something About All Matter

The second objection which can be made to using substantial change as a starting-point for the philosophy of nature is that even when we succeed in establishing the occurrence of substantial change beyond any doubt, we still have to prove that such an occurrence is typical of matter as matter and not of a certain kind of matter. This was precisely the objection made to those philosophers who chose as an indisputable starting-point the fact of transition from non-living to living matter. For by what means can we know that all matter is subject to such transition? Certainly there is no philosophical evidence; at best it is only a scientific probability.

A good starting-point should from the very beginning say something about all matter. For in the philosophy of nature we deal with the general nature of matter. Therefore, only those features of matter should be considered which are characteristic of *all* matter and *all* material phenomena. Here again the examination of the presuppositions of science can be of great help. For if we take as a starting-point something that science presupposes about matter, we can be sure that it is a characteristic feature of all matter.

There is a third advantage connected with choosing a presupposition of science as a starting-point for the philosophy of nature. By doing so, we cannot only be sure that our starting-point is characteristic of all matter, but we also eliminate the dispute with science. Not that the philosophy of nature has to fear such a dispute, but such a dispute involves the danger that philosophical concepts will be mixed up with scientific ones. And then the philosophic concepts seem not only entirely superfluous but also meaningless, for the philosophical problems are lost sight of. The fate of the 17th century philosophers should be a warning.[2] So the search will be for a starting-point that is not open to dispute, that is characteristic of all matter, and that is really philosophic. The presuppositions which science makes about matter are very likely to fulfill these desiderata.

4. THE SPECIES-INDIVIDUAL STRUCTURE OF MATTER AS A STARTING-POINT FOR THE PHILOSOPHY OF NATURE

Introductory Remarks

In discussing the philosophical system of Aristotle in Chapter II, Section 3, it has been shown that his matter-form doctrine not only

---

[2] Cf. p. 74.

accounted for the possibility of substantial change, but for the *species-individual* structure as well. This is interesting, because it suggests the possibility of developing the fundamental ideas of Aristotle from quite another angle than that of substantial change. We can perhaps start with the fact that all matter has a species-individual structure and so arrive at the same conclusions as Aristotle did. Starting with the species-individual structure has all the advantages outlined in the last section. This structure is obvious; it is characteristic of all matter; and it is presupposed by science. It is therefore quite logical to start with it.

Not so logical, of course, is the desire to arrive at the same fundamental conclusions as Aristotle did. After all, twenty-five centuries have passed since Aristotle developed his system. And the study of nature has not only undergone a tremendous development, but has even taken quite another direction than Aristotle had outlined. And as far as philosophy is concerned, the philosophy which has inspired natural science was not Aristotelian, but mechanistic. However, the development of science in the last twenty-five years shows a definite tendency to get rid of the traditional bond which in the past connected science with a mechanistic philosophy. Science was forced by its own development to abandon the idea of unchangeable particles as elements of matter. The changes in matter which science comes across are much more radical than can be accounted for by a mechanistic philosophy.[3] Therefore, science itself points in the direction of a philosophy of nature which has a broader concept of change than a mechanistic philosophy can give. The development of science suggests the idea that perhaps Aristotle was right after all in his conception of matter as fundamentally subject to more than accidental change.

Philosophy, however, can never be based upon scientific suggestions alone; it must follow its own course, guided by philosophic considerations. It has been seen that, notwithstanding the fact that both modern science and common experience suggest the idea of substantial change, such a change is not clearly enough established by primary experience to form an indubitable starting-point for a philosophical doctrine about matter. Nor can science furnish the necessary material, for it does not classify changes according to philosophic distinctions. Science therefore can at the utmost only suggest certain distinctions.

---

[3]Cf. *From Atomos to Atom*, pp. 185 ff.

It is clear, however, that such a suggestion makes it worthwhile to study again Aristotle's philosophy of nature. Perhaps it is possible to approach the Aristotelian doctrine of substantial change from another angle and to base it upon a datum of experience that can be established beyond any doubt. Now the Aristotelian doctrine which accounts for both the species-individual structure and the possibility of substantial change appears in a new light. For it justifies the attempt to construe Aristotle's philosophy of nature by beginning with the species-individual structure. And once given a philosophic doctrine of matter, the possibility of substantial change may be seen as the conclusion of that doctrine.

There is still another reason for studying again Aristotle's doctrine. In this doctrine the basic concepts are matter and form. A little reflection shows that these concepts are still at the root of all thought. The human mind always thinks in terms of matter and form. Moreover, a man not only *thinks* in terms of matter and form, but also his working with, and his domination of, the material world shows the use of the matter-form schema. Any human action on the material world consists in reshaping some material element that is given. This reshaping is sometimes nothing more than giving a new shape, as in making a statue or a table; sometimes it is a rather complicated process of uniting several given parts, by giving them an appropriate shape, as is the case with the construction of an engine. Sometimes, however, human actions go so far as to make even new materials. Yet, even in this instance, there is reason to speak of "reshaping" because there are always some material elements that are used for the preparation of the new material; these material elements obtain a new form. In view of the almost infinite possibility of making new materials, there seems to be in nature an almost infinite capacity for receiving forms. The trend of thought which Aristotle followed when proposing his hylomorphism represents, therefore, something which is fundamental.

The present problem is, therefore, to study more closely the *individual-species* structure to find out whether or not this structure really reveals the same fundamental non-simplicity in matter as Aristotle had in mind when he spoke of hylomorphism in his effort to explain substantial change. If so, the possibility of substantial change in matter can be established, and, what is more important, deriving the possibility of substantial change from the fundamental structure of matter has the advantage that one can determine beforehand what will be the typical feature of a substantial change in matter. Substantial change is then no longer a kind of primitive concept, known only through a certain feeling. For that was precisely the difficulty in starting with substantial change. The concept is not clear enough. We have a notion that it can be applied to matter, but we do not know how and to what extent. This weakness of the concept leads us to attempt to clarify the concept of substantial change with the help of scientific knowledge. But this obscures the concept more than it clarifies it. For the only way a philosophical concept can be clarified is by a philosophical analysis. Otherwise we get lost in a multitude of scientific concepts, none of which is designed for philosophical purposes.

Analysis of the Species-Individual Structure

In the first chapter it was pointed out in a general way what species-individual structure means. It is necessary, however, to analyze the concept more profoundly in order to avoid certain misconceptions.

The Meaning of the Species-Individual Structure. Species-individual structure means that any determination or form in matter, whatever the nature of such a determination or form may be, is realized in such a way that it is, in principle, not confined to just one particular individual material thing or event. The same shape, color, atomic structure, weight, and so on, which is present in this individual thing or event can also be realized in another individual thing or event. In this phase of the analysis, "things" or "events" are spoken of quite indiscriminately. For it does not matter what the ultimate constituents of reality are: "events" or "things." Both have a species-individual structure.

Another point that should be stressed and kept constantly in mind during the current discussion is that the term "specific" is not used in opposition to "generic." Nor is the term meant to indicate a "substantial essence" in the sense in which Aritotelian philosophy distinguishes this "essence" from that of an accident. "Specific," in the sense in which it is used here means exclusively to be in opposition to "individual." So the concept of "specific" covers all kinds of "essences," specific as well as generic ones, both in the way of substances and in the way of accidents.

The reason why these distinctions are not made is that at the moment they are not needed. The species-individual structure is so fundamental that it pervades all matter and all material phenomena. Therefore, we do not even need to know, philosophically speaking, what things are substances and what things are accidents, what are generic determinations and what are specific. For even before we know whether or not the said distinctions can be applied to the material world, we do know with certainty that the distinction indicated by the species-individual structure does exist in matter, both with respect to "things" and their "properties," and with respect to "material events."

Species-Individual Structure in Things. Let us now first think in terms of "things" and see how the species-individual structure is applied.

Being a bird, a rose, or an electron is, so to speak, not the privilege of one individual "thing"; the specific nature expressed by the concept "bird," "rose," or "electron" belongs to different individual "things." The same holds good for all that we usually call properties of things. All properties we ascribe to birds, roses, or electrons fall under the same fundamental law; none of these properties are characteristic of an individual thing as such. All properties are specific in the sense that "red" or "green" or "having certain dimensions" or "a certain charge" is not confined to just one individual thing. All those properties by their very nature can be attributed, in principle, to several individuals.

Species-Individual Structure in Events. The same structure exists in events. Each individual event is, of course, somewhat unique, as is each thing. The actual fall of this apple at this moment is not identical with the fall of another apple or with another fall of the same apple. Yet all that characterizes such an individual fall, all properties of the event are specific, i.e. they apply, in principle, to other events of the same kind. All features characterizing an actual transition of electrons into γ-rays[4] are specific in the sense that they are not just limited to this actual case, here and now.

Species-Individual Structure Does Not Suppose the Actual Existence of More Than One Individual of a Species. Before going further with the analysis, an obvious objection to what has just been said must be considered. Is it really true that all that characterizes an individual thing or event is of a specific and not of an individual char-

---

[4]This process is sometimes called a dematerialization-process, which is a misnomer, for γ-rays belong as well as electrons to the material world.

acter? Is it unthinkable that a certain characteristic is typical for just one thing or event? Such a possibility is not only not unthinkable, but perhaps not even so unusual. We may safely assume that many a property (for instance, a certain shade of red) exists only in just one individual case.[5] However, that is not the point. The point is that nothing in the content of the concept of such a particular property prevents its being realized also in another individual. This fact is so evident that nobody, merely because only one actual instance of a certain property is known, will refrain from attempting to materialize the same particular property in another individual. Thus the supposed uniqueness of that particular property is never an uniqueness with respect to its essence; it is an uniqueness with respect to its existence. Thus the species-individual structure does not necessarily suppose the actual existence of more than one individual of a species. The structure expresses only that all material phenomena are of such a nature that more than one individual can exist.

Another important point that deserves our attention is that probably no two individual things are exactly alike. Suppose we have two pieces of glass, two tumblers of the same set. Roughly speaking, all their properties will be alike, their size, color, weight, chemical composition, physical properties. But that is only roughly true. If we could determine several properties with precision instruments, we should certainly find minor differences.

In our every-day language we are inclined to speak of the said minor differences as individual differences, because they do not seem to have any bearing on the observable specific properties of the set of glasses under consideration. The specific properties are not so exactly determined as not to allow for a certain tolerance. Yet, speaking of individual differences is an incorrect way of expressing ourselves. Strictly speaking, those minor differences fall under the category not of individual differences, but of specific differences in the sense which was outlined above. If for example the chemical composition of both glasses is slightly different, then there is a specific difference. By the very fact of that difference the glasses belong in two different categories![6]

Individual Differences. In order to get a correct idea of what is meant by individual differences, let us imagine two glasses which are exactly the same in all respects. Yet they are different. Their dif-

---

[5]See p. 89, where this problem has been discussed.
[6]The differences between these categories are, of course, only accidental.

ference is, however, not of a specific nature; the only difference is a difference in individuality. *This* individual glass is not *that* individual glass, notwithstanding the fact that both have all properties in common.

It is of importance to note that the individual difference is not a difference in position. It is, of course, true that the two glasses have a different position; but that is the effect, and not the cause, of their difference in individuality. For if we would change the places so that glass No. 1 occupies the place of No. 2 and vice versa, then their individualities would not be changed. It is true, of course, that we always *distinguish,* both in daily life and in science, two individual things or events with, practically speaking, the same properties by their different positions in space and time. It is the only possibility we have. Yet, space and time do not create a difference in individuality. This point will be dealt with later on, when the nature of space and time is discussed.

The Exclusion Principle of Pauli. Before continuing the analysis of the species-individual structure, another objection which is worth consideration must be mentioned, because it helps to clarify further the correct meaning of the structure under consideration; that objection is based upon the exclusion principle of Pauli. According to that famous principle, no two electrons belonging to the same system can be in exactly the same state. This principle plays an important rôle in the atomic theory. It explains, among other things, the distribution of the orbital electrons over several orbits. All electrons in one orbit must be in a different state. Therefore, if all possible states of one orbit are occupied, a new electron will move into another orbit.

So the exclusion principle brings up the question as to whether two things can have the same determinations. Was the example of two glasses not a bit too simple? We can perhaps imagine two things with the same determinations, but has not science proved that this situation is not possible? Did not the exclusion principle, discovered after a thorough experimental study of nature, prove once again how dangerous it is to draw speculative philosophical conclusions from simple examples?

The answer to this objection can be very brief. The exclusion principle does not in the least contradict the species-individual structure. On the contrary, it confirms this structure by presupposing it. For the said principle speaks of the distribution of the composing electrons in a certain whole, namely, the orbits of an atom. By the simple fact that the principle is a *general* one, it presupposes that there are more atoms of the same kind, i. e., the same distributions of electrons. Each atom of oxygen has a distribution of electrons which is specific for oxygen, each atom of sulfur one which is specific for sulfur, etc. Thus each possible *specific* distribution of electrons is realized in many *individual* atoms.

So it is correct to say that Pauli's principle presupposes the species-individual structure, precisely because the principle is meant to explain the specific differences between atoms of different elements. As a matter of fact, in speaking of electrons, atoms of hydrogen or oxygen, molecules of water, etc., science continually presupposes the existence of objects which have exactly the same nature. Of course, even apart from the exclusion principle of Pauli, science never does contend that two molecules of water are in exactly the same state. For each molecule has *in concreto* a set of relationships to the whole of the universe, which set, however slightly, differs from the set of relationships any other molecule of water has. But that is not important with respect to our problem. For science presupposes that each individual molecule of water is capable of possessing any of the above sets of relationships. In this fundamental sense each molecule of water has exactly the same specific nature. What was said in Chapter I should be remembered: namely, that science would be impossible if it did not presuppose the species-individual nature. For that reason there is no need of discussing possible objections any longer; it is more important to focus the attention now on the philosophical consequences of the species-individual structure.

The Meaning of the Term "Structure." The most important point to be examined now is the exact nature of this structure. The term "structure" is a familiar one. We use it constantly in daily life, in mathematics, in science, and in technology. In all these instances "structure" indicates the manner in which the different parts of a whole are joined together; the parts are discernable as separate entities; they are located outside each other, notwithstanding the fact that they form a whole. The different parts of a human body, of a house, of a chemical formula are, as parts, discernable. Each part has a certain position with respect to the other parts, and with respect to the whole.

Speaking, however, of the "species-individual structure," the situation is different. It is true that here too it may be said that the individuality and specificity are "parts" and that together they form a "structure." The difference from the normal use of the term "structure" is, however, that the two parts are not, strictly speaking, outside each other.

Let us return to the example of the two glasses in order to show what is meant. There is a definite distinction between the individuality and the specificity of such a glass. For being a glass of a certain species (e.g. a standard set), does not determine whether it is "this" or "that" individual glass. Thus the "thisness" or "thatness" indicates definitely something else than "being a glass of that particular species." Something can be a glass with all the specific requirements and yet not "this" glass. Thus "thisness" and "glassness"[7] refer to different aspects or "parts" of the same concrete thing. It is precisely for this reason that we are justified in speaking of species-individual structure, a term which indicates that there are parts to be distinguished.

However, the peculiar point is that these parts are not at all outside each other as hand and foot are. For when all the specific properties of the glasses are enumerated, then no reality is left unconsidered. There is no reality in an individual glass that is not mentioned when mention is made of any of the specific properties. Yet these specific properties do not cover the full reality, for if they did so, there would be no reason to distinguish between the "thisness" and the "glassness," as must be done. The same result can be reached when the problem is approached from a different angle. The individuality, the "thisness," does not exist separately. The "thisness" exists only as a concrete thing with specific properties. So the structure meant in the term "species-individual structure" is of a very special kind. It is not a structure of parts existing outside each other. The "individuality" and "specificity" represent, so to speak, two fundamental aspects of the same reality. There is a real distinction between these aspects,[8] but they always exist together. Specific properties exist in *this* or *that* individual being; and *this* or *that* individual being exists only with specific properties.

Conclusion. The conclusion to be drawn from this analysis is that species-individual structure refers to a fundamental non-simplicity that is present in each material thing or event, whatever its character may be. Each thing or event belongs to one or more categories; it has

---

[7]For brevity's sake the term "glassness" is used to indicate in one term all the specific properties of the glasses which belong to the same set.

[8]The distinction is real because the different aspects are not a result of a different *look* at the same reality. It is reality itself that offers different aspects.

properties in common with other things or events and yet it has its own inalienable uniqueness, its own individuality.

Thus it is evident that because the species-individual structure is something that is characteristic of all matter, the fundamental non-simplicity, too, is characteristic of all matter.

Species-Individual Structure and Hylomorphism

The next problem is whether or not the fundamental non-simplicity to which the species-individual structure refers is the same conception Aristotle had in mind when he spoke of a matter-form structure. If it is, then it is not difficult to prove the possibility of substantial change and to determine its exact status in matter.

The content of Aristotle's hylomorphism is that all matter is composed of both a material and a formal principle. The material principle, called primary matter, is pure potency, pure capacity for receiving forms; whereas the form is nothing but a certain determination of that potency. Therefore matter and form never exist separately, but always together.

Species and Form. It is easy enough to see a close correspondence between the species-individual structure and that of matter and form. Both structures have in common that their parts do not have a separate existence. Moreover, from the way we have determined the concept of "species" in the foregoing discussion, it is clear that "species" is related with the concept of form. Both concepts have the same broad analogous possibility of application, and both indicate, in general, determination.

The point that comes up for special examination is, however, whether the concept of "individuality" implies a potency as fundamental as does the concept "primary matter". If this question can be answered in a positive sense, then one can be sure that the concept of specific determination also covers, among other things, that basic and essential determination that is attributed to the substantial form.

Individuality and Pure Potency. It is, as a matter of fact, not difficult to show that the concept of individuality, as it is used in connection with the species-individual structure, implies the nature of pure potency. For individuality as such does not include one single determination.

In the analysis given some pages ago[9] of the species-individual structure, whatever has the nature of a determination was placed on

_____

[9]See pp. 118 f.

the side of a specific properties. Therefore, whatever a thing or an event is, is wholly determined by the specific properties. The only function of the concept "individuality" is to safeguard the fundamental fact that an individual thing or event is more than what its specific properties indicate, for these properties never make a thing or event *this* or *that* thing or event. Thus individuality has a definite function, but not a determining function. The only function of individuality is to account for the possibility that the same determination, or rather the same complex of determinations, can exist as different individuals with the same specific properties. Because the said possibility does not include any determination whatsoever, it can justly be termed a pure potency, i.e., a pure capacity for receiving determinations. Its only function is to individualize these determinations. It does not itself add any determination to existing things or events; it only makes them *individual* things or events.

Species-Individual Structure Indicates the Possibility of Substantial Change

The fact that individuality does not include any particular determination leads to an important conclusion. No particular determinations or complex of determinations is exclusively connected with a certain individuality. All determinations can exist in other individuals too. And what is perhaps still more important, the actual determinations of a certain individuality are not the only possible determinations. For if individuality is pure potency, it is not directed exclusively toward any *special* determination. All determinations are, in principle, equally possible. If this is true, then the conclusion follows that all kinds of changes are possible, both in accidental and substantial determinations.

Thus far the distinction between substantial and accidental determinations or forms has been avoided for the simple reason that the distinction was not needed. All that has been said thus far was valid for all possible kinds of determination. Therefore, if it makes sense (and that will be examined in the next section) to distinguish between substantial and accidental changes, then it follows that *both* kinds of changes are possible in view of the fundamental non-simplicity of matter. That fundamental non-simplicity opens up the possibility of fundamental mutability. The same individuality can be successively determined by different determinations.

5. SUBSTANTIAL CHANGE IN MATTER

The Analogy of Substance

Before speaking of substantial change in matter, it must first be known what substance means. The curious fact is that, whereas the meaning of this term seems at first sight quite clear,[10] the more we think about it, the more difficulties we meet. These difficulties are so great that many modern philosophers reject the concept entirely or else they claim that it has only a certain meaning in daily language, but not in philosophy.

The Concept of Substance Is Necessary. Yet the rejection of the concept "substance" does not bring us any further, for it leads, in its turn, to tremendous difficulties which become clearly apparent when we speak of human beings. Avoiding the concept "substance" with respect to human beings produces not only an unbridgeable gap between our most fundamental spontaneous convictions about what human beings are and the way these convictions are repudiated in a philosophical analysis, but it also makes this philosophical analysis itself highly unsatisfactory.

There is, of course, a close relationship between both consequences. A philosophy which repudiates our spontaneous convictions can never give satisfactory results, especially not when these convictions are of such a nature that they resist all attempts of philosophers to eliminate them. There is certainly more in such a concept as "substance" than Hume could see in it, interesting as his analysis may be. A spontaneous conviction tells us that human beings are more than the sum total of their activities or properties. The concept of substance refers to the common origin of these activities and properties, an origin whose existence is immediately evident in a self-reflection.

Different Use of the Concept of Substance. The difficulty with the concept of "substance" is that it is an analogous concept. This explains why its use in daily language (both explicitly and implicitly) shows such a variation of application, and also why the meaning is sometimes clear and sometimes vague and confusing. The concept *substance* as included in the concept *person* is clear. It still is not very difficult when we thing of the concept of "substance" as it is implicitly present in the concept of "animal" and in that of "plant".

The real difficulties begin when we speak of "things." The con-

---

[10]Cf. what has been said about it on pp. 39 f. in connection with Aristotle's analysis of Parmenides' concept of being.

cept of "thing" implicitly contains the concept of substance. However, the use of the concept "thing" is very vague. We call all kinds of objects "things." We find "things" in nature, we ourselves make "things." We discover "things" in science which are never given in immediate sense-experience, such as molecules, atoms, electrons, protons, and the like. Further, we sometimes call an aggregate of things a "thing." An automobile is a "thing," but its parts are also "things."

These difficulties connected with the use in daily language of terms implicitly connoting "substance" are not the only ones. In those philosophic circles which still consider the concept of "substance" fundamental, we also come across very important differences of interpretation. To mention only one, sometimes the term "substance" seems more or less to mean that which is permanent. Consequently, "energy" is called a "substance," not because it is thought of as something "thing-like," but because of the fact that the law of conservation of energy expresses the permanency of energy. In the Aristotelian use of the term "substance," on the other hand, no absolute permanency is connoted, as witness the use of the term "substantial change."

It is not possible, of course, to discuss all problems connected with the different use of the term "substance." The discussion here will be confined to the Aristotelian use of the term, for that is, practically speaking, the same as that of daily language. In philosophy, however, "substance" ought to be free from the vagueness of daily language.

The only way to get the necessary clarification without violating the reality to which this term refers is to account for the analogy of the term and of the reality involved. The general analogous meaning of "substance" refers to all being that does not exist "in-something-else." A human person, for example, forms a substance because he exists "not-in-something-else." He exists in himself. A human action, on the other hand, is not a substance, for such an action exists only in a human being.

The Concept of Substance and Material Being. According to definition, "substance" can be applied to God, to pure spirits and to material beings. Since here only the latter category is of interest, the other categories may be disregarded. It would, however, be a serious mistake to think that, because the discussion of "substance" is limited to the realm of matter, there is no longer any analogy in the concept to be considered. This mistake is the main cause of many difficulties in the philosophy of nature. Let us consider, therefore, some analogous distinctions which are of interest.

The first distinction is a direct consequence of the species-individual structure in matter. This fundamental non-simplicity in matter pervades all that is material. It therefore also has a bearing upon the application of the concept of substance to material beings. The following question may illustrate this. If we speak of man as a substance, what do we mean: the concrete individual person, or the essence of a human being as contrasted with the accidents? Traditionally both are called substance. The individual substance, i.e. the concrete individual with its essence, is called *substantia prima,* primary substance; whereas the abstract essence alone is referred to as *substantia secunda,* secondary substance. In philosophy, especially when we think of non-living things (see p. 47), we usually speak of the latter because there we are interested in the specific nature of a certain kind of being, and not so much in individuals as individuals. Consequently, what is foremost in our minds is that abstract specific nature, the *substantia secunda.* But we realize also that *in concreto* such a specific nature exists only as an individual. Hence the distinction between *substantia prima* and *substantia secunda.*

This is, however, not the only important distinction that should be made. There is another one which concerns the degree of "self-existence" of a substance. Let us explain this curious expression, "self-existence."

Difference in Degree of Self-Existence. "Substance" has been defined above as a being whose nature it is to not-exist-in-something-else. Now it is clear that this negative definition refers to something positive, and this can best be described by the term "self-existence." Considered from the positive point of view, it is clear that there can be degrees of self-existence. Not degrees in a quantitative sense, but a difference in perfection with respect to status of being. A human being, for example, has a higher degree of self-existence than a stone has. Although both are substances because they do not exist in something else, yet their degree of self-existence—the way in which they express their being a substance—is not the same. A human being has something that properly can be called a kind of self-possession; he governs his own activities; he knows himself. His self-existence is, therefore, far more pronounced than that of a piece of inanimate matter. As a consequence nobody seriously doubts that a human being is a substance and just one substance. His individual existence as a substance is more intensely expressed, more marked, and therefore more recognizable, than that of any other material being. We shall return to this problem after consideration of the consequences which the distinction between *substantia prima* and *substantia secunda* has in regard to the concept of substantial change.

Two Kinds of Substantial Change

The first important conclusion to be drawn from the preceding discussion is, of course, that not all substantial changes are alike. If there is a distinction to be made between *substantia prima* and *substantia secunda,* the logical consequence is that there must also be two kinds of substantial change, one in which *substantia prima,* and another in which *substantia secunda* changes. In order to see the difference, let us consider an example. Suppose we have one individual substance of a certain species. (For the present the criteria by which *one* individual is distinguished from an aggregate of several individuals, are of no importance. Likewise, it is of no interest to know what precisely constitutes a species in the strict sense of that term, namely, a class of beings which are characterized by the same substantial form. These problems will soon come up for discussion when the different degrees of self-existence of a substance are discussed.)

To an individual of a certain species two things can theoretically happen. The one individual can be divided into two individuals of the same species. The fact that some kinds of worms can be cut in two and still function as two distinct worms proves that the supposition is not too unrealistic. Since the division results in two individuals there is a change in *substantia prima*. The division represents a substantial change, notwithstanding the fact that *substantia secunda,* the essence, did not change. There is still the same substantial form, the same specific kind of matter.

It is also possible to conceive that while no division of the individual takes place, the old species can be superseded by a new species. With this type of substantial change, the term "substantial" refers, first of all, to *substantia secunda,* the essence of the kind of matter involved. When speaking of substantial change, we usually think of this second type, or preferably of a combination of both; for a substantial change with respect to *substantia secunda* usually results in a division of the one individual.[11] The death of a worm, for example, means a

---

[11]It is, of course, clear that after the substantial change the same *substantia prima* would no longer exist, even if there would be no division of the individual.

substantial change in a double sense. The one living animal changes into a conglomeration of chemical compounds. The mortal remains are only seemingly *one* being. But that is not the point now, for the only purpose of this discussion is to point out the fundamental distinction that should be made between the two kinds of substantial changes, the one in which a specific change occurs, and the one in which an individual is merely divided without the emergence of a new kind of substance.

The difference between these two kinds of substantial changes is a direct consequence of the nature of material being, with its species-individual structure. Therefore, whatever may be the outcome of the examination of the factual changes in matter with respect to their classification into substantial and accidental ones, this we know for sure, there must be two kinds of substantial changes.

6. WHAT ARE THE INDIVIDUAL SUBSTANCES IN MATTER?

The Standards Are Set With Respect to Human Individuals

The preceding section has outlined in general and theoretical terms the content of both the concept "substance" and that of "substantial change," but it has left untouched the crucial problem of what should be considered the concrete individual substances in the material world. It must be remembered that this constitutes a two-fold problem. First, there is the problem as to the criteria by which a distinction is made between one concrete individual and another. These criteria deal with *substantia prima*. They should, therefore, provide an answer to such a question as this: Is a piece of gold *one individual* substance or a collection of individuals? Secondly, there is a problem with respect to *substantia secunda*. The criteria to distinguish one substance from another must be known. Such questions as the following must be answered: Is gold another substance than silver or do both form only different aggregates of the same substances?

Thus far the problems have been dealt with only in a theoretical way. One exception must be made. In discussing the analogy of the concept "substance," it has already been pointed out that human beings are undoubtedly to be considered individual substances. Why are we so sure that they are? In trying to make explicit the reasons for our conviction, it should be mentioned that there are three different levels on which the individual self-existence of human beings expresses itself:

1. The level of intellectual knowledge and free will.

A human being knows himself as an original centre of activity in the midst of a world to which he undoubtedly belongs and which he needs, but in which he is not just a part of a whole.

He knows he has personal existence and personal responsibility, both of which set him apart as an individual and as specifically different from the rest of the material world.

2. The level of organization characteristic of the biological unity which is called "animal."

3. The level of physical objects. The human body is a physical object with a natural coherence in space and time which makes that body clearly discernable from all other physical objects.

On all three levels there is, therefore, reason to speak of an individual. The classical definition of an individual, *indivisum in se et divisum ab aliis,* "undivided in itself and divided from others," applies prefectly to all levels, but more meaningfully at the higher levels of individual existence. The concept "individual" is analogously applied to the different levels.

It should be pointed out that the simple fact of making a distinction between the three levels on which a human being can be said to be an individual does not imply the idea that these three levels exist only in a kind of accidental relationship. It may be that intellectual self-knowledge and free-will do not necessarily imply a being with a biological and therefore also a physical body. It is obvious that in a *human* being the bodily functions condition the kind of self-knowledge and exercise of free will which that being has. On the other hand, the very fact that a human being is more than an animal also lifts the biological unity to a plane above that of a biological unity alone. It gives this biological unity a new sense and significance.

The same applies to the physical object that the human body is. This particular physical object too has a very special place in the midst of other physical objects, as will be seen later when the problems of determinism are being discussed. For the present, the point to be stressed is that the obvious unity given already on the third level acquires a new significance because of the unity on the second level. The physical object with its coherence in space and time (i.e. with a "thing-like" character) is not an accidental aggregate of matter; it is a whole which is carefully selected on behalf of the biological functions.

A similar consideration can be made with respect to the biological organization. This organization is such that it makes intellectual life possible. As a result, the striking substantial unity on the first or highest level, which leaves no doubt that a human person is one individual substance, communicates itself to the lower levels. There may be some doubt about the substantial unity of a human body considered exclusively as a physical object, but that doubt disappears when we see that physical object in the light of its functions on higher levels. Therefore, when we speak of the substantial unity of an individual with respect to human individuals, the content of that concept is quite naturally determined by the unity which exists on the highest level.

Individual Substance on the Sub-Human Level. The very fact that there are physical bodies which have only the unity of the third level, or the unity of the second and the third combined, makes it a matter of necessity to give the concept of an individual substance a content which also satisfies these objects. The danger exists that the obviousness of the substantial unity of a human being captures our attention so strongly that the standards set by this unity are considered the only possible standards. All that does not meet these standards is in danger of not being considered worthy to be brought within the category of substantial unity. In other words the analogy of the concept "substance" is forgotten; and that is the main reason why it seems so difficult to speak of individual substances in the material world. The concept has, perhaps unwillingly and unconsciously, a content which is colored by its application to human beings. This does not cause too much trouble with respect to higher animals because of the close resemblance between animals and human beings. Animals, too, have a kind of cognition which guides their action toward self-preservation. But the real trouble starts when non-living material beings are dealt with. Then we are at a loss as to the standards to be used.

A great many of the difficulties disappear, however, when we realize that the lower *status of being* of matter has its consequences as to the kind of individual existence and substantial differences to be expected. With non-living matter there is not much left of self-existence. Yet the material world shows clearly something that may be properly called "individual substances" if we lower our standards enough to meet the status of being that is characteristic of non-living matter. The only type of unity to be considered is the type of unity that has been described as that of the third level, namely, a certain natural coherence in space and time. So far this has been only a phrase. Let us try to make it more concrete.

Natural Coherence in Space and Time

Although space and time will be discussed later on, something must be said about it now. Spatial extensions and temporal succession mean a diminishing of the substantial unity of a being. All that exists in *time* exists *now*; but existing *now* does not guarantee existence in the *future,* certainly not existence as the same being. Extension in *space* means ex-tended *parts*; such extension opens the possibility of *division* and consequently of the destruction of the unity of a being.

Speaking, therefore, of something that shows a coherence in space and time, stresses the fact that the thing under consideration shows a unity that will resist the possibilities of destruction implied in the very reality of space and time. It survives the flux of time and it remains undivided in space, at least to a certain extent.

The term "natural" added to that of "coherence in space and time," expresses the fact that this coherence is something natural, originating in the nature of the thing involved. The term means that there are natural kinds of matter, types of organization-patterns given in nature. That nature shows such fixed patterns in the organization of matter cannot be doubted. Thus a thing may be identified as an individual substance if it meets two requirements: first it must be *one* piece of matter (i.e., coherent in space and time); secondly, it must have just one natural organization-pattern. Theoretically speaking, these requirements seem clearly enough established.

Application Is Difficult. The difficulty begins, however, when the attempt is made to apply these requirements to actual "things." Then several terms used in the formulations of the requirements seem to become vague. For example, things with a different organization-pattern can be joined very easily in such a way that they have a coherence in space and time; for instance, two pieces of metal soldered together. Now it can be argued, of course, that this coherence is not natural. It all depends, however, on how we define "natural." Nobody can deny that the forces which make possible the process of soldering things are *natural* forces. And whoever tries to escape from this consequence by saying that the arrangement of the different pieces is artificial and, therefore, not natural, overlooks the simple fact that nature offers us many examples of such arrangements. There is, therefore, nothing unnatural about it.

A Partial Solution. A partial solution to this difficulty is found if "natural coherence" is defined more precisely as a coherence according to a fixed type of organization. Now the point can be made that in the example discussed (two pieces of metal soldered together), there is not just one organization-pattern, but two, or even three. And the way they are connected is not itself a fixed organization-pattern, because it all depends on casual circumstances just what will be the accidental form of the unity that comes into being. Therefore, our example seems to be a clear case of an aggregate of at least three individual substances.

However, this way of looking at the problem certainly does not solve all difficulties. For what would be said when two metals are welded together instead of soldered? Welding seems to result in just *one* natural organization-pattern. The difficulty behind the whole problem is that all the evidence points in the direction that there exists, practically speaking, a gradual transition from clear-cut aggregates to what can properly be called a natural unity.

Nature Shows Gradual Transitions. An interesting point is that the evidence for the existence of gradual transition is already given in every-day experience. It is not just science which has brought this fact to light. Science has only confirmed it. Every-day experience sharply distinguishes between the accidental unity of a heap of stones, held together only by gravitation, and the substantial unity of a crystal of ice. But the simple fact remains that there are still all kinds of intermediate unities. The gap between the "accidental" unity of a heap of stones and the "substantial" unity of a crystal can gradually be bridged by such examples as a clod of earth, a piece of mortar, a brick, and different crystals melted together. It is difficult to say where accidental unity ends and substantial unity begins. And if we turn to science in order to get an answer, we meet with precisely the same difficulty.

Science started out by making a rather sharp distinction between a chemical bond and a physical adhesion. Philosophers have made use of that distinction by considering the chemical bond as representing a substantial unity, and the physical adhesion an accidental unity. Clear examples are, respectively, a chemical compound of two elements and a simple mixture, such as an alloy. However, there are all kinds of intermediate forms in which it is hard to say whether the bond is chemical or purely physical. And a more profound theoretical knowledge of the respective nature of a chemical and physical bond makes it clear why the transition is so gradual.

To make things still more difficult, it can be argued that the so-called pure chemical element or compound, which should be the only piece of matter under consideration to be classified as *"one* individual substance," never exists in reality. There may be found in reality things which come so close to a state of purity that they may be said to have only *one* natural organization-pattern. But there is reason to believe that the concepts of pure chemicals, such as pure iron or pure salt, are, strictly speaking, idealized physico-chemical concepts of something that probably never does exist in reality. If this is true—and all scientific evidence points in that direction—then the concept "individual" has importance only when used in connection with elementary particles. All macro-things seem to be aggregate. The only real individual substances are the elementary particles. This conclusion seems to be inevitable. This is one of the reasons why the mechanistic conception of matter is so attractive in the eyes of scientists. The discussion of this conception however, is better postponed till some other difficulties which the term "natural coherence in space and time" presents are outlined.

Other Difficulties. Besides the impossibility of applying that formula in an unambiguous way to existing things, there is another much greater inconvenience connected with it. The formula takes care only of solid bodies. An application to liquids, to gases, and to light does not seem to make much sense. There can be no doubt that the phenomena in these different fields demonstrate the existence of fixed patterns of organization. There is also something that can be called a certain coherence in space and time, (a beam of light, a drop of water, a volume of gas), but it is pretty hard to call these "things," possessing such a weak coherence, individuals. The coherence in space and time is too little pronounced to justify the use of the term "individual" in the strict philosophical sense.

Proposed Solutions. Again the solution seems to be that such things as a volume of gas or a drop of water or a beam of light are conceived of as aggregates of invisible, elementary particles. Only these particles are the real individuals. This mechanistic solution is, however, not the only solution. There is a fundamentally different one which considers the whole material world, the whole universe, as one individual substance. This substance is the only existing material reality of which all "things" are but parts. A part can sometimes distinguish itself with such a clearness from its surroundings that we call it an individual "thing"; but it never has the degree of substantial unity required for an individual substance. Nor are the differences between these "things" of such a nature that they should be considered *substantially* different. The transitions are too gradual. Thus a whole series of difficulties can be put forward to show that the formula of "natural coherence in space and time" is extremely difficult to apply and can give rise to entirely different solutions of the factual problems.

It must be remembered that the difficulty connected with the application of the formula does not find its origin in exclusively scientific considerations. The gradual transition between different types of unity appears already on the level of a primitive pre-scientific experience. Science only confirms the graduality of the differences, and shows thereby that the difficulties we are facing are essential. They do not disappear with growing knowledge. Before drawing a fundamental philosophical conclusion from this state of affairs, let us first examine the two solutions thus far mentioned.

The Whole Universe as One Substance

It is undoubtedly true that much can be said in favor of a solution which considers the whole universe as one and, consequently, the only individual substance. With one large gesture we get rid of all attempts to make artificial distinctions between aggregates and genuine unities in the material world, between accidental and substantial differences. However, here also are serious objections; and they are so serious that we are forced to abandon the idea of considering the whole universe as one individual substance.

The first objection arises when the place human beings occupy in the universe is considered. Human beings are undoubtedly "part" of the universe. They are subject to all laws of the material world; they need other "parts" of the universe for their preservation (food, water, air, and the like); and they are in continual interaction with these parts. Briefly, nature is inside man. If we speak of the universe as a whole, then human beings must be included; they form a part of it. On the other hand, human beings are individual substances. Hence their being a part of the universe cannot mean that they are a part in the strict sense of that term.

Here again we come upon the greatest difficulty in philosophy, namely, the analogy of philosophical concepts and terms.[12] "Part" is

[12]See pp. 141 f.

an analogous concept. It is correct to call a hand a part of a body, a drive-shaft a part of an automobile, a human person a part of the society to which he belongs. However, "part" has in each of the given examples a different meaning, as also does the "whole" to which the parts refer. In order to see the difference more clearly, let us think of what happens to the part when it is removed from the whole to which it belongs. A hand is essentially different when it is not any longer a part of a human body. It is even, strictly speaking, not any longer a hand. The very essence of a hand is "to be a part" of a body. The hand exists only as part of the body. A drive-shaft, however, is exactly the same thing whether or not it is an actual part of a car. It is still a drive-shaft when it is outside a car. A human being is still a human person when he does not any longer belong to the society of which he was a part.

The fact that a human being is an individual makes it impossible to consider him *merely* as part of the universe. The universe may be a whole; but the very existence of human beings within this universe indicates clearly that the universe does not have the unity of *one* individual substance. If this were the case, then it would not be correct to speak of *human* actions. The person would not act; but his action would be, properly speaking, an action of the universe. For the action of a *part* in the strict sense of that term is never the action of a *part*, but the action of a *whole*. The hand is not acting, but the human being acts by means of his hand. From this it can be seen that the universe can be said to be a whole, but not in the strict sense that an individual substance can be so considered.

Closely connected with the foregoing objection to considering the universe as one substantial individual is another. This objection can, however, more appropriately be discussed later when we speak of the problem of determinism. Then it will be shown that the theory which considers the universe as one whole, with one substantial nature, leads to insurmountable difficulties.

The Mechanistic Conception

The mechanistic conception gives an opposite solution to the problem of what the individual substances in the material world are. According to the mechanistic doctrine, only elementary particles can be said to be individuals. Thus all difficulties connected with distinguishing between aggregates and genuine unities in the visible world are avoided. All sensible "things" are aggregates of invisible elementary particles which are the true individuals. As a point in fact, the mechanistic doctrine makes the sharpest possible distinction between individual unities and aggregates of these unities, but it shifts the distinction from the level of the macro-world to that of the micro-world. Each elementary particle is one individual thing. It may have parts, but the assumption is that an elementary particle cannot be divided; it never changes its nature. Briefly, it remains exactly what it is. It may become part of a whole, but that does not affect its nature. The whole is merely accidental, a pure aggregate.

As to the problem of substantial difference, two opinions are possible. The classical view of Democritus considers all "elementary particles" as having the same nature. But it is, of course, also tenable to accept substantial differences between the elementary particles. Substantial changes are, however, excluded by a mechanistic philosophy.

It cannot be denied that the mechanical solution has, at first sight, many advantages. The concept of individual substance seems to have a clear meaning; and the application of the concept does not give any difficulty, at least so long as we speculate exclusively upon theoretically assumed elementary particles. For these particles are tailored to what we think an individual should be.

Yet, a closer look at the mechanistic doctrine and its basic concepts reveals many scientific and philosophic difficulties. For the present, the philosophical, not the scientific, difficulties are going to be considered.

The Mechanistic Concept of Individual. Let us begin with the main objection. In Section 4 of this Chapter it has been shown that individuality as such does not include any form or determination. That was the result of the analysis of the species-individual structure. Mechanicism, however, provides the individual particles with determinations (size, shape, mass and sometimes charge) which are intrinsically bound to the individual as such. Each individual has its own permanent determinations. This gives the concept of material individual quite another significance than it has according to a careful analysis of the nature of matter. The material individuals have a permanency which is not compatible with the fundamental non-simplicity which characterizes material being.

Distinction Between Individual Substance and Aggregate Is Too Sharp. A second objection concerns the sharp distinction which the mechanistic doctrine makes between individuals and aggregates. This distinction seems much too sharp. For nature shows us a very gradual transition between instances of one individual substance and those of an aggregate. So the peculiar difficulty which we experience when we try to apply to the things of the macro-world the concept of individual substance is not that there seems to be no occasion at all for application. The specific difficulty is that there appears to be no sharp distinction between the instances where possibility of application is obvious and those where there is certainly merely an aggregate. The experience we have of the material world does not point in the direction of such a sharp distinction between individual substances and aggregates thereof, as the mechanistic philosophy wants us to believe. And this leads to a third objection.

Mechanism and the Difference Between a Chemical Compound and a Physical Mixture. The more or less gradual transition between clear instances of aggregates and those of substantial unities does not take away from the fact that there is a distinct difference between these two types of unities. There are in nature organization-patterns which show a strongly marked constancy: for instance, the pattern of chemical elements and compounds. The number of the elementary chemical patterns is limited. With that limited number many different chemical compounds can be built, but all have that strongly-marked constancy characteristic of chemical compounds. External circumstances have an influence upon the realization of a compound, but they are not able to vary the fundamentally constant pattern.

On the other hand, however, organization-patterns are found which, although a certain underlying constancy cannot be denied to them, show an almost infinite variation due to circumstances. Consider, for example, the ways that two metals can form an alloy. This can take place in, practically speaking, all proportions. Compare this behavior to the way in which two elements can form a chemical compound, and it should be clear that nature shows different types of organization-patterns. These different types do exist, although the transition between the two types is not as sharp as classical chemistry supposed them to be when it made a distinction between chemical compounds and physical mixtures.

Mechanicism cannot very well account for that difference. It uses a matter-form schema in which the form is nothing but the external relationship between intrinsically unchangeable elementary particles which play the role of matter in the schema. The one-sidedness of the form in the mechanistic schema, which allows only for a variation in configuration of the particles, makes the existence of organization-patterns in nature with a strongly pronounced constancy difficult to comprehend.

One can perhaps imagine that such a matter-form schema, as used in the mechanistic doctrine, can explain organization-patterns which have been described above—those with little constancy; but it can certainly not explain organization-patterns with pronounced constancies.

The latter objection can be formulated in a more general and more fundamental way.

Narrowness of the Mechanistic Matter-Form Schema. Because of the very limited content of the concept "form" in the mechanistic schema, the full burden of explaining the richness of the organization-pattern in nature falls upon the elementary particles. These particles are supposed, however, to be unchangeable and possessed of very few, if any, qualitative differences. They are, therefore, extremely unfitted for this function of explaining. They could fulfil this function only if they themselves were full of properties which would give them the plasticity and mutability necessary to account for the richness and variety of nature's organization-patterns. In other words, the elementary particles themselves must have a more profound matter-form structure than that of the mechanistic schema which allows only for different configurations of unchangeable particles. This matter-form schema is too limited to serve as an *ultimate* explanation of the nature of the material world.

From this it does not follow, of course, that the schema cannot be very useful for a more limited purpose than for an ultimate explanation. The mechanistic matter-form schema undoubtedly satisfies existing situations, such as are studied in mechanical models. Then we have the case in which the elements of the structure do not change. This also explains why the science of the 17th century could so wholeheartedly adopt mechanistic atomism as its philosophical background.[13] Science then was chiefly theoretical mechanics and applied mechanics. The matter-form schema of mechanistic philosophy seemed sufficient to explain all that was within the reach of the science of these days.

The development of science was bound to show the limitations of the mechanistic matter-form schema. For this schema is contrary

---

[13]Cf. *From Atomos to Atom*, Ch. III.

to the real nature of matter, as should be clear from the preceding analysis.

Before turning our attention to the development of science, however, it is worth stressing still another reason why the mechanistic matter-form schema is so attractive.

The Analogy of the Matter-Form Schema

In order to understand why the human mind thinks easily in terms of a mechanistic matter-form schema, the following consideration is important. The mechanistic schema may be too limited, yet it is the clearest example of a matter-form schema in general. The reader might recall that Aristotle also started his intellectual analysis of change by considering a change of external form, a piece of clay that becomes a statue. Without a clear understanding of intellectually more accessible instances of change, other more radical changes can never be understood. This fact contains a profound lesson. The matter-form doctrine of Aristotle, stating that all material things are composed of primary matter and substantial form, can be understood only as an analogous extension, or rather deepening,[14] of the better known matter-form schema, used for the explanation of a purely accidental change. We have even seen, when speaking of Aristotle, that the transition from the idea of an external form to that of an internal form is achieved by the intermediary idea of the internal form (structure) of an artifact. The function of the two matter-form schemes, borrowed from the construction of artifacts is not only to supply

---

[14]The use of the terms "extension" and "deepening" is in itself a very good instance of analogy. All that is said in the text with respect to the analogy of matter and form also applies, *mutatis mutandis,* to the way in which we use the terms "extension" and "deepening." Strictly speaking, "extension" and "deepening" refer to spatial relationships. In this sense, they cannot be applied to knowledge. Yet, it makes sense to use them also with respect to knowledge. And this use is not purely metaphorical. We find something in our knowledge that has some points in common with a physical process of extending or deepening. Yet it is different. Because of the presence of both similarity and difference, the philosopher speaks of analogy. Something in the content of a certain concept can be used elsewhere, where the strict use of that concept is impossible. The point to be stressed is that we are not able to express the reality of "deepening our knowledge" without using concepts which have, strictly speaking, an exclusively spatial sense. This is not only the result of a certain poverty of language; the problem is much more fundamental. If it were only a problem of language, i.e. of terminology, we could easily coin new terms to express the different analogous meanings of one concept. The trouble is that in order to *understand* these different analogous meanings we must have the original spatial meaning in mind. We can never dispense with it. This proves how strongly human knowledge is sense-bound. Yet, there can be no doubt that there is definite meaning in speaking of the "extension" of our knowledge. Our knowledge may be sense-bound; but it is not restricted exclusively to sense-knowledge.

the terms for the more fundamental matter-form schema of Aristotle; it goes much further than that. Even the *content* of the terms "primary matter" and "substantial form" can be understood only in relationship to the meaning the terms "matter" and "form" have in the better-known schemes. This meaning must be constantly in our minds, although we must at the same time transcend this meaning. This transcendence is necessary, for the original meaning of "matter" and "form" is in itself not what we want. Yet something in the content of "matter" and "form" carries the meaning of what we are trying to express. In other words, we use these terms analogously. And this is the only way available to the human intellect, as has been explained in the footnote dealing with the analogous use of the terms "extension" and "deepening."

The fact that philosophy must of necessity always make use of analogous concepts and terms is what makes philosophical understanding so difficult. There is always the danger that we shall fall back on the more ordinary meaning a term has when not used in an analogous way. This may make the meaning clear but it does not solve the philosophical problem.

So two points are important with respect to the matter-form schema. First, the mechanistic schema is undoubtedly the clearer one. It is useful in order to understand certain simple situations in nature, but it is also indispensable to understand the more profound matter-form structure. Thus we are bound to make use of it. On the other hand, there is a natural tendency in the human mind to make the mechanistic schema the exclusive one, because it is so much easier to understand than the more profound hylomorphistic structure of primary matter and substantial form. Hence the constant temptation to use both concepts in a more physical sense. "Primary matter" is then to be identified with elementary particles or elementary waves, and "substantial form" with the structure thereof. In doing this we miss the analogy and revert to a strict mechanistic schema.

Science and the Use of a Mechanistic Schema

In the 17th century science worked on a mechanistic schema. This was certainly not accidental. Science will always use this schema because it is indispensable. Even philosophy cannot fully dispense with it. True, philosophy has to transcend it. Philosophy must apply the matter-form schema analogously in order to explain the nature of matter; but the very fact that it is an analogous application shows how indispensable the mechanistic schema is.

The difference between science and philosophy is that science is allowed to use a limited schema if such a schema is helpful in understanding a certain group of phenomena, whereas philosophy is not allowed to do so. Philosophy is from the very beginning directed towards the understanding of matter as matter. A limited philosophy is therefore a wrong philosophy. A limited science can be a correct science with respect to a limited field of phenomena. The kinetic gas theory, for example, explains certain phenomena with the help of the external behavior of molecules which are supposed not to change during the processes covered by the theory. If science can correctly explain the phenomena at issue on the basis of a limited mechanical schema, nothing is wrong. Science does not contend that molecules are unchangeable; science says only that as far as the explanation of the kinetic gas theory goes, molecules can be considered as unchanging. If science should go further and use the assumption of the immutability of molecules outside the field involved, then it would have to prove for each field of phenomena that the assumption is true. If philosophy, however, uses a mechanistic schema as the ultimate explanation of the general nature of matter, it has to prove from the very beginning that this schema can explain all the general features of matter. Nothing in the field of the general features of matter could be left unconsidered. It is when measured by philosophical standards that the mechanistic doctrine fails. This doctrine can explain some particular phenomena, but not the fundamental features of matter.

The failure of mechanism as an ultimate philosophical explanation remained almost unobserved during the 17th and following centuries. Not that the philosophical reasons could not be grasped as to why mechanism failed, but the seemingly universal success of that system of thought distracted attention from these reasons. It seemed as if science had sufficiently proved the universal value of a mechanistic schema. The truth was, however, that science could explain only a very limited group of phenomena. It could perhaps suggest a possible explanation of some others; but that science could explain all phenomena on the basis of a mechanistic schema was certainly not a justified extrapolation.

In proportion as science developed, it became clear how limited the mechanistic schema was. It is a simplification and it holds good as long as the simplification is irrelevant with respect to the phenomena under consideration. The chemical atomic theory of the 19th century, for example, could simplify the atom, considering it as something unchangeable, as long as that theory focused attention on the factor "weight," which does not change during a chemical reaction.[15] The weight of an atom remains the same in all kinds of compounds. This fact was the basis on which Lavoisier and Dalton built up the system of elements and compounds. Practically all other properties of atoms did not reveal a comparable consistency, but chemistry was not yet ready to pay much attention to an explanation of these other properties. It was simply assumed that one day they could also be explained according to the same mechanistic schema. This expectation, however, was not realized.[16] Contemporary science still works with elementary particles, but these particles do not in the least show the permanency required by mechanistic philosophy. The schema is still useful, but its limitation is clearly established by science. None of the "particles" has a "permanent" existence. All are open to fundamental changes in which they simply cease to be the particles they were before.[17]

Consequently, science has lost even the appearance of favoring the mechanistic answer to the question of what individual substances in the material world are. The progress of science has shown that changes are more radical than a mechanistic philosophy can account for.

The Relativity of the Concept "Individual"

Considerable time has been devoted to the alternative solutions of the problem of what should be considered an "individual" in the material world. None of them proved satisfactory. The conception of the whole universe as one individual led to insurmountable difficulties with respect to the place of human beings within that one

---

[15]At least not to such an extent as is observable by the classical methods of weighing.

[16]It should be stressed that the mechanistic principle was never a presupposition of science in the strict sense in which we have used this term in Chapter I. Therefore, science could abandon this principle the moment it discovered the limitation of the mechanistic schema.

[17]See, for example, Francis Bitter, *Nuclear Physics*, Cambridge, Mass., 1950, p. 11.

For a description of the development of science which gradually undermined the idea of permanent elementary particles, the reader may be referred to *From Atomos to Atom*, Ch. IV ff. The fact that science still uses the concept of "particle" without its former connotation of immutability is nicely indicated by the quotation-marks in the title of J. D. Stranathan's book, *The "Particles" of Modern Physics*, Philadelphia-Toronto, 1943.

universe. The once highly favored conception which considered "elementary particles" as the only individuals is, at least in its mechanistic form, not tenable because its basic conceptions are in conflict with the general aspects of nature.

This state of affairs forces us to reconsider the several difficulties which exist regarding the application of the formula "natural coherence in space and time," a term used to characterize a material individual. Although the concrete application of the formula may not be always clear, the alternative solutions lead nowhere. It must be possible to apply the concept "individual" to a reality somewhere between "elementary particles" and the universe as a whole. The great advantage of the formula "natural coherence in space and time" was that it could without great difficulty be applied to human beings, to animals, and even to plants, with this restriction as to plants that it is sometimes difficult to say whether we are dealing with one plant which has several parts or with a combination of several plants.[18] The real trouble starts, as has been pointed out, with non-living things. Among them it is the rule rather than the exception that no sharp distinction is possible between aggregates and real unities, i.e. between an accidentally connected collection of individuals and just one individual.

Two Views are Possible. Now one can take two views of the situation. One can say, the formula used to characterize an individual is not adequate; it is too one-sided, too much tailored to fit human beings and animals. But another view is also possible. The fact that there is an increase of uncertainty with respect to the application of the formula when we descend the line from animals to non-living things can also be an indication that the concept of "individual" is gradually losing its significance. It is quite possible that nature itself gives the term "natural coherence in time and space" a gradually decreasing significance. After all, the term "natural" is derived from the term "nature."

Natural Coherence is Subject to Gradual Decrease. The second view is no doubt the correct one. On the level of human beings and animals, nature shows such "natural coherences" that being an individual on that level means something. The "natural coherence" of

---

[18]As to the difficulty of applying the concept "individual" in biology, see M. Jeuken, "The Concept, 'Individual' in Biology," in *Acta Biotheoretica*, Vol. X (1952), pp. 57-84.

the parts is caused by a nature which possesses a kind of self-preservation that gives the individually existing being a distinctive individuality And not only that, but an individual also has a pronounced organization-pattern which clearly marks it as an individual of a certain species. With plants the natural coherence is much less, but still noticeable. However, to divide a plant is very easy; it can sometimes be performed without any damage to the plant.

When we get to non-living matter, we still find "natural coherence," but it is as if nature were not any longer interested both in keeping its organization-pattern pure and its individuals clearly distinct. A piece of impure gold has as strong a "natural coherence" as a piece of pure gold. There is really no reason to call only the second an individual and the first an aggregate because it does not have one organization-pattern. Nor does it seem to make much sense to say that a piece of metal consisting of two parts soldered together is not one individual but only an aggregate. Its "natural coherence in space and time" is hardly discernible from that of a piece of metal with just one organization-pattern. Nature does show the different possibilities just described, and we have to acknowledge them when speaking of individuals.

So the conclusion from this state of affairs should be that it is a violation of nature to make sharp distinctions between aggregates and natural unities. Nature also gives many so-called aggregates a natural unity. Or let us put it this way: individuals can very easily, and in a natural way, so combine that they together form a new individual.

What About the Substantial Form? But now the question comes up as to what the substantial form of that individual is, e.g., two pieces of copper soldered together with tin. If there is reason to call such soldered pieces *one* individual substance, then they must have also *one* substantial form. The question is crucial. At first sight, the question may even seem fatal, because it seems immediately to expose the weakness of the solution given to the problem of what the individuals in the material world are. The reader who up till now has carefully followed the arguments put forward to show the relative value of the concept of "individuality" and has thought them convincing, will feel embarrassed (as did the author) when confronted with this question of substantial form. "Substantial form" seems too dignified a concept to be subject to the same kind of relativity as the concept of individuality perhaps might be.

Yet the conclusion is inescapable. If the concept of "individual" has a relative meaning, then the same seems to apply to that of "substantial form."

Relativity of the Distinction Between Substantial and Artificial Forms. In order to remove some of the embarrassment, it may be pointed out that Aristotle would have solved the difficulty by saying that the individual under consideration (two pieces of soldered copper) had an artificial form. The concept "artificial form" was a kind of counterpart of that of "substantial form." An "artificial" form was a form given to things by man, not by nature. Strictly speaking, Aristotle considered such a form an accidental form of a very special type. This proves that Aristotle was aware of the problem. The trouble is, however, that the distinction which Aristotle made between "artificial" and "natural" forms is artificial. It has been pointed out in a preceding section that nature also offers examples of such artificial forms as are being considered at the moment. "Soldering" may be an artificial way of uniting things, but nature unites them in exactly the same way. The "natural" stones Aristotle speaks of are, as a matter of fact, "soldered" stones.

It therefore seems safe to say that the distinction between substantial and artificial form has to be taken in a relative sense.

There undoubtedly are in the material world very definite and mutually different substantial forms, that is, forms possessing different, clearly marked fundamental patterns of organization. The usefulness of such concepts as electron, proton, neutron, pure chemical element, pure chemical compound proves that sufficiently. The concepts of pure chemical elements or pure chemical compounds are, however, more or less idealizations. In reality there are no pure chemical elements or compounds. Nature knows only approximations thereto. It is as if matter were not capable of realizing in a pure way its fundamental organization-patterns. The potency of primary matter makes its influence felt. The indeterminateness of primary matter which causes it to be able to be determined in so many ways prevents, as it were, the actualization by just one pure organization-pattern in greater unities than the elementary patterns.

So the actual substantial forms, the actual fundamental determinations of matter do not have the idealized form which they have in our theoretical concepts. They are realized in a deficient, or rather mixed, way. For this very reason the distinction between substantial and artificial form has to be taken in a relative sense. And one should not hesitate to speak of *one* substantial form, even when he is able to discern more than one pure organization-pattern. If these patterns are united in a natural way, then there is only one *substantial* form. For the important point is that not one of the pure organization-patterns has actualized primary matter; but an impure or mixed pattern has. That is the only one which is present in reality. That is the only substantial form which makes the thing that which it is.

It may be noted that the above solution of the problem, as to what the individual substances are, does not imply that there is no difference at all between aggregates and substantial unities. What has been stressed is that the transition is rather gradual; this fact has been the guide to the discussion. It is clear, however, that there are instances of obvious aggregates. Mechanical artifacts especially should be so considered. However, there is no essential objection to also calling such an artifact an "individual." It is an individual with an "artificial form," because of the fact that the principle of unity is not given by nature, but by the way in which the different parts are artificially adapted for the combination. The analogy of the concepts *individual* and *substantial form* makes it possible to use these terms also in this case; but the analogical use is obvious.

Individuality in Non-Solids

So far our discussion has exclusively dealt with solid bodies, but not with other material phenomena, such as liquids, gases and the phenomena of light. The last category especially does not seem to allow us to speak of individuals.

Classical physics seemed to suggest a certain solution for these problems in so far as it made an essential distinction between two fundamental kinds of matter, so-called ponderable and non-ponderable matter. With ponderable matter the elementary particles (atoms, molecules) could be supposed to be the individuals, at least with liquids and gases, whereas with solids there was always the opportunity to consider unities greater than elementary particles as individual substances. As to light and other electro-magnetic phenomena, these were supposed to happen in the ether. The ether was considered as one continuous individual substance of a special kind. It was imponderable and pervaded all ponderable matter. So the problems of individuality could be solved with relative ease in classical physics. The classical picture of the world, however, is not any longer tenable. The sharp distinction of all material phenomena in discontinuous ponderable and continuous non-ponderable phenomena has been proved wrong. There is no such sharp distinction. Both the phenomena of radiation and those of the ponderable matter show the same fundamental properties. Modern physics knows even instances of transition between phenomena of radiation and ponderable matter. The radical mutability of matter, so much stressed above, exists also with respect to these two kinds of matter, formerly so sharply distinguished. The two realities, that of continuous matter (ether) and that of discontinuous ponderable matter, merge into one and the same reality.

As a result of this scientific development, the idea of elementary particles and that of continuous waves are therefore no longer to be considered adequate representations of different realities, but models of the same reality. Sometimes the one model is more appropriate, sometimes the other. The difficulty is, however, that both models exclude each other; therefore neither can be adequate. This should not surprise us too much, for both models stem, as a matter of fact, from a mechanistic view of reality. We have seen, however, that although this view has certain advantages, yet it cannot provide the final view of reality. The sharp distinction which classical physics made between ponderable and imponderable matter makes the impression that the distinction resulted from the absolute significance given to something that had only an introductory and relative value. So it seems, philosophically speaking, that the modern physical conception which makes use of the mechanical models, though not in an absolute sense, has more truth in it than the old conception had. The material reality has both aspects, the aspect of discontinuity and the aspect of continuity. Sometimes the reality shows its continuous aspect, and then the continuous model can be used; sometimes it shows its discontinuous aspect, and then the discontinuous model can be used.

The question to be asked now is, of course, whether or not the results of modern science can indicate a solution of the problem as to what should be considered individuals in the material world. Let us try to evaluate the above conceptions of modern science in terms of our problem. In view of the fact that much remains obscure, we can only make some hesitating remarks.

The material world has partly the character of a continuous medium, a general substratum, which as such does not show individual substances but has a definite tendency to form such substances.

This may be shown by the fact that with each group of physical phenomena it is possible to discover something that can properly be called a corpuscular aspect. Even on the level of the most elementary forms of matter such as photons (particles of light), there seems to be a hesitating beginning of forming individuals in the general substratum of matter. With electrons, this corpuscular aspect becomes more strongly marked, but the influence of the general substratum of matter is still noticeable in such a way that the individuality remains very weak and easily disappears again in the general substratum of matter.

Not until the stage of molecules is reached does the corpuscular aspect become strong enough to allow us to speak of real individuals (the molecules of a gas). Molecules exhibit also the tendency to form greater individual unities such as crystals. Yet, even with crystals, the individuality has only a relative meaning, as has been seen above. With crystals, we can only speak of a cumulation of the same elementary form. Nevertheless, there is sufficient natural coherence in space and time to call a crystal an individual. As to other "aggregates" of molecules, such as liquids and gases, these do not show clearly enough pronounced "natural coherence in space and time" above the level of molecules to justify calling anything other than molecules individuals. There is some evidence that in liquids, and even in gases, the molecules are united in larger unities (witness the regularity shown by X-rays and electron diffraction by gases and liquids), but these unities do not shown enough coherence to be called individuals. The existence of these unities confirms, however, how gradual the transitions in nature are. Gases and liquids already make a beginning with structures of a higher order. But only when this hesitant beginning is completed in a solid body are we justified in calling these higher structures "individuals."

With living beings the individuality becomes more pronounced, there is something of a self-existence. Many elementary patterns of matter work together in forming a living individual, which is sufficiently distinct from the rest of the material world to enable us to use the term "self-existence." There is still another point. Although the substantial form of such a living individual exists only as a determination of matter, yet it has a certain independence insofar as the form maintains itself throughout a continual stream of material processes. After some time, all the material elements of an animal are replaced, but the animal is still there. Thus the distinction of the individual from the rest of the material world (the general substratum), although in no way absolute, is pronounced enough to call an animal an individual substance. Even with human beings, in which the individuality of the material world culminates, there is not an absolute distinction, but there can be no doubt about their self-existence.

7. RECAPITULATION

If a retrospective view is taken of the results obtained in this chapter, then two points deserve special attention: first, the profoundness of Aristotle's analysis of the essence of matter; and, secondly, the reason why this analysis is very often neglected.

As to the first, during the last centuries it may have appeared that Aristotle's analysis was entirely wrong. This appearance resulted from a very superficial analysis of the then existing science. That science seemed to confirm the mechanistic philosophy with which it was connected, whereas a more profound analysis of the basic pre-suppositions of that science would have revealed that at least one of these presuppositions, namely the species-individual structure of matter, was incompatible with a mechanistic philosophy. The further development of science has demonstrated that a mechanistic philosophy and science are two entirely different things. This development has confronted science with changes of a much more radical nature than a mechanistic matter-form schema can account for. No material organization-pattern which science comes across has a "permanent" character with respect to the individual representatives of these patterns. Nature is organized in electrons, photons, protons, neutrons, atoms, molecules, crystals, plants, and animals; but no individual electron, etc., has a permanent existence.[19] In nature there is a continual changing from one organization-pattern into another, and this is exactly what, in Aristotelian terms, should be called "substantial change" with respect to *substantia secunda*. Beside this type of sub-stantial change there is place for "substantial change" with respect to *substantia prima*. In this case there is no change of pattern but only a break in the pattern. *One* individual becomes two or more. Finally,

---

[19]It is of interest to note that the "particles" of modern science are much closer to the *minimum naturalia* of the Greek and Medieval Aristotelians than to the atoms of Democritus. For the doctrine of *minima naturalia* see *From Atomos to Atom*, pp. 41 ff., pp. 46 ff., pp. 58 ff.

there are accidental changes. These changes do not destroy either the fundamental pattern or the unity of the pattern.

In view of the fact that the basic ideas of Aristotelian philosophy are especially suited to the philosophical needs of modern science, it is strange that this philosophy is in many circles still considered as too old-fashioned. This misconception shall be considered again in the last chapter. For the present, one reason for the misconception may be mentioned in connection with what has been said in the present chapter. Philosophy must always use analogous concepts. This explains, of course, why scientists have a natural dislike for the philosophy of nature. They miss the exactness of scientific terms and concepts. They miss also the possibility of verifying the outcome of philosophic reasoning by sense-experience. However, this dislike of the scientist is not the point to be discussed now in connection with the analogy of philosophic concepts. It is not the scientist, after all, who has to work in the field of the philosophy of nature.

It has been shown in this chapter, however, that the scientist is not alone in his dislike of analogy. The philosopher joins him, and that fact is most dangerous for philosophy. This chapter has shown clearly that the greatest difficulty in handling such philosophical concepts as "substance," "substantial change," and "individual" comes from the natural tendency of the philosopher to neglect the analogy of these concepts. He has in mind some clear-cut applications of these concepts as they relate to human beings. That fact colors the content of these concepts. Consequently, when it comes to applying these concepts to other levels of matter than that of human beings, the philosopher runs into difficulties. He does not see any possibility of applying such concepts as "individual," "substance," and "substantial change" to material phenomena. There seems to be nothing on the level of matter alone which is worthy of being called "individual" and which can be put on a par with human individuals. No event in matter seems important enough to be labeled a "substantial change." No difference seems fundamental enough to be considered a "substantial" one. Only two ways are now open. Either the philosopher stays in an ivory tower, in which case he speaks only in general terms of "substance," "substantial change," and "individuals" and refrains carefully from confronting physical reality with his abstract terminological system; or else he abandons the whole Aristotelian system as though it were built only upon the primitive concepts of daily life.

The result in both cases is the same. The outsider is confirmed in his conviction that Aristotelian philosophy is an old-fashioned system not suited to modern use. Yet nothing is further from the truth. Provided that their analogous meaning is understood, the Aristotelian concepts are extremely useful for analyzing the fundamental nature of matter.

This will be demonstrated again when we turn our attention in the next chapters to the problems connected with the quantitative and qualitative character of matter, and with the way matter acts. These chapters will also provide the opportunity to discuss some problems which in this chapter were only touched upon. To mention only one, it has been shown in the beginning of this chapter that the conception of "substantial change" as a change for which science could not give an explanation was highly unfortunate. This notion of substantial change has nothing at all to do with substantial change. It is even the opposite of the spirit of Aristotelian philosophy, as will be discussed in Chapter VI.

SUGGESTED READINGS

P. Hoenen, *Cosmologia,* 4th ed., Rome, 1949, *Liber* IV.

Louis de Raeymaeker, *Philosophie de l'Etre,* Louvain, 1946, *2e section.* English translation, *The Philosophy of Being,* St. Louis, 1954, Part 2.

Bernard Bavink, *Ergebnisse und Probleme der Naturwissenschaften,* Leipzig, [6]1940, Chapter I, Section 19.

A. G. van Melsen, *From Atomos to Atom,* Pittsburgh, 1952, Ch. V.

H. Weyl, *Philosophy of Mathematics and Natural Science,* Princeton, 1949, Appendix F.

CHAPTER FIVE

QUANTITY

1. QUANTITY IN GENERAL

Discrete and Continuous Quantity

One of the most striking traits of all material things and events is their quantitative character. Things are extended in time and in space. But not only that. The fundamental quantitative character of matter is more than just its temporal and spatial *extension*. Quantity pervades matter in all its aspects. To mention just one example: A material quality, say a color, is always the color of an *extended* thing. But that is not the only relationship between quality and quantity. A color also has intensity. And intensity has a quantitative character of its own, different from that of extension. Accordingly, intensities have specific mutual quantitative relationships.

Let us first discuss, however, the nature of quantity in general, and then draw attention to the different forms in which quantity manifests itself in reality. The notion "quantity" is one of our first concepts, hence the impossibility of giving a strict definition of it. No definition can avoid the use of concepts which already presuppose the concept "quantity" in one way or another. The only thing we can do, therefore, is to stress several characteristics of quantity and the common root of the main forms in which quantity appears.

It should be clear from the previous discussion of the nature of material being how closely quantity is connected with that very nature. As a matter of fact, in the preceding chapter the investigation of that nature was begun by reflection upon the species-individual structure. In this structure, the notion of quantity is already present. The complex notion "many individuals of the same species" implies the notion of number, of what is called *quantitas discreta,* discrete quantity.

Another aspect of the fundamental character of the material world was exhibited when the "extension" in space and time possessed by all material things was spoken of. This form of quantity is usually called *quantitas continua,* continuous quantity.

There is an obvious relationship between these two fundamental forms of quantity. Extension provides the possibility of indicating several parts in the same extended thing; thus we can number the parts.

154

Thus extension—*continuous quantity*—leads immediately to *discrete quantity*. If we go the other way around we come to the same result. Two things are discernable, i. e., knowable as *two,* only if they occupy a different position with respect to time or space, both continuous quantities.

The Object of Mathematics Is Quantity

In regard to the nature of quantity, it is important that we can study quantity and its relationships without paying attention to the way quantitative relationships are realized in the material world. The science of quantity has its own degree of abstraction. In accordance with the obvious distinction between continuous quantity and discrete quantity, classical mathematics had two main branches: arithmetic and geometry, and their derivatives. It is not surprising, however, that both branches of mathematics have fused together in later times. The close connection between the two forms of quantity indicates a common root. And it was only natural that after a certain development of both branches of mathematics, the attention of mathematicians should turn toward the study of what both branches had in common.

There is some terminological confusion nowadays about the proper way to indicate the common object of all mathematical activity. The obvious term for that object is, of course, quantity. But that term has in mathematical circles a much more restricted meaning than it has in philosophy. It seems that mathematicians, when speaking of quantity, think, first of all, of something that can be measured or counted.

Now it is clear that not all branches of mathematics are interested in measurement and calculation. That only quantity in the just-mentioned restricted sense should be the subject matter of mathematics is therefore opposed by mathematicians. On the other hand, however, it is equally clear that the most abstract branches of mathematics also deal with quantity, if we take that term in the general sense. Since the development of mathematics can greatly help us to discover the fundamental nature of quantity, let us consider for a moment some aspects of this development, especially that of geometry.

The Development of Mathematics. Mathematics began with the study of numbers and of geometrical figures as were provided by sense-experience. The very name "geometry" (measurement of earth) indicates both the practical orientation of the early phase of mathematics and the close connection with sense-experience. The main purpose was to deduce from some obvious and simple relations between certain geometrical elements, such as points, lines, and the like, other more complex relations between the same elements, and also relations between more complex geometrical entities defined with the help of the elementary ones. This latter especially opens a never-ending field of investigation. The Greek geometers were impressed by the possibility of constructing a whole system starting only with some simple elements and the relations between them. As a result they studied such a system for its own sake and not exclusively for its practical use. The Greek mathematician Euclid is, as a matter of fact, the father of the idea of axiomatic construction of mathematical systems.

The first important development in mathematics was the discovery of the possibility of "translating" geometrical systems into algebraic ones and *vice versa*. That discovery showed that there was a certain irrelevance as to the *kind* of mathematical entities that are in a system. A second even more important development was the discovery that it was possible to build a mathematical system upon relationships which were assumed to be different from those suggested by sense-experience.

Abstract Systems. The construction of such non-Euclidean systems stressed the view that the characteristic of mathematics did not lie so much in the material content of the original axioms and original elements as in the way conclusions could be drawn from them. This led to the development of systems in which even the character of the original elements was no longer indicated. They were no longer lines or numbers. Their only definition existed in the rules of the system; these rules prescribed how the elements were to be handled[1]. After a system is completed it might be possible to interpret the symbols representing the elements, as for example, geometrical entities, but such interpretation forms no part of the system. The construction of the system, and especially the deductive part of it, is independent of such a geometrical interpretation. In other words, what we are allowed to do with the elements of the symbolic system is exclusively determined by the rules of operations and axioms of the system and not by the connections which exist between those mathematical entities which can be considered the "real" meaning of those

---

[1] The reader unacquainted with mathematics may be referred to the game of chess which possesses some features of modern abstract mathematics. In chess the different pieces are not defined by what they represent in a symbolic way, a king, a queen, a castle, and the like. The rules of how to handle the different pieces are the only definitions of these pieces.

elements. Hence it will be easily understood in the light of the development of mathematics why mathematicians claim that quantity is not their subject matter. For numbers and lines have entirely disappeared in some abstract branches of that science.

The relevant problem is, however, whether or not quantity as such has disappeared too. The close connection between the two forms of quantity was pointed out above, and in that connection mention was made of a common root. What is this common root? The following consideration may perhaps help to answer this question.

The Use of Symbols and the Species-Individual Structure. When mathematicians construct their abstract systems, they necessarily work with symbols. These symbols are merely the individuals to which certain properties and relations, e.g. those expressed in the axioms, are attributed. What properties and relations are attributed is a matter of choice on the part of the mathematician. Yet it is of interest to note that material symbols as material symbols have certain characteristics which the mathematician can never dispose of. Symbols can never be deprived of their fundamental properties, which are implied by the fact that they are symbols. As such they do have certain properties of their own.

Consequently, the construction of even an abstract mathematical system is never entirely free. It is free only within certain limits. It is free insofar as the elements of an abstract system do not have special properties which the elements of a non-abstract system necessarily have. For example, if the elements of a system are surfaces, lines, and points, then certain properties and relations of the system are determined by the very nature of the elements. Determinations of *this* kind are absent when the meaning of the elements of the system is not interpreted, i. e. when we have an abstract system. In an abstract system the mathematician is entirely free to choose the relations between the elements himself. In other words, he has complete freedom in the choice of whatever axioms he wishes to establish. However, there is one limitation: his freedom is limited by the fact that his elements are necessarily represented by symbols. The necessary use of symbols with their inherent properties restricts his freedom.

What exactly are the properties of a symbol as symbol? A symbol expresses the fact that a certain element with its properties is present in whatever formula the symbol appears. In other words, the symbol is the expression of the species-individual structure. A symbol can be repeated, and in every repetition the same specific set of properties is present. The nature of these specific properties is not determined from outside in an abstract system. The elements are not lines, numbers, and the like. Therefore, the properties are determined only by the way in which the mathematician has decided that the elements of his system are related to each other. But once this decision is made, i.e., once his set of axioms is chosen, then the symbols represent certain specific properties. The nature of an abstract mathematical system means that these specific properties never have a material but always a formal character. That is to say, the specific properties *can* be given different material content by interpretation and application. But the mathematician is interested only in the different formal systems he can construct.

This precisely marks the difference between the attitude of the mathematician and that of the scientist. The latter is interested in mathematics, too, but only insofar as mathematical systems can be interpreted in a physically useful way.

Abstract Mathematics and Science. It is an interesting fact that practically all abstract mathematical systems can be interpreted in a physically useful way, notwithstanding the fact that the mathematician is interested only in formal systems. What is the explanation of this fact?

The explanation appears to lie in what has been said about the relationship between the use of symbols and the species-individual structure.

All the investigations of the mathematician remain within the framework of the species-individual structure. That is inevitable from the simple fact that he must necessarily use material symbols. Thus we may say that the mathematician investigates all the possible formal relations that can exist within the species-individual structure. This being so, it is clear why abstract mathematical systems can be interpreted in a physically useful way. Abstract mathematics studies the possible relations of all that is built according to a species-individual structure. A mathematical system, therefore, always reflects a certain fundamental aspect of matter, namely, that all relations which exist in nature are within the framework of a species-individual structure.

It is also clear that mathematics gives only one part of the picture of physical reality. Mathematics has made abstraction of the material content of what exists in nature. It studies only the formal aspects of an underlying universal pattern which can be diversified in several ways, but which still possesses the same general pattern.

It is necessary to retain for that universal pattern the term "the quantitative aspect of matter," because it is this aspect that both number and continuum represent. It is that which both discrete quantity and continuous quantity make *quantity*.

Quantity and Species-Individual Structure. The close relation that exists between the species-individual structure of matter and the quantitative character of matter has been shown. The quantitative character is the first effect of the species-individual structure. It is the universal property of any being having a species-individual structure. Because quantity manifests itself most obviously in number and extension, mathematics set out to study both separately. But mathematics gradually discovered that both had a common root, namely, quantity in general. Modern abstract mathematics studies, therefore, the formal aspects of quantity in general, i.e., a field of relationships that necessarily exists in a being with a species-individual structure. This problem will be discussed again in the following chapter when quality is taken up.

It is time to turn attention to the several ways in which the quantitative character of matter manifests itself concretely. That means that the famous problems connected with space and time must be discussed.

2. SPACE

Different Opinions About Space

The first problem that presents itself when we think of space is the way it exists. It is clear that there exists something that we call space, but what kind of existence does it have? Three theories can be distinguished. The first holds that space is a reality in itself, a kind of general receptacle, in which material objects have their place and can move. In this conception space has only mathematical properties; it is exclusively extension. Well-known holders of this theory are Democritus and Clarke, a contemporary of Newton.

A second theory takes an opposite view. It denies that space has any reality in itself. According to Kant, the most famous formulator of this theory, the fact that we perceive things in space (and time) is a result of the organization of our sense organs. Space is, as Kant has called it, an *Anschauungsform a priori,* a form imposed upon reality by our perception.

Between these two extremes, a third theory acknowledges the reality of spatial dimensions, but denies space an independent and separate existence. What is called space is nothing but an abstraction, an *ens rationis* based upon the existence of spatial dimensions of material things. This theory is held by Aristotle and St. Thomas and by a great number of our contemporary philosophers. It is also the theory implicitly accepted by modern science, as will be seen. Let us consider each of these theories more closely and in particular the arguments pro and con.

Space as Reality in Itself

As to the first, which holds that space is a reality in itself, the following argument can be offered to support it. It seems that when we think away all physical objects, space still remains. Moreover, in our immediate experience we always have a certain space partly filled with objects. The idea of space as a separate being, as a separately existing pure "extensum," seems more or less obvious. A material object necessarily appears to be somewhere in space, because a material object itself has extension.

Closer examination of this fact, however, shows that in this case, as in so many others, the obvious is not necessarily true. It is true that in our daily experience we can make a distinction between solid objects and the space in which these objects are placed, but it is quite clear that this space is not just quantitative space without any physical quality. As a matter of fact, this so-called "empty" space is full of physical phenomena such as gravitation, light and other electro-magnetic waves.

Modern physics, therefore, never speaks of empty space, but of a field of gravity, or of an electro-magnetic field, to indicate that where no "matter" in the ordinary sense is present there is still found physical activity. This means, philosophically speaking, that so-called "empty" space is as material as is ordinary matter. Physics has sometimes spoken of the opposition between ordinary matter and empty space with its physical qualities as the opposition between matter and ether. This is an unfortunate expression, for it suggests the idea that ether must be something immaterial. The origin of this misunderstanding lies, of course, in a mechanistic way of thinking.

In this way of thinking, matter is identified with particles of ponderable mass. If science is right in assuming the existence of ether, then the only conclusion would be that ether and ordinary matter are two fundamentally different kinds of matter.

Since it is not the task of the philosophy of nature to theorize about the different kinds of matter, nothing will be said here about the existence of ether, beyond what has already been said at the end of the foregoing chapter. As far as the problem of space is concerned, the only point of importance is that not even classical physics with its theory of a separately existing ether supported the idea of space as a being deprived of any physical quality.

The fact that space as an extension without any quality can be so easily imagined proves nothing but our capacity for abstraction. What exists in reality is, however, not pure extension, but extended matter with physical qualities.

Space as "Anschauungsform a Priori"

A thorough discussion of the position of Kant lies outside this study, because such a discussion belongs to epistemology.

It should be recalled, however, what has been said in Chapter I. Kant's epistemological convictions originated partly in certain ontological difficulties he came upon in the philosophy of nature. Kant rejected the reality of space because he thought that the acceptance of the reality of spatial extensions led to contradictions. His argument can be summarized as follows:

It is possible to prove that any compound must be composed of simple things (For if not, there would be nothing but composition.).

On the other hand, it is also possible to prove that no material thing can be simple for the very reason that a part of an extended being is always extended. Therefore, every "simple" part occupies a certain space and is thus open to division. Hence every "simple" part is at once simple and non-simple.[2]

This difficulty of Kant, known as the antinomy of the continuum, reveals how carefully one should proceed in the philosophical analysis of matter and its properties. Only if he always keeps in mind the philosophical meaning of the terms used in his analysis is it possible for him to avoid those misunderstandings which immediately lead to contradiction. In Kant's antinomy the difficulty lies

---

[2]*Critique of Pure Reason*, Part I, Division II, Book II, Chapter II, Section 2.

in the meaning of the term "simple." As has been shown in the foregoing chapter, the term "simple," as applied to matter, can have only a limited and relative sense. Material things can be said to be simple only with respect to a relative criterion of simplicity.

In an absolute sense material things are never simple, because of the fundamental non-simplicity of matter. If we speak, therefore, of the simple physical entities which built up a whole, then "simple" means that in a certain order no further division or analysis is possible. This does not mean, however, that such a simple thing is also simple with respect to its other aspects. For example, the parts of a machine can be called "simple" with respect to the whole, whereas they are themselves still complex. The elements of a chemical compound are also only relatively simple.

The particular difficulty with which Kant was dealing, namely, the fact that simple things are always extended and therefore non-simple, originated from the fact that simple and non-simple refer to *different criteria*. It is quite possible that a certain thing, considered as a physical being, is not further divisible, whereas, mathematically speaking, it can still be divisible.

The very fact that a certain entity has extension makes it subject to a division in the mathematical sense. For extension as extension is divisible. However, the nature of the entity involved can resist physical division. The distinction between physical and mathematical divisibility is the basis of all atomic, minima- and quantum-theories, both of the past and of modern times. Democritus' atoms, for example, had extension but could not be divided.

In the modern theory an atom is not absolutely indivisible. It can be divided, but then it loses its nature. The resulting parts do not have the same nature as the atom had. Whether or not there are in nature entities which are absolutely indivisible, and therefore, "simple," is not important at the moment. Important is the fact that an extended being is never simple in the absolute sense. Extension is a token of that fundamental non-simplicity which was discussed earlier.[3]

There is consequently no need to reject the reality of spatial extension because of the alleged contradictory properties to be ascribed to extended material things. There is no contradiction involved. And

---

[3]It should be noted that the same applies to all entities which have quantitative values, for instance, a minimum quantum of energy. All such entities are tokens of the non-simplicity of matter.

with the contradiction removed, there is not much left in favor of Kant's conception of spatial relationships. For if these relationships did not exist in reality, how could we explain why one instance differs from another in spatial relationship? To borrow an example from Bertrand Russell, why do we always see people's eyes above their mouths and not below them?[4] There must be a reason for that particular spatial arrangement in reality. The mere fact that an "Anschauungsform" gives presentation in space, does not explain the difference in spatial relationship. There must be a kind of underlying fundamental structure in the world of the "things in themselves," which perhaps may be not spatial but which has nevertheless all the spatial relationships.

This brings us to the third theory which conceives of space as an *ens rationis* based upon the extension of material things. It is the only theory that remains, if space is neither a reality in itself nor the result of our way of perception.

Place

A consequence of the conception that space is only an *ens rationis* is that "place" is a more important concept than is "space." For "place" refers to the position of a certain object in relation with other objects. "Place" refers, therefore, to *real* relationships within the material world. If material things are extended, then there exists also such a thing as "place," the position one material object holds with respect to another.

The problems of space and place are very interesting, both from a philosophic and a physical point of view. Here the discussion will confine itself to a strict philosophical consideration of the problems of space and place. Its purpose is to determine what kind of *being* space and place are.

Aristotle's Definition of Place. Instructive is the definition which Aristotle gives of place. The place of a body is "the innermost, immobile boundary of that which immediately surrounds that body."[5]

Several points require our attention in this definition. First of all, this definition is more complete than the way the concept of place is used today, both in every-day language and in science. In every-day language, the place of a certain body is indicated by referring to the

---

[4]Bertrand Russell, *History of Western Philosophy,* London, 1946, p. 741.
[5]*Phys.* IV, 4, 212a 20.

surroundings, but practically never to the immediate surroundings. For such questions as "Where is he?" or "Where is it?" are answered by mentioning, for example, a certain town, a certain house, a certain room. It is clear, however, that such a reference indicates place only in an inexact way. The real place is more limited and is to be described by indicating the immediate surroundings. Scientific language is usually more exact, but it schematizes both object and place. The place of a body in science is usually indicated as the place of a point in a system of coordinates. Science has, of course, a very good reason for using such a concept of place, but it is clear that what science is describing is not the real place, but only a schematized one. The real place has extension since the object of which it is the place is extended, too.

Place as Surface. A curious point in Aristotle's discussion of place is that he defines it as a surface. At first sight, one is more inclined to think of place in terms of a portion of space. Yet, Aristotle's definition is correct. For as we have seen, there is no such thing as just a portion of space; there are only extended bodies. Thus if we indicate a certain portion of space in order to indicate the place of a body, we indicate only the body itself and not its place, for "place" essentially refers to something outside that which has a place. "Place" must be where a body contacts its surroundings.[6]

Relative Immobility of Place. A difficult point with respect to the definition of "place" is the immobility which Aristotle requires for a place. Let us first examine the reason why immobility is important. If a body moves it successively occupies different places. Thus, strictly speaking, place does not move with a body, because place is not something inherent in the body. Place is outside the body and in the extension that contacts a body. The reality of place lies, therefore, in the dimensions of the surrounding extended body. Hence it is entirely correct to say, with regard to a body which is in a certain place, that the place of that body is immobile. This simply means that a place does not move with the body of which it is the place because place is no part of that body. On the other

---

[6]Hoenen (*Cosmologia,* 4th ed., Rome, 1949, p. 66) gives a very interesting application of Aristotle's definition under the assumption that there exists an ether in the sense as defined by H. Lorentz. If ether were a physical reality which pervades all material objects, then a physical body would always occupy a certain part of the ether. The contact would be a kind of internal three-(or even more) dimensional contact.

hand, however, since place is nothing but a certain part of a surrounding extensum, which itself is a physical entity, it follows, that no place is *per definitionem* immobile in an absolute sense. For a physical entity usually is not supposed to be immobile.

Only if there existed an ether in the sense used by Lorentz, could place be considered absolutely immobile. For the ether of Lorentz was supposed to pervade all physical bodies. It would be, therefore, an ideal "localization medium," as Hoenen has called it. All physical bodies would be in immediate contact with the immobile ether.

It does not appear, however, that place requires the existence of such an absolutely immobile physical extension. This may be for the present a sufficient discussion of "place." Place appears to be much closer to reality than space is. Space is an abstraction based upon the existence of extended physical entities. But place is a *reality* consisting of the external relationship between the extension of one body and the extension of another.

There are, of course, more problems involved than those discussed here, but all aspects of the quantitative character of matter are so closely connected that it is preferable to discuss some of the other aspects first.

3. MOTION

Importance of Motion

One of the most important concepts of the philosophy of nature is the concept "motion." As a matter of fact, material being is often defined as *ens mobile,* mobile being. In this expression, the concept *mobile* has a broader meaning that that connected with local motion. It indicates all kinds of change in matter. These kinds are substantial change, change in quality, and local change. In the previous chapter substantial change was dealt with. The next chapter will be partly devoted to qualitative change. The present chapter will concentrate on problems connected with local motion, although a few words will be devoted to motion in general.

Local motion is one of the topics which has always occupied a very important place in the philosophy of nature. Aristotle was very much interested in it, and analyzed it thoroughly. The thinkers of the 17th century directed one of their severest attacks against Aristotle's analysis of the phenomena of motion. It is even justifiable to say that the different point of view toward the problems of local motion in the 17th century was one of the main causes for the fall of Aristotle. The new natural science of the 17th century was above all a mechanics. It was mentioned in Chapter II that this new mechanics did more than merely correct several mistakes in Aristotle's mechanics. It showed the possibility of a new approach to the phenomena of nature. Whereas Aristotle's analysis of local motion was a mixture of philosophical and scientific analysis, with the result that both were distorted, the new mechanics was, on the contrary, exclusively scientific.

This being so, a discussion of the problems of local motion should give an opportunity for illustrating several points already discussed in previous chapters, such as: first, the fundamental difference between a scientific and a philosophical analysis; next, how easily this fundamental difference is lost sight of, with all the unfortunate consequences thereof for both philosophy and science; and finally, the fact that all philosophical concepts are analogous.

Aristotle's Definition of Motion

Aristotle's definition of motion leaves no doubt that his approach to the phenomena of motion is, above all, philosophical. He defines motion as "the actualization of that which is in potency, insofar as it is still in potency."[7]

It should be understood that this is a genuine philosophical definition. Aristotle is defining motion in the metaphysical terms of act and potency. It is also clear that the definition applies to all kinds of motion; there is no special reference to local motion, for instance.

The definition is not exactly easy to comprehend and, therefore, warrants consideration in detail. The definition says that motion is something between potency and act. Motion is neither a static act nor a static potency. As long as a certain thing is still entirely in potency, it is not yet in motion. Hence the definition speaks of the actualization of that which is in potency. On the other hand, when the potency is entirely actualized there is no motion either. Motion is the very process of actualization. For this reason Aristotle adds the words "insofar as it is still in potency." Motion is the actualization of a potency as long as the potency is still present and not fully actualized.

---

[7]*Phys.* III, 1, 201a 10.

The Unity of Motion. The most important point in Aristotle's definition is that he sees motion as a *unity*. Motion is conceived as one continuous process of actualization. The goal to be achieved, the end, is already present in the beginning of a motion. It gives the motion its unity. It connects the successive phases of a motion as steps towards a common end. Thus the end of the motion, which comes into existence as final actualization of this motion only after the motion is over (or rather at the very moment the motion stops), must already have a certain existence during the entire motion. For without existing it cannot direct and unify the motion. What kind of existence is that?

The obvious answer that it is a potential existence does not explain much. A potency can never exist alone; it can exist only as connected with an actuality. A *potential* oak exists as an *actual* acorn. So we want to know in what actuality the end of a motion potentially exists during a motion. In order to prepare the answer, the consideration of a concrete instance of motion, such as an arrow flying to its goal, can be of great help. A concrete instance offers the opportunity to clarify the abstract notions involved.

Strictly speaking, the only thing that actually exists at a certain moment during the motion of the arrow is a *particular phase* of that motion. If the arrow is in the air and on its way, it has left its starting-point behind. The part of the motion that lies between the starting-point and the actual phase under consideration no longer exists, whereas the different phases between the actual phase and the goal do not *yet* exist. Thus it seems that motion is built up of individual phases which never exist together. It seems that only parts of the motion exist, but never the whole. To a certain extent this is correct. Motion is a so-called *continuum fluens,* a flowing continuum, a kind of continuum whose parts never exist together.

On the other hand, it is also clear that a motion has a unity which is more than just a series of successive phases. The *actual* situation of a certain phase, existing at a certain moment, already possesses in potency what will be the next step in the process of actualization. The arrow has in each phase a certain direction. In that actual direction the end is already present in potency, even at the beginning of the motion. The constant presence of such an actual direction connects the different phases of a motion and gives it its own and specific type of unity. This unity is the gradual actualization of an inherent potential goal. It is entirely possible, of course, that the final end of the motion will never be reached since the goal is present only in potency and does not exist in act. The motion of the arrow can be broken at any moment by an external cause, but the tendency to reach the end is present in every phase of the motion.

There can be no doubt that Aristotle's definition expresses in an exact way the status of being which is specific for a motion. His definition accounts for the unity of a motion as well as for its extension in time. It is a being under way with all the risks connected with that situation, but it is a being under way with a definite goal. One is almost tempted to say "with a definite goal *in mind.*" This reveals the first of a series of objections to the definition of Aristotle which must be discussed.

The Concept of Finality

The first objection to Aristotle's definition of motion is that it is anthropomorphic. Is it not based upon an analysis of motion which can make sense only when human actions are involved? If the end of a motion is not only an end point in time, but also a final goal to be achieved which from the very beginning directs the entire course of the motion, is it not then necessarily presupposed that such a final goal is *known* by somebody who imposed that final goal upon a motion?

The Analogy of Finality. This objection undoubtedly reveals a danger that should be avoided, but it does not destroy the analysis of Aristotle. The analysis itself is not based upon anthropomorphism, but it must be correctly understood. It is true that when speaking of such concepts as "goal," "end," or "finality," we think, first of all, of human actions. As a consequence there is a natural tendency to fill the content of these concepts with characteristics found only when these concepts are used in connection with human actions.

The same kind of difficulty existed with respect to the content of the concept *substance.*[8] The concept *substance* has a clear meaning when applied to human beings. Hence the tendency to apply such a concept in exactly the same way to material objects. In doing so we forget that the concept "substance" is analogous and has to be used in an analogous way.

---

[8] See pp. 130 ff.

With respect to the concepts of finality and the like the same tendency to neglect analogy exists. When human actions are involved, it is perfectly clear what "finality" means. A certain action is undertaken with a certain goal in mind. Thus the goal directs the action. The goal does not yet exist in reality, but it exists in the human mind and is, therefore, able to direct the action. There is no violation of the law which says that a non-existing thing cannot act. When we consider, however, a motion at the level of matter it seems that there is no possibility of giving the end of a motion a kind of existence apart from the existence which lies in the realization of that end at the very completion of the motion. There is no mind in the moving object that *knows* its end and that, therefore, can direct the motion. Hence the objection that Aristotle's analysis is based upon anthropomorphism. Yet, this is not the case. There can be a tendency towards a certain goal without the consequence that this goal has to be known.

Inherent Tendency of a Motion. Once again, the example of the flying arrow can help us to understand the nature of such an inherent tendency. The example is particularly interesting, because it seems to be a clear-cut instance of an anthropomorphic example. The motion of the arrow is the result of a human action, and the goal of that motion is determined by the archer. However, the fact that human action gives the arrow its direction is irrelevant to the existence of an inherent tendency in the motion itself.

In order to understand this, let us consider the case where the arrow is given a wrong direction, so that it will miss its intended goal. There is also in this instance a tendency which is objectively realized, but which is different from the tendency which was intended. When finality with respect to a moving body is spoken of, then this term does not refer to the *intended* aim, but only to the tendency which is objectively realized in the direction of that moving body. The goal of the motion is, therefore, in an objective way present as a tendency—that is, a direction by which the course of the motion is determined at every moment of that motion. This tendency is not necessarily known and is not necessarily an intended tendency. It exists as a determination by natural forces. It is not the good intention of the archer which directs the motion, but the tendency which is realized in the material object as a result of the working of certain mechanical laws.

Science and Finality. The existence of such tendencies in nature is obvious, not only with respect to local motion, but also with respect to motion in general. Two chemical elements, such as sodium and chlorine, for instance, react in a definite way according to their nature. "Reacting in a definite way," however, is tantamount to *"tending* to a certain result."

The existence of tendencies with respect to locomotion provides science with a special method to handle most of its mechanical problems. This method can be illustrated by a concrete example, such as water running down a hill. There are two possible descriptions of this phenomenon. The first is that the water is attracted by gravitational forces; the combination of these forces with those caused by the resistance of stones determines the route the water takes. We are even able to calculate from point to point the actual course of the water. The second description is, more or less, made in terms of tendencies. For example, the water tries to reach a place of less potential energy, i.e. a place as close as possible to the centre of the earth. It seeks to do so with a minimum of work. This is the principle of least action which B. Russell has called "a law of cosmic laziness."[9] The law states that a moving body always chooses the route which involves least work. There are other similar minimum principles; one, which is the principle of Fermat, states that a beam of light follows the route which involves the least time.

Causality and Finality Are Co-principles. The interesting point now is that science is able to describe any motion in these two ways. Any one motion can be considered the result either of the acting forces or of the tendencies expressed in the minimum principles.[10] It should be stressed that both descriptions are two sides of the same picture. Sometimes both advocates and opponents of the final aspects of the material world seem to think of "finality" as something superimposed upon the acting forces. This is a serious misunderstanding. The acting forces act in such a way as to realize the final aspects. The final aspects are nothing but the inherent tendencies of the acting forces. That is the reason why the actual course of a motion can be followed by studying either the acting forces or the finality of that motion. Causality and finality are co-principles. Where causality is, there is also finality. Moreover, the type of finality corresponds with the type of causality. If the causality is deterministic, then so is the

---

[9]*Human Knowledge, Its Scope and Limits,* London, 1948, p. 328.

[10]The difference is, technically speaking, the difference between an integral relation and a set of differential equations. See Henry Margenau, *The Nature of Physical Reality,* New York-Toronto-London, 1950, p. 423.

finality. If the causality is free, then so is the finality. Only in the latter instance can finality be identified with "purpose." Stressing the fact that there is finality in nature does not imply therefore, the existence of "purpose" in a human sense.

Aristotle's Physical Conception of Motion

A second objection to Aristotle's definition of motion deals with the fact that his concept of motion was closely connected with an erroneous physical conception of the world. So the legitimate question arises as to whether his philosophical analysis was not dependent upon his erroneous physical theory. The question is particularly pertinent when local motion is considered. Let us first consider Aristotle's ideas about local motion.

Aristotle divided local motion into two categories, natural motion and violent motion. The fall of an object offers an example of a natural motion. According to Aristotle, each "heavy" body has a natural tendency to fall, whereas "light" bodies have a natural tendency to rise. Because these motions occur under the influence of natural tendencies caused by the nature of the objects involved, Aristotle calls them "natural" motions. Besides these "natural" motions, "violent" motions are possible: A stone can be thrown away, an arrow can be directed toward a goal. These motions are called "violent" because they violate the natural tendency of a stone or an arrow to move toward the centre of the earth, which is the *locus naturalis* (the natural place) for a stone or an arrow because these objects are "heavy." The *locus naturalis* of light objects is located in the outer sphere of the universe. Hence the natural tendency of light objects to rise. To understand this conception of Aristotle, it should be remembered that according to him the earth was the centre of the universe (see Ch. II, 3).

It is clear that in Aristotle's conception of the physical world the concept "natural tendency" plays a much more important role than in modern physics. With Aristotle a natural motion ends, if nothing interferes, in the *locus naturalis*. In that place the motion stops because the object has reached its natural goal, the place where it belongs on account of its nature. There is a fundamental difference between the state of motion and the state of natural rest in the *locus naturalis*. In view of this conception of Aristotle, his philosophical definition of motion appears in a new light. For example, is the fact that Aristotle stresses the finality of a motion independent of his ideas of natural place? Is not his analysis of a motion as a process of actualization determined by his physical views? The end of a motion is called an act. This suggests that the end of a motion has a higher status than the beginning. It is all perfectly understandable if *end* is interpreted as the *natural place,* the natural destination of all motion. All motion stops there because the natural tendency is satisfied. As to violent motion, its goal is, of course, not natural, but it still has something of a goal to be achieved, namely, one imposed upon the object by force. The moment the force stops working, the violent motion stops too.

Before an examination is made of the extent to which Aristotle's philosophical analysis depends upon his physical conceptions, it is important first to have a look at modern physical ideas.

The Modern Physical Conception of Motion

Modern physics is entirely different from that of Aristotle. According to the mechanics established by Galileo and Newton in the 17th century, there is no reason to distinguish between natural and violent motion; there is no such thing as a *locus naturalis.* Modern mechanics holds that, once in motion, an object maintains this motion unless it is stopped by some physical force (the law of inertia). This means that no physical force is needed for maintenance of a uniform motion. A physical force accelerates or decelerates a motion.

Two points require attention. First, there is the fact that there is no essential difference between the status of rest and the status of uniform motion. If an object is at rest, it will remain in this state unless a physical force acts upon it. Physical objects everywhere seem to be in a *locus naturalis* when no physical force is working on them.

The second point is that a motion has a natural tendency to continue. There seems to be no natural goal for motion, no act to be achieved.

There can be no serious doubt that the description of motions in terms of the mechanics of the 17th century is much more exact than Aristotle's. Thus the Newtonian mechanics should be accepted as true.[11] Consequently, the all-important problem, whether or not the

---

[11]There is no need of discussing here certain improvements and new theoretical points which the theory of relativity has brought forward. See pp. 181 ff.

new mechanical views on motion have invalidated the *philosophical* analysis of Aristotle, must be discussed. It must be determined whether the elimination of the concepts *locus naturalis* and *natural rest* leads to the result that the Aristotelian definition of motion also is erroneous. It must further be determined whether the mechanical law that a uniform motion has no end can be reconciled with the Aristotelian idea that every motion has a determined tendency towards an end.

Aristotle's Analysis of Motion Is Not Based Upon His Faulty Physics

Locus Naturalis and Natural Tendencies. The solution of the first problem, the elimination of the concept *locus naturalis* and *natural rest,* is not difficult after what has been said earlier in this section about the existence of a determined tendency in any motion. This was a philosophical conclusion based upon the simple fact that there are laws which govern all motions and changes in nature. The fact that Aristotle erred in his understanding of the physical and chemical content of these laws is not important. His philosophical conclusion was based upon the *existence* of such laws, not upon their specific content. Once again the fundamental difference between philosophy and science should be stressed. Philosophy discusses the general characteristics of matter. Science, presupposing these characteristics, tries to give them specific content.

Aristotle was interested in both science and philosophy. As a result, his conclusions in both fields sometimes so overlapped that their difference can hardly be distinguished. The concept *locus naturalis,* for example, had a double sense with Aristotle. It indicated both a *physical place* and the fact that each local motion had a natural and inherent *tendency*. Nowadays it is known that Aristotle was wrong in his idea that all heavy things had a natural tendency to a *place* located in the centre of the earth. He was not wrong, however, in observing that there were definite ·*tendencies* working in nature. We know now that there is no such thing as a *locus naturalis* for each particular kind of matter. Matter can move to all places, depending upon circumstances. Each motion, however, is determined by certain laws which give that particular motion its particular inherent direction or tendency. It should be stressed that the knowledge that such a direction exists does not in the least imply a knowledge of the specific character of this direction. Where modern physicists speak of "gravitation," Aristotle spoke of "tendency towards the natural place in the centre of the earth." The *physical* implications of both descriptions are quite different, but they both express the same philosophical truth, namely, that there is a definite tendency in all motion.

The Law of Inertia. The second difficulty is related to the law of inertia. This difficulty can be formulated as follows: If the law of inertia, that a local motion never stops of its own account, is true, then the conclusion seems obvious that a motion does not have an "end" in the Aristotelian sense of this term. No *de facto* end of a motion can be considered the *actualization* of a tendency present in a motion. Consequently, it seems that the analysis of motion in terms of potency and act assumes the existence of a definite end of each motion as the natural achievement or perfection of that motion. This assumption is proved to be wrong with respect to what are called uniform motions. In such motions there seem to be eternal potency but no act. Such a situation seems to deprive the whole analysis of its meaning in terms of potency and act.

In a substantial change the natural end of the motion is the new substantial form. In a local motion under influence of gravitation there is a tendency to reach a lower state of energy. There is, therefore, in both instances something that seems to have the nature of an act to be achieved. But in a uniform motion no such act seems to exist.

Since the second difficulty deals with the analysis of a motion in terms of potency and act, that difficulty involves the very definition of motion. Accordingly, a careful consideration of the difficulty is a matter of necessity.

The Law of Inertia Deals With Real Motions. The problem cannot be solved by such a superficial argument as that such motions as the law of inertia describes do not exist. The law of inertia is not supposed to speak of real motions, for it assumes the absence of physical forces, which, as matter of fact, are never absent in reality. Since Aristotle's analysis deals with real motions, the difficulty does not exist.

Such an argument does not seem to solve anything. For the reason science established the law of inertia was not because it was interested in non-existent motions, it did so because the law of inertia is of great help in analyzing *real* motions. It points out an important tendency in all motions, namely, the tendency to continue a motion; and that tendency is real.

The Solution of the Difficulty. The solution of the difficulty should be sought in another direction than by disparaging the value of scientific data. It should be asked whether the analysis of a motion in terms of potency and act requires a final act in which motion comes to rest. It is of interest to note that Aristotle himself would certainly have answered no to that question. He would have referred to the eternal circular movement of heavenly bodies as an instance of ceaseless motion. So it must be possible to apply analysis in terms of potency and act to motions which are endless.

The difficulty is, of course, not that such a motion does not reveal the actualization of a potency. The moving body goes continuously from one place to another, say from A towards B, from B towards C, etc. If this body is actually in place A, then it is *not* in place B, but is moving towards B. Therefore, there is a definite potency of being at B. The arrival at B means the actualization of that potency. But this actualization is no final act, yet such a final act seems necessary to give to the motion its unity. However, the arrival at B includes the potency of going on to C, etc. In other words, each moment of the motion has a definite tendency towards further actualization, and it is this which gives the motion its unity. There may be, therefore, no *final* act which gives the motion its unity, but such a final act is not necessary for motion to possess unity. The process of gradual actualization in a definite direction is sufficient.

It is now clear why the law of inertia seems to affect so much the analysis of motion in terms of potency and act. It was because of the kind of example used to clarify this definition of motion. The example was misleading because the *goal* of the arrow assumed too much importance in the explanation. As a matter of fact, the goal was quite irrelevant as concerns the unity of the motion of the arrow. The goal was important only for the *intended* direction, not for the *inherent* direction of the motion itself. And it is this latter alone that is important, as has already been revealed in the discussion of anthropomorphism.

The reader with a scientific background is perhaps a little annoyed that no scientific development seems to have any important bearing upon the philosophical analysis of motion. Yet, that is the simple truth. Aristotle's analysis of motion was based upon the general character of motion. The fact that he had many erroneous physical ideas did not prevent him from recognizing the general character of motion.

Hylomorphism and Motion

This discussion of motion may be concluded with a brief consideration of the relationship between some of the fundamental aspects of motion and the general doctrine of hylomorphism. Speaking of the nature of matter, it has been seen that matter is essentially changeable. Matter is constantly changing, acting, and reacting, according to fixed patterns. So we recognize two characteristics inherent in the very essence of matter,—a certain restlessness and the stabilizing influence of form. The same characteristics are found in local motion. Restlessness is dominated by certain definite tendencies. Just as no material substance is pure act, but is always mixed with potency, and is therefore subject to change, so no local motion ever achieves a state of pure act. It is always in potency to further motion. Matter is moved by tendencies which never have complete fulfillment. Matter is restless, in principle, as an immediate consequence of its hylomorphic composition of potency and act. Matter is never pure potency, but it is also never pure act.

Thus it appears that the dynamic picture of the structure of the universe that modern science gives is really more in accordance with the principles of Aristotelian philosophy than is the static conception of Aristotle himself. Thus the principle of inertia, instead of being a fundamental obstacle to Aristotle's philosophical analysis of motion, rather confirms it if we take the trouble to understand the philosophical implications of the principle.

4. TIME

Similarity Between Time and Space

Closely related to motion is time. Without motion it is not only impossible to measure time, but it is even impossible to know of the existence of time. Thus the question arises as to how close the relationship between time and motion is. Before discussing this problem, however, the attention must be focused on other aspects of time which show how much time and space have in common. Spatial distance corresponds with distance in time. "Being at the same place" finds its counterpart in "happening at the same time." As there is a "before" and "after" with respect to distance in space, so is there a "before" and "after" in time.

It is somewhat difficult to realize that there is a difference between spatial and temporal "before" and "after." The reason for this difficulty is that in thinking of spatial "before" and "after" we think in terms of going from one place to another, and that immediately involves temporal aspects. For example, in travelling from New York to Washington, Washington is reached "after" Philadelphia. "After" has here a temporal sense because we think in terms of moving from one place to another. It is clear, however, that there is also a spatial "after" involved. On the road from New York to Washington, Philadelphia is situated "before" Washington and Washington "after" Philadelphia. It is also possible to say that Philadelphia is "after" Washington, namely, when we speak of the road from Washington to New York.

This indicates that in space "before" and "after" are to a certain extent relative, whereas temporal "before" and "after" are not relative. Spatial "before" and "after" refer to an existing order; there is definitely a certain spatial sequence of the different parts of the road between New York and Washington, but what has to be called "before" and "after" depends upon where we want to start enumerating them. That is to say that once a certain directon has been chosen, the sequence of "before" and "after" is determined by the spatial order of the different parts. In time, however, the direction is not open to choice. The direction is determined by the very nature of time. Time goes from past to future, and not conversely. We can *think* backwards in time, but we can not go backwards. This indicates a distinctive difference between the spatial and temporal order, and will require discussion later on.

Theories About Time. In view of the great similarity between time and space, it is not suprising that in discussions of the status of time the same diversity of opinion will be found to exist that was dealt with when discussing the status of space. For Kant, time was simply a pure intuition (*Anschauungsform*) of our sensibility. As a result of the way our sensibility is structured, we perceive things in time, but in reality there exists no such thing as a temporal order. Other thinkers give time a separate existence apart from that of matter. For them matter exists in time just as it exists in space. The majority of philosophers look upon time as something which does exist in reality, but not separately from matter. Time exists in matter and seems to be an essential aspect of it.

After what has been said about space there is no need to discuss the first two theories about time. Both are based upon the same considerations as were the corresponding theories about space, and the same objections can be made to them.[12]

As to the third theory, that which holds that time is a real aspect of the material world, the difficulty lies in the necessity of determining more precisely the nature of the aspect that is responsible for the temporal character of the world. In order to discover this aspect the relationship between time and motion will first be studied.

Time and Motion

It has previously been shown that time is closely connected with motion. Among other things, both have in common the fact that each is a flowing continuum (*continuum fluens*). The time-continuum never exists as a whole; only "now" exists. The fact that time is a flowing continuum indicates its main difference from space, with which time has otherwise so much in common. Because time is a *continuum* it is related to space, because it is a *flowing* continuum it is closely connected with motion.

In order to understand the relationship between time and motion on the one hand, and time and space on the other, what was said about the existence of both a temporal and a spatial "before" and "after" should be recalled. For example, in a local motion, one part of the path is in a spatial "before" with respect to another part. From this follows the fact that the different phases of a motion come into existence one "after" another. The motion reaches *first* this part and *then* that part, which is exactly the temporal order. Time, therefore, expresses the fact that the different phases of a motion come successively into existence.

Definition of Time. Aristotle's formulation of the above result is made in the following definition: "Time is the numerable aspect of movement in respect of the before and after".[13] That is to say, the different phases of a movement are distinguishable with respect to the "before" and "after." Consequently, they can be numbered.

Time does not, therefore, exist in itself. It is an aspect of motion. It will be understood that time is an aspect of any motion, not only of locomotion. A change in intensity, for example, is also successive. Since time exists only as an aspect of motion, and since there are many motions, it follows that every motion has its own time. On the other hand, however, much can be said in favor of the idea that

---

[12]Cf. pp. 159 ff.
[13]*Physics* IV, 11, 220a 24-26.

there is only one time. To mention only one argument, all motions are measured with just one time. There seems to be a contradiction between the conception of the universality of time and the conception that there are as many particular times as there are motions. Let us examine whether this contradiction is real.

The Universality of Time. To begin with, it is undoubtedly true that any successive motion is sufficient for establishing a temporal order; in this sense every motion has its own time. This does not mean, however, that the individual or specific differences between motions also create a corresponding difference in time. Any motion creates a definite order of "before" and "after." The different motions in the material universe all contribute to the establishment of exactly the same order of "before" and "after." This order exists only in the different motions and not apart from them. But this temporal order is not the privilege of one particular motion. If a certain moment in a certain motion corresponds with a certain moment in another motion, then all that preceded this moment in the first motion also preceded this moment in the second motion. If the end of a certain motion coincides with the beginning of another, then the whole order of "before" and "after" in that second motion comes "after" the whole order of the first motion. Thus all motions contribute to one and the same order of "before" and "after" in the universe. For that reason we may speak of one universal time, of one universal order of "before" and "after."

In recent years the theory of relativity has cast doubt upon the correctness of this analysis because of the use of the concept "simultaneity." That concept has been used when a certain moment in one motion that corresponds with a certain moment in another motion was spoken of. "Corresponds with" is the same as "is simultaneous with." The theory of relativity is said to have proved the limited significance of the concept *simultaneity*. The concept is supposed to have no universal value. Consequently, no universal time exists. The next section will be devoted to this problem.

Topological and Metric Structure

Up to now only the structure of "before" and "after" in time has played a role in the discussion. This structure is called the topological structure, because it considers only the order of the parts of time and not their distance. If the distance is considered also, we then speak of the metric structure of time. Consequently, such a question as "When did that happen, before or after the birth of Christ?", refers to the topological order. If it is asked, however, "How long before the birth of Christ did it happen?" in order to answer, reference must be made to the metric structure.

The Measurement of Time

In order to measure time any motion can be used, although for practical purposes a uniform or an approximately uniform, endless, periodic motion is preferred. *Uniform,* because we want a fixed standard; *periodic,* because the parts of such a motion are discernible. *Endless,* because such a motion includes the time of all other motions which therefore can be measured by that motion.

The Motion of Celestial Bodies as Standards of Time. The rotation of the earth upon its axis and its revolution around the sun offer practical examples of such a uniform periodic motion and are for that reason chosen as standards of time. The regularity and imperturbability of the motion of the celestial bodies gave Aristotle reason to believe that the matter of which these bodies was composed differed specifically from the elements of the earth. As a result he also thought that the motions of the celestial bodies were regular and imperturbable by the very nature of these bodies. Furthermore, he thought that the celestial motions, because of their higher status, must be circles, since a circular motion is without beginning and end, and, therefore, it must be considered the more perfect. Thus for Aristotle the celestial motions were not only a very practical standard of time, they were the *natural* standard in virtue of their perfect nature.

Confusion between Philosophy and Science. Aristotle's treatise of the motions of celestial bodies is another example of his confusing the philosophical and the physical levels of consideration. It makes sense in philosophy to call one kind of being more perfect than another, because of its higher status of being.[14] Such a consideration does not make sense in physics. If we use the term "perfect" in physics, then the only sensible meaning it can have is that a certain thing is a more or less perfect realization of a mathematical or physical prototype. We say, for example, that a certain motion follows a perfectly straight line or a circle. It does not make sense in physics,

---

[14]Cf. what has been said on pp. 128 f. about the different degrees of self-existence.

however, to call a circle a more perfect figure than an ellipse or a straight line. Certainly not if we connect with this idea of perfection a higher status of being. The conception of Aristotle and other Greek philosophers that celestial motions must be circles on account of philosophical considerations was one of the reasons why the replacement of circles by ellipses in 16th century astronomy seemed much more than just a matter of a more exact description.

The too narrow relationship between philosophical and physical considerations in the system of Aristotle did more harm to his physics than to his philosophy. For it is easy to see that his philosophical analysis of time as "the numerable aspect of movement in respect of before and after" is independent of his conception of celestial motion. There is no need for a privileged motion to give time its status of being. Any motion is sufficient. Nor is a perfectly regular motion needed in order to measure time.

5. THE THEORY OF RELATIVITY ABOUT SIMULTANEITY

No Universal Time

Mention has already been made of the fact that the theory of relativity, proposed by Einstein to solve certain difficulties in classical mechanics, has something to say about the use of the concept *simultaneity*. According to Einstein, the concept *simultaneity* makes sense only when used in connection with events happening at the same place. When events happen at different places they can be called simultaneous only in a relative and not in an absolute sense. Thus one observer will call two events simultaneous, whereas another observer, whose state of motion differs from that of the first, will observe these events as happening at different times. According to him the events are not simultaneous. The different states of motion of the observers— for example, one on earth and one flying with enormous speed through the air—are responsible for their differences in observation.

It is even possible that according to one observer, event A happens before event B; according to a second observer, B may happen before A; whereas a third observer may call them simultaneous. Since there is no physical possibility of preferring one state of motion to another there is no possibility of deciding which of the observers is right and which is wrong. Therefore, no absolute statement about simultaneity can be made. The only thing that can be said is that, considered from the standpoint of one observer, the events are simultaneous; whereas they are not simultaneous, considered from the standpoint of another observer.

There seems, therefore, to be no universal "before" and "after" in time. From this it would follow that there can be no such a thing as universal time.

Contradiction between Philosophy and Science. Before discussing in detail some of the conclusions of Einstein's theory, some remarks about so-called contradictions between the outcome of a philosophical analysis and the content of physical theories based upon experiments should be repeated again with special emphasis. It will be understood that according to the basic philosophy of this study, as expressed in the theory of the different degrees of abstraction, such a contradiction is impossible, at least in principle. The reason is that each method of consideration, the philosophical and the scientific, moves on a different level and deals with different kinds of problems. Therefore, there can be no contradiction one of the other. However, this is true only if the philosophical analysis is purely and exclusively philosophical and if the scientific theory is purely and exclusively scientific. This, however, is not always the case. On the contrary, it has been shown earlier in this study how easily the philosopher can mistake certain data of common experience which belong to the primitive sector of human experience for philosophical data.

This danger of mistaking primitive for primary data is especially great when the philosopher deals with things which have a certain obviousness to the imagination, such as spatial and temporal relationships. Moreover, philosophy is an abstract system of knowledge, and the philosopher has a natural desire to complete his abstract knowledge with data on another level. Thus there is occasion enough on which non-philosophical data can intrude into a philosophical analysis. This being so, it is clear that the development of science can show mistakes in a philosophical analysis because science can expose the spurious nature of some philosophical data. On the other hand, the scientist is always projecting his scientific (and therefore abstract) knowledge upon a philosophical background. Thus it can happen that he will draw conclusions which *seem* to be consequences of a well-established scientific theory, whereas they are *in reality* consequences of a faulty philosophical background.

So the point at issue in the present discussion is whether or not the philosophical analysis of time in the previous section was based upon genuine primary experience. The theory of relativity says no.

It claims that the development of science forces us to abandon the idea of an universal time, for this idea is not based upon primary experience, but only upon a seeming obviousness due to the limitation of our daily experiences of temporal relationships.

In order to find out the truth, it is necessary to begin with a brief statement of the theory of relativity.

The Principle of Relativity

It is not possible within the framework of this book to give a description of the whole theory of relativity or the reason for its development. The reader may be referred to one of the many physical works on the subject.[15] Discussion must be confined to some very brief remarks about its origin and content.

The theory of relativity is divided into the special and the general theory of relativity. For our purpose, only the special theory is of interest. This theory was proposed by Einstein as an extension of the classical principle of relativity, well-known in classical mechanics. This classical principle states that mechanical events which occur in a system moving with uniform speed cannot be distinguished from similar events which occur in a system at rest. This means that the occupants of a smoothly running train would not notice any motion if they do not look outside. All phenomena within the moving train happen exactly as when the train is not moving. Only changes in the state of motion (i.e. deviations from the uniform motion), such as acceleration or deceleration of speed, change of direction (curves) are noticeable within the train; then all objects within the train have a certain tendency to move from their place.

One of the consequences of the principle of relativity is, that observers inside and outside the train will give a different description of what occurred inside the train. If inside the train a ball were to be thrown upward, each observer inside the train would describe the motion of the ball as vertical; observers outside the train, however, would speak of an oblique motion. The motion which they observe is a combination of the vertical motion of the ball and the horizontal motion of the train.

The special theory of relativity extends the classical principle of relativity. The theory states that not only mechanical but also electro-magnetic phenomena fall within the scope of the principle. This

---

[15]An excellent introduction is offered by A. Einstein, *Relativity, the Special and the General Theory,* New York, 1921.

would explain why the velocity of light is exactly the same whether measured in the direction of the motion of the earth or contrary to that direction. This phenomenon is the experimental starting-point for the theory of relativity. The velocity of light does not seem to obey the so-called Galileo-transformation.

Galileo- and Lorentz-transformation

A simple example may show what the Galileo-transformation is all about. Suppose we want to calculate the speed of a man walking on the deck of a boat. If the boat has a speed of 10 miles an hour and if the man walks with a speed of 3 miles in the same direction in which the boat travels, then his speed with respect to the shore is 13 miles an hour. In this instance the Galileo-transformation amounts to a simple adding of both speeds, the speed of the man in respect with the first system of reference (the boat) and the speed of that system with respect to another system of reference (the shore). As a result the man has a different speed with respect to different systems of reference. Similarly we can calculate his speed with regard to the sun or to the fixed stars.

Difficulties Arise When Light Is Involved. Light seems to have exactly the same speed in all systems of reference; it does not obey the Galileo-transformation. To overcome this difficulty, H. Lorentz proposed a transformation in which light always has exactly the same speed. In this transformation not only are the different spatial coordinates indicating distances transformed (which is also true in the Galileo-transformation, although the equations are not the same), but the time-coordinate is also transformed. This means that the time in one system differs from the time in another system. If System II moves in the direction of the x-coordinate of System I the formula is

$$t' = \frac{t - \dfrac{v}{c^2} x}{\sqrt{1 - \dfrac{v^2}{c^2}}}$$

in which t' indicates the time in System II; t the time and x the place-coordinate in System I, v the speed of the second System with respect to the first, and c the speed of light (300,000 km. per second). This formula makes several things understandable.

First, when v is not very high, $\dfrac{v^2}{c^2}$ and $\dfrac{v}{c^2}$ are practically zero because of the high value of c. As a result $t' = t$.

Secondly, when two events in System I happen at the same time and at the same place, an observer in System II will also observe them as simultaneous. Only his time will differ from that of the observer in System I.

Thirdly, when the events in System I happen at the same time, but at different places—that is to say t is the same and x is different—then different times will be observed in System II.

Finally, in the case of two events happening at different times, t_1 and t_2, and at different places, t'_1 and t'_2 will be, generally speaking, also different. However, it can also happen, with appropriate x and v, that t'_1 and t'_2 are the same. It can even happen that whereas, for example, t_1 is greater than t_2, t'_1 is smaller than t'_2. This means that observers in System II see the events happen in reverse order. All these possibilities are clearly expressed in the transformation formula which itself is based upon sufficient physical evidence to be accepted. The conclusion about the observation of different physical times is, of course, not verified. For the time being, this verification is impossible because of the enormous speeds involved. Even the fastest airplane represents, in terms of the theory of relativity, slow motion.

There are, however, other consequences of the theory of relativity which are in agreement with experimental data, so that there is sufficient reason to believe that the time-transformation is real.

Theory of Relativity Deals With Measurement of Time

The crucial question now is whether the supposed correctness of Einstein's theory about the relativity of the concept *simultaneity* affects the philosophical analysis of time based upon this concept. To begin with, Einstein's theory reveals fundamental difficulties as to the *measurement* of time only. In order to measure time we must have a periodic motion which can be used as a clock. Now it is clear that observers in different systems (that is to say, systems in different states of motion) will not use the same individual clock. One clock will be used in only one system. Thus observers in different systems have to use different clocks. This seems to offer no great difficulty, for we can imagine two clocks, made in exactly the same way, and perfectly synchronized. As a matter of fact, nature provides us with such clocks in the form of the frequencies of atoms.

This, however, does not solve the problem. According to the theory of relativity, the frequency of a clock is altered when the state of motion of the clock is altered. Thus two observers in different systems, using clocks which were perfectly synchronous before one system started to move with respect to the other system, will actually read different times on their clocks. This is precisely the theory of relativity.

Let us consider, however, another possibility. Let us imagine that there is a clock in the universe which can be read by all observers, regardless of their distance or their state of motion. The same difficulty will still exist; for no observer who is at a certain distance from the clock can observe the periodical signals, indicating seconds, at exactly the same time as they are sent off by the clock. He can observe the signal only after a passage of time, and according to his state of motion the intervals between the different signals will be shorter or longer. Thus the seconds do not have the same duration for all observers. An observer who is not in the same state of motion as the clock is will reckon with another system of second than an observer whose state of motion is the same as that of the clock.

The difficulty is that no observer can claim to know his absolute state of motion. He knows only his state of motion with respect to another system. That makes it impossible to correct the differences between the observed time-units. This being so, no universal clock is available. Observers in different states of motions will, therefore, differ in their observations of the time at which certain events in the universe happen. It is even possible that they sometimes differ with respect to "before" and "after," as was explained above. Events which one observer calls simultaneous, are observed by a second observer as happening one after another, whereas a third observer sees them happen in reverse order.

The Theory of Relativity Alone Has No Philosophical Consequence

The preceding discussion should have made clear that Einstein's theory deals exclusively with the *observation* of simultaneity and the order of "before" and "after" insofar as events happening at a certain distance from each other are involved. Nowhere does the theory of relativity itself lead to the conclusion that simultaneity in the universe does not exist or cannot exist in reality. The theory of relativity is simply not concerned with it. There is then no immediate contradiction between the philosophical analysis of time and the physical theory of relativity.

Those scientists or philosophers who contend that such a contradiction does exist are not able to prove it upon scientific data alone. They can do so only if they combine their scientific data with some philosophical principle. Sometimes this is done in a very superficial manner. Without further analysis, sometimes without even being aware of it or mentioning it explicitly, the results of the theory of relativity are combined with some general philosophical principle such as, for example, the maxim: "That which cannot be measured or observed does not exist." Then the conclusion that simultaneity does not exist is obvious; however, it is not on account of scientific consideration alone, but on account of an implicitly presumed philosophical principle.

Therefore, the contradiction which is supposed to exist between the philosophical analysis of time and the theory of relativity is not a contradiction between a scientific and a philosophical doctrine, but between two philosophical doctrines.

A comparable refutation can be offered when the theory of relativity is said to prove that it does not make sense to speak about simultaneity of events which happen at a certain distance from each other.[16] In this instance, the theory of relativity is combined with the philosophical principle which says that it does not make sense to speak of something that cannot be observed or measured. It is obvious that the theory of relativity itself does not lead to this proof. The so-called proof has conclusive force only if the implicit philosophical principle is accepted as well. Since neither this philosophical principle nor that used in the former argument is valid, as has been shown in the first chapter, there is no reason to ascribe to the theory of relativity the power to prove anything about the *existence* of simultaneity.

The Theory of Relativity Does Provoke Philosophical Problems

Thus far our discussion of the philosophical consequences of the theory of relativity has been negative. It was shown that the physical theory alone does not have any philosophical consequence, and therefore that there could not be any contradiction between the

---

[16]The reader must keep in mind that the difficulty with respect to simultaneity exists only when events happening at a distance from each other are involved.

physical theory and the philosophical doctrine about time.   However, the mere absence of contradiction between a physical theory and a philosophical doctrine does not establish anything in favor of the philosophical doctrine involved.   It is, therefore, worthwhile again to review carefully the philosophical analysis of time made in the preceding section.   Perhaps something was said there that seemed very obvious, but which no longer seems so obvious now that the theory of relativity has been developed.   In other words, it is always possible that in the philosophical analysis of time a primitive datum has been mistaken for a primary one.

Moreover, such a philosophical principle as "that which cannot be observed or measured does not exist" may be wrong as a *general* philosophical principle, but this does not mean that it is also wrong when given a limited sense.   So it is correct to say that "If time has a metric structure, then it must be possible, at least in principle, to measure time."   A universal time having a metric structure which, in principle, cannot be measured does not make sense, because it belongs to the very nature of a metric structure to be open to measurement.   Therefore, if it can be proved that an objective measurement of time is not possible in principle, then we are pretty close to the conclusion that the universally objective metric structure of time does not exist.

A comparable difficulty exists with respect to the universal topologic structure of time.   If the theory of relativity is right in denying the possibility of determining "before" and "after" in an unequivocal way, then there is reason to believe that time has no universal topological structure.   Thus there is plenty of reason for a careful reëxamination of the philosophical analysis of time.   But before doing this, something should be said concerning the impossibility of determining the topological and metric structure of time.   And more in particular about the phrase "impossible in principle," used in that connection.   What is the exact meaning thereof?

The Meaning of "In Principle"

In order to understand the meaning of the phrase "impossible in principle," used in connection with the measurement of time it is necessary first to consider other instances in which measurement is also impossible, such instances as those in which the impossibility is caused by the imperfection of the available means of measurement. It is not possible, for example, to determine the exact number of human beings on earth. This impossibility, however, is not an impossibility in principle. If there were a well-organized civil registration for the whole world having the cooperation of everybody, the number of all human beings living at a given moment could be determined. So the impossibility of making the count is due to the fact that we simply do not have at our disposal the ideal means of determining the world's exact population. The difficulty is a practical one.

Precisely here lies the difference between the example and the problems of the theory of relativity. The alleged impossibility of observing or measuring simultaneity seems to be an impossibility in principle. The impossibility is not based upon the fact that we do not have ideal clocks or ideal observers at our disposal. According to the theory of relativity, ideal clocks and ideal observers do not exist *even in principle*. No observer escapes the necessity of using signals travelling with finite speed (at the utmost, the speed of light). Any clock an observer carries would be affected by his own state of motion; and he would have no possible way of determining his own state of motion in an absolute way. So the impossibility of determining simultaneity is an impossibility in principle. Only if physical means were discovered beyond those known at the present, means not subject to the principle of relativity, would the said impossibility be no longer an impossibility in principle.

The possibility of this discovery, which limits the absoluteness of the impossibility, may seem somewhat speculative from the physical point of view. It has, however, philosophical importance. For the possibility of such a discovery indicates clearly that the impossibility of determining simultaneity is not the result of the nature of time itself. Time itself does not exclude, in principle, the possibility of determining its topological and metric structure; the exclusion is entirely the result of the kind of physical means at our disposal.

So the phrase "impossibility in principle" has only a limited meaning. It is correct to use it in connection with the observance of simultaneity, but not in an absolute sense. It is not the nature of time itself which causes the impossibility under consideration.

So once again the conclusion is reached that the theory of relativity does not contradict our philosophical analysis of time. But, as has been said, that conclusion is only negative. It does not in the least confirm the positive value of the philosophical analysis. It must still be determined whether or not all elements of this analysis are of a philosophical nature. Are perhaps some of these elements open to attack by science, and so not philosophical? The safest way to

check this is to examine whether all the data on which our philosophical analysis was based are also implicitly presupposed by science.

The Theory of Relativity Presupposes Simultaneity

The first philosophical datum used in the analysis of time was
that time is an aspect of motion. It was said that time is the numerable
aspect of movement with respect to before and after. This point does
not cause any difficulty, because all physical theory, relativistic or
not, presupposes that. For time in physics is always measured by
the parts of a motion, especially a periodic one.

The real difficulty lies in a second point, namely, that there is
only *one* time, *one* order of "before" and "after" in all the motions
of the universe. This fact, to put it mildly, does not seem to be presupposed by what the theory of relativity says about time. For the
theory of relativity states explicitly that no universal simultaneity
can be observed, and, since a science cannot speak about what
cannot be observed, it could hardly be expected that science would
presuppose the existence of suc.. an objective universal simultaneity[17]
as is required for the existence of one universal time.

Yet, strange as it may sound, there is no convincing evidence
that the theory of relativity does not presuppose an objective, universal
simultaneity and, consequently, an objective universal order of
"before" and "after." On the contrary, there is evidence that the
theory of relativity does presuppose objective simultaneity.

The Physical Content of the Theory of Relativity Is Not at Stake.
To avoid any misunderstanding, it should be stressed from the very
beginning that the above opinion is not based upon a lack of confidence in the *physical* content of the theory of relativity itself. So
it will be assumed in the following analysis that the theory of relativity
is true and that the Lorentz-transformation, which involves a transformation of time, is correct. This assumption does not, of course,
mean that the analysis holds true only when the physical theory is
also true. To hold such a view would be a serious misunderstanding.
What is being done is simply in line with the general policy of this
book, which is based upon the belief that *any* physical theory as physi-

---

[17]The term *universal* expresses the fact that simultaneity exists for the
whole universe. According to the theory of relativity, objective simultaneity
makes sense only when two events at the same place are involved. Otherwise
there is no way of observing the objectivity of simultaneity. Within one system,
however, there is a subjective simultaneity.

cal theory must of necessity presuppose some philosophical principles about matter and its properties.

Thus a physical theory about time has to accept implicitly some philosophical principles about time. Otherwise this theory could not be workable. The attempt in these pages, therefore, is to find out what principles about time are necessarily presupposed by the theory of relativity because of the very fact that it is a *physical* theory. The actual specific content of a physical theory is, of course, not determined by these implicitly presupposed principles. The actual physical content is determined only by specific experimental data and their theoretical evaluation. This being so, our aim must be to find certain implicit principles about time which are presupposed by the way the theory of relativity works.

The crucial point in the theory of relativity is the Lorentz-transformation, in which time is also transformed. For *one* and the same event the measured time in one system is not the same as the measured time in another system. Consequently, a certain event does not seem to mark an objective universal moment of time, and it is possible that that which happens simultaneously in one system does not happen simultaneously according to an observer in another system.

Any Transformation Presupposes Simultaneity. At this point it is necessary to examine what is presupposed by the very use of a transformation of one system into another. "Transformation" means that the place and time of a certain event expressed in coördinates of one system can also be expressed in coördinates of another system which moves with respect to the first system.

Let us assume two points, E_1 and E_2 in System I. These points, according to the transformation, correspond with two points, E'_1 and E'_2, in System II. Actual values have no significance here, because such values are not important. With regard to our problem, only the following is important. Let E_1 and E_2 represent in System I two events happening at a distance from each other. The place-coördinates P_1 and P_2 are therefore different. Now the transformation-formula says, in principle, that the places P_1 and P_2 in System I correspond with certain places in System II. For System II, which moves in relation to System I, is supposed to be in a *continual* contact with System I. Any event happening in System I can also be recorded in System II. This means that at any moment of time all points (in the spatial sense) of System II coincide with certain (unknown) points of System I. Otherwise, it would be impossible to record also in System II any event happening in System I. There is a continual correspondence between the two Systems of reference.

The very existence of such a correspondence presupposes something about time apart from the measurement of time. It presupposes that *at the same moment* when P_1 in System I coincides with P'_1, P_2 necessarily coincides with another place in System II. Otherwise the two Systems would be partly out of touch that moment, and the use of the transformation-formula would not make sense. The very use of the transformation-formula presupposes therefore that at *any* moment, for example, the moment marked by a certain event at P_1 in System I, all the places in System I, regardless of their distance from P_1, coincide with certain points of System II. In this fundamental sense, and in this sense only, there is simultaneity. This does not mean that clocks indicate the same time—simultaneity only says that a certain moment of time is not confined to just one place. Or to put it another way, simultaneity in the fundamental philosophical sense means nothing but the fact of the coexistence of the parts of the universe.

The Presupposition of Simultaneity Does Not Imply the Possibility of Objective Measurement

It is of great importance to note that the presupposed existence of a simultaneous coïncidence of places of one system of reference with those of another system does not imply anything about the possibilities of objective measurement. In order to understand this, consider the following instance.

Suppose that at a certain moment, place P_1 of System I coïncides with place P'_1 of System II. Let the moment be measured as t_1 by an observer in System I. Let the place be measured as x_1.[18] It was said above that at that very moment another place of System I, say P_2, coïncides necessarily with a place of System II, say P'_2. The difficulty is now that different observers will give different values to the places P_2 and P'_2. An observer in System I will determine the value of P_2 as x_2. According to the Lorentz-formula, x_2 will coïncide at the moment t_1 with

$$x'_2 = \frac{x_2 - vt_1}{\sqrt{1 - \dfrac{v^2}{c^2}}}$$

---

[18] If the motion of System II is in the direction of the x-coördinate of System I, as we have supposed in introducing the Lorentz-transformation on p. 184, then the other place-coördinates are not important.

No one, however, can be sure that the time t_1 at the place x_2 is the same "real" time as t_1 at the place x_1. Observers in System II at places corresponding with x_1 and x_2 will deny that their colleagues at the places x_1 and x_2 in System I are using the same time. According to them t_1 at x_1 has the real value:

$$t'_1 = \frac{t_1 - \dfrac{v}{c^2} x_1}{\sqrt{1 - \dfrac{v^2}{c^2}}}$$

whereas t_1 at x_2 has the real value:

$$t'_2 = \frac{t_1 - \dfrac{v}{c^2} x_2}{\sqrt{1 - \dfrac{v^2}{c^2}}}$$

Consequently, the observers of System II claim that their colleagues in System I were mistaken in their determination of what place of System II coïncided with x_2 at the moment that x_1 coïncided with x'_1. They would say that the coïncidence of x_1 with x'_1 was not simultaneous with that of x_2 with x'_2.

The observers of System I would, however, maintain that it was simultaneous. Here is exactly the same situation as was mentioned in the beginning of the discussion on simultaneity. The presupposed existence of a simultaneous coïncidence of places of one system with those of another system of reference does not imply anything about the possibilities of objective measurement. Two events, happening at x_1 and x_2 at the same time, according to an observer in System I, would, according to an observer in System II, happen one before the other.

There is no physical means to determine an objective simultaneity of the two events. It is correct, therefore, when Einstein says that the concept objective simultaneity does not make sense in physics; there exists no means by which to observe simultaneity in an objective way. And for a scientist, a simultaneity which cannot be observed has no meaning within his science. On the other hand, to say that because no way exists of observing simultaneity the whole concept therefore does not make sense is too extreme a statement. For, as was previously explained, transformation of the data of one system into data of another system, which moves with respect to the first, presupposes correspondence in time, and therefore presupposes objective simultaneity.

This conclusion may be repeated in terms of a philosophical analysis of time. According to that analysis,[19] any motion marks time. For example, take the moment that the clock of an observer at x_1 in System I indicates t sec. This particular moment x_1 coïncides with x'_1 and, according to the presupposition of the transformation-formula, at that very moment x_2 coïncides with a certain point of System II, notwithstanding the fact that x_1 and x_2 are at a distance from each other. Consequently, before any observation of time can be made at x_2, it is presupposed that there is simultaneity. The contacts or the coïncidences of points of System I with points of System II are supposed to be simultaneous by the very use of the transformation-formula. Otherwise there would be no correspondence.

6. SPACE-TIME CONTINUUM

The Objective Distance in Space-Time

The fact that it could be shown in the foregoing section that the existence of an objective universal simultaneity is presupposed by the theory of relativity also warrants something being said about another so-called consequence of the theory of relativity.

According to many scientists, the theory of relativity has proved that the fundamental distinction which philosophers have always made between spatial distance and temporal distance is erroneous. They base this opinion upon the possibility of fusing together into one distance in a space-time continuum the spatial and temporal distances between two events. This "distance" has an objective and absolute value, independent of the state of motion which influences the measurement of both temporal and spatial distances. The quantitative value of such a distance can be expressed only in units which are neither purely spatial nor purely temporal, but of a kind of combined nature. That is why scientists deny that there is any fundamental difference between space and time. The possibility and usefulness of combining space and time proves that they are not fundamentally different.

---

[19]Cf. p. 179 f.

Objective distance in the space-time-continuum cannot be directly measured. Only temporal and spatial distances are directly observable. Out of necessity, therefore, an observer will separate this objective distance in the space-time continuum into a temporal distance and a spatial distance, according to his state of motion. He will say, for example, that event A happened t seconds after event B, and at a distance of x miles. An observer in a different state of motion will, however, tell a different story. According to him the temporal distance was t' and the spatial distance x'. Each of the observers has his own manner of dividing the same distance in space-time into separate temporal and spatial components. It is possible, however, to calculate from each separate set of subjective temporal and spatial distances, the objective distance in the space-time continuum.[20]

The Fundamental Difference Between Space and Time

Because of the mathematical-physical way of handling space-time problems, the philosophical problem arises whether or not the sharp distinction between spatial and temporal distances is justified. Does not the unification of these distances in a single space-time distance prove that the absolute distinction philosophers make between space and time is incorrect?

It seems that there is no reason to distinguish fundamentally between a permanent continuum (*continuum permanens*) and a flowing continuum (*continuum fluens*) if both can be combined in such a way that the distinction vanishes entirely. The irrelevance of the distinction is all the more conclusive since only distances in a space-time continuum can have an objective or absolute value.[21] Therefore the division of space-time continuum into a spatial and temporal con-

---

[20]A simple illustration of the way in which different sets of separate values combine to one value is offered by the well-known thesis of Pythagoras which states that in a rectangular triangle the square of hypothenuse is equal to the sum of the squares of the other two sides, i.e. $d^2 = a^2 + b^2$. Now different rectangular triangles with the same hypothenuse but with different sides are possible. The separate values of the squares of the sides of these triangles differ from a^2 or b^2, but their sum is always d^2. The hypothenuse represents the objective distance in the space-time-continuum. The different possible sides of the triangles represent the different values of temporal and spatial distances which all result in the same objective distance.

[21]It is of interest to note a frequently misunderstood aspect of the theory of relativity. Relying on the term "relativity," some philosophers, without much knowledge of the theory itself, seem to think that the theory of relativity proves that all human knowledge is relative. Even apart from the fact that a physical theory can never prove anything about *all* human knowledge, this idea about the theory of relativity is wholly wrong. For the very aim of the theory is to find *absolute* values for certain physical quantities.

tinuum seems to be based on our way of perceiving, and not on reality.
As it would be foolish to assert that the sun is a disk because we see
the sun always as a disk, so would it be equally foolish to maintain the
idea of separate time and space after a successful theory has shown the
existence of a space-time continuum.

Yet, there is a big difference between the two instances. The fact
that we always see the sun as a disk can be easily explained by relating
it to the real shape of the sun as affected by the position of an observer
on the earth. In the case of the time-space continuum, however, the
situation is entirely different. If time and space have exactly the same
character, how then is the fundamental difference between the nature
of the time continuum and the space continuum to be explained? The
typical fluent character of time, the impossibility of reversing the order
of time, is something which clearly distinguishes time from space. The
objection, namely, that the theory of relativity has shown that the
order of time is not absolute but can be reversed because of the relativity of the concept simultaneity, is based upon a misunderstanding.
This being so, the solution of the seeming contradiction between the
possibility of combining space and time in one continuum and the fundamentally different character of both must be found in another way
than that which disregards the fundamental difference between time
and space.

Temporal and Spatial Distances Cannot Be Measured Independently

The fact that temporal and spatial distances could be easily combined should not surprise us. Space and time have much in common.
Both can be measured, and their values can be expressed in units.
The actual course of a motion can, therefore, be reproduced in a
graph in which the time coördinate differs not at all from the space
coördinate, except in the fundamentally different character of the
respective units. But this difference is important only in the actual
process of measuring, not in the mathematical reproduction. The
procedure of combining time- and space-coördinates in one graph is
generally used in physics. The fact that space and time are reproduced
by the same type of mathematical dimensions does not imply, of
course, that there is no fundamental difference between space and time.

The theory of relativity introduced a new element into the gen-
ral procedure of mathematical reproduction, insofar as it stated that
the measurements of time and spatial distance are not mutually
independent. This is in no way a contradiction of the statement that

there is a difference in nature between space and time. For in order to measure the time at which an event happens at a certain distance, the observer also has to know, and therefore to measure, the distance. The greater the distance, the more time a signal needs in order to reach the observer. Thus in this instance measuring time is necessarily connected with measuring distance. This means that the measurement of time is not only a measurement of time, but that it also includes a measurement of a distance. The theory of relativity claims that the direct outcome of such a combined measurement is not independent of the state of motion of the observer. The theory also has shown the possibility of putting the outcome of the combination of the measurements of time and distance in a form which is not dependent on the state of motion of the observer.

From this it follows that there is no reason whatever to conclude that the theory of relativity fuses time and space together in one continuum, and so erases the fundamental difference between them. The theory tries to find a value for the combined measurement of distance and time which is independent of the state of motion of the observer. This combination is not the result of a theoretical consideration of the nature of space and time; it is simply the result of the fact that in actual measurement space and time are already combined. In order to understand the necessity for this combination, it should be kept in mind that space and time are not realities in themselves, but aspects of the same reality. However, they are aspects with a different nature.

7. SUMMARY

The discussion of the quantitative aspects of matter has many times required the examination of the apparent contradictions between the philosophical analysis and the results of science. Again and again we have come to the conclusion that the contradictions are only apparent. A more profound analysis both of the correct meaning of philosophical terms and of the results of science can in each instance solve the difficulties. Such an analysis is therefore healthful for both philosophy and science, because it purifies both of those extraneous elements which do not belong to their level of abstraction.

In discussing the quantitative aspects of matter, the philosopher is interested only in the status of being of these aspects. So the question has been asked what kind of beings are space and time. The answer has been that neither space nor time are realities in themselves, but essential aspects of material, i.e. mobile, beings. The same kind of question has been asked about motion. This has been answered by establishing the mode of being of motion in terms of the metaphysical concepts of act and potency.

All these problems are purely philosophical. Science does not concern itself with such aspects of matter. Science presupposes motion, time, and space. It deals exclusively with specific kinds of motion. It measures certain stretches of time and certain spatial relations. It does not discuss their general nature. It cannot do so for the simple reason that scientific methods presuppose the existence of time, space, and motion.

Suggested Readings

Aristotle, *Physics,* bk. IV.

P. Hoenen, *Cosmologia, Liber* I and *Liber* III.

Albert Einstein, *Relativity, the Special and the General Theory,* New York, 1921.

Alfred Tarski, *Introduction to Logic and to the Methodology of Deductive Science,* New York, [2]1946, Chapter VI.

P. Henry Van Laer, *Philosophico-Scientific Problems,* Pittsburgh, 1953, Chapter II.

Henry Margenau, *The Nature of Physical Reality,* New York-Toronto-London, 1950, Chapter VII.

Peter G. Bergmann, *Introduction to the Theory of Relativity,* New York, [6]1953, Chapters I-V.

CHAPTER SIX

QUALITY

1. THE REALITY OF QUALITIES

Introduction

The purpose of this chapter is to determine the nature of material qualities. What is meant by the term *quality* is obvious. It refers directly to a certain kind of sensory experience which teaches us the existence of qualities. Colors, sounds, smells, and the like are observed. Consequently, in daily and even in scientific language, qualities are ascribed to objects. For example, we make a distinction between a piece of iron and the heat thereof. The heat is said to be a quality of that piece of iron. And we distinguish further between that quality itself and the quantity of that quality, when we speak of a temperature of 100 degrees. So there is reason enough to examine the general nature of a material quality and of its relationship to quantity.

As it was not possible to give a definition of quantity, so is it not possible to give a real definition of quality. A more primary concept than quality, one that can be used in a definition of quality, cannot be found. Quality is one of the primary categories, as are substance and quantity. To determine the nature of qualities, therefore, does not mean the attempt to find a definition; it means an examination of the rôle quality plays in the material world and of the relations quality has to substance and to quantity.

Are Material Qualities Properties of Matter?

Several questions about the nature of quality can be asked. The first and most important one doubts the very existence of qualities in matter. Are not the qualities we experience more the result of the reaction of our sense-organs to certain external stimulations than they are properties of matter itself? A great many philosophers and scientists have not hesitated to answer that qualities exist only in our sense-organs. In matter itself there is only quantity. To a certain extent, the denial of the real existence of qualities in matter is nothing but the counterpart of the denial of the real existence of quantity, which came up in the discussion of space.

199

Yet, there is a distinct difference between the reasons for denying the existence of quantity and for denying the existence of quality. The denial of quantity is based entirely upon certain ontological and epistemological considerations, without any evidence from the field of science. So the denial of quantity is an exclusively philosophical affair, and is a problem discussed only among philosophers. The denial of quality, however, is discussed among scientists as much as among philosophers. Scientists, especially physiologists, perform experiments which show that certain sensations with qualitative content can be produced just as well by stimulating certain spots of the nervous system as by normal sensory perception. Moreover, it seems that the history of science proves that such a philosopher as Democritus, who said that all qualities were the result of certain quantitative arrangements in matter, was right. To a continually increasing extent science explains differences in observed quality by differences in quantity. The differences between red and green, for example, are reduced to a quantitative difference of wave length. The old conception of Aristotle, which ascribed, in agreement with immediate sense-experience, a typical set of qualities to each kind of matter seems entirely abandoned by modern science. Science explains away an apparent multitude of qualities. It seems that Democritus was not only right in predicting the course of science, but also in the argument upon which his prediction was based. For Democritus' argument was that differences in quality are unintelligible and, therefore, have no existence. Explaining qualities should, therefore, be a matter of reducing qualitative differences to exclusively quantitative differences.

Thus there seems to be plenty of reason for accepting the philosophical position that there is no such thing as quality in matter. Quality seems to be a concept that belongs entirely to the human sphere of perception, with which the philosophy of nature has no concern.

The Reduction of Quality to Quantity Is Never a Total Reduction

The reasons have been given as to why many philosophers and scientists think that qualities do not have an existence outside sensation. These reasons, however, are not conclusive. The following consideration should show this. It may be true, for example, that there is a procedure known as the reduction of qualitative to quantitative differences, but this reduction is not absolute. Differences in color are indeed expressed by differences in the value of certain quantities, such as wave length and amplitude, which form a part of mathematical formulae. But this does not deny the fact that these quantities are not exclusively *mathematical* entities; they actually refer to certain material dispositions.

Studying the phenomena of sound, we come across the same kind of formulae and the same kind of mathematical entities as are used in the study of colors. But these formulae refer to material dispositions of quite another nature. Even according to physics, a sound wave is something other than a light wave. The identical mathematical formulae refer to different things in matter. This difference is not difference in quantity. The best way of expressing it is to say that it is a difference of a qualitative nature. According to science, sound is a mechanical vibration of the molecules of the air, whereas light is a fluctuation of intensity of certain electric and magnetic properties.

Thus the simple fact that science uses mathematical formulae to express its theories about the nature of qualities is not proof that science reduces all qualities to quantity. On the contrary, a careful examination of the way science works will show that what has been seen with respect to the scientific descriptions of sound and color is universally valid. A mathematical formula used in science is not merely a mathematical formula.

Empirical Science Presupposes Quality

If science uses a mathematical formula, then this formula always contains certain quantities which refer to a certain sense-experience of physical reality. This means that in order to know what a certain quantity represents it is necessary to refer to the specific way in which that quantity is observed and measured. Such a reference is incompatible with a purely quantitative world. For if such world existed, there would be no possibility of observing anything in that world. A purely quantitative world would be a world in which only topological and metric structures would exist. We must take the term "quantitative world" seriously. Much confusion with respect to our problem stems from the fact that the term "quantitative" is used in an inexact way. If, however, the term is used according to its strict meaning, then it is immediately clear that observation of an exclusively quantitative world is impossible. Even the simple measurement of a certain length requires that there be an observable difference between the end-points of the length under observation and the medium in which it is found.

Observation and measurement require qualitative distinctions, because they require at least a distinction in intensity of a certain quality, and that means a qualitative difference. From this it follows that an empirical science presupposes that matter is more than mere quantity. An empirical science presupposes in matter a factor which makes things discernible. And that factor is quality. Quality gives quantity the possibility of being observed. This indicates already how intimate the relationship between quality and quantity is. But the relationship is even closer. For it is not only true that quantity never exists without quality; but the reverse is also true. There is no quality in matter without intrinsic quantitative relations. First it is necessary to make clear the nature of these relations. When that is done it should be possible to discuss the philosophical source of this close relationship between quality and quantity.

2. EXTENSION AND INTENSITY

Science Presupposes That All Material Phenomena Are Subject to Mathematical Methods

The best way to determine the relations between quantity and quality is to examine somewhat further the fundamental methods used in science. It has been shown in the previous section that science presupposes the existence of quality in matter by the very fact that it uses empirical observation. Facts, stubborn facts, enjoy absolute supremacy in science. Science knows that it has no immediate insight into nature, that it has to rely in the last instance on sense-experience.[1] And sense-experience implies that there is more than quantity. For quantity alone is not observable.

On the other hand, science[2] also presupposes that the use of mathematics in scientific theory is, in principle, unlimited. This means two things. First, mathematical consequences are valid in any part of a scientific theory, for once it is found that certain aspects

---

[1] In this fundamental sense, science presupposes the old and famous scholastic thesis of the infallibility of sense-knowledge. Cf. St. Thomas, *Summa Theologica*, I, q. 17, art. 2.

[2] We deliberately use the term *science* instead of *scientists,* notwithstanding the fact that science exists only in scientists. The reason for using the term "science" is that when speaking of presuppositions, the personal philosophical opinions of scientists have no special interest. The important factor is what was called, in the method of science, incarnated philosophical convictions.

of reality satisfy a certain set of mathematical axioms and definitions, all the mathematical consequences should follow in order. Secondly, the unlimited use of mathematics means that science is further convinced that there can always be found such a mathematical set of axioms and definitions. Science feels that no observable feature of nature is beyond the reach of mathematics. The important point here is not whether that conviction is or is not entirely true. The important point is that science has this conviction and that science has been very successful in the unlimited use of mathematics.[3]

Quality Has Extension and Intensity

There are two ways in which science establishes quantitative relation between observable, and therefore qualitative, data. The first way is based upon the fact that a quality is always present in *extended* matter. This means that there are places where a certain quality is found and places where it is not found, or at least, not in the same degree. Consequently, we are entitled to speak of the *extension* of a quality, referring to the extensions of the objects having that quality. Mediaeval philosophers called this the extension *per accidens* of a quality. Such an extension can, of course, be measured in the same way as extensions are always measured, and the results can be expressed in the units used as standards for the measurement of extension.

In addition, a quality has something that is usually called intensity, a kind of degree of perfection. A quality can be more or less intensive. This intensity of a quality can also be measured and expressed in certain units. This can be done in several ways, which need not be discussed in details.[4] One of the most important ways is that in which the scientist makes use of the quantitative effect of a certain quality. The degrees of temperature, for instance, are usually measured by the expansion of a certain liquid, mercury or alcohol. This expansion is nothing but the quantitative effect of the quality involved.

The Difference Between Intensity and Extension

The fact that intensity can be measured does not mean that intensity and extension are not essentially different. The essential difference is easily understood when we compare the properties of intensity with the properties of extension. Two pieces of wood, each a meter

---

[3]The justification of this conviction of science has been given on p. 158.
[4]Cf. P. Hoenen, *Cosmologia,* pp. 184 ff.

long, have, if joined together, a length of two meters. However, two portions of water, each with a temperature of 50 degrees, do not yield, if added together, a temperature of 100 degrees. The difference is striking, but it does not take away from the fact that an intensity as well as an extension can be measured and mathematically handled. Mathematical relations between intensities can be established, and they reveal something of the nature of the quality involved. The knowledge, for example, of the mathematical structure of sound waves gives us a good idea of what sound really is. It makes the relations between such properties of sound as pitch, intensity, and velocity understandable. Mathematical relations are not only external concomitants of quality, they express intrinsic aspects. Material qualities have essentially a mathematical pattern. This mathematical pattern is not the whole quality, but it is an essential aspect of it.

3. QUALITY AND QUANTITY IN THE LIGHT OF HYLOMORPHISM

The foregoing section has shown how intimately quantity and quality are related. The best way to express this relationship is perhaps to say that any material property is essentially of a quantitative-qualitative nature. Quantity is imbued with quality; quality exists only in a quantitative pattern.

This method of expression shows a great similarity with the method used to express the relationship between matter and form. And it is no coïncidence that we have to use similar phrases to express both relationships. For the distinction between matter and form, which is a distinction within the substance of a material being, finds its natural consequence in the accidents of matter. The fundamental non-simplicity, characteristic of matter, is present not only in the substance, but also in the accidents. This is not surprising if we realize the correct distinction between substance and accidents. An accident is not something glued onto the substance as if both were separate complete beings. An accident is a determination of a substance. Therefore, the fundamental non-simplicity of a material substance continues its influence in the determinations of the substance, i.e. even in the accidents. In the accidents this non-simplicity expresses itself in the distinction between quantity and quality. The distinction is real, but it is not a seperation; no more than the distinction between matter and form is a separation. Quality and quantity are always found together.[5]

---

[5]Cf. L. de Raeymaeker, *The Philosophy of Being,* pp. 193 ff.

From this it follows that there is nothing wrong if science stresses the mathematical aspects of a physical thing. The mathematical aspects are an inherent part of physical qualities. And it is natural, in view of the fact that the human mind has better insight into quantity than into quality, that theoretical consideration in physics have a mainly mathematical character. The necessary bond of physical theory with the qualitative aspects of nature is preserved by the fact that the mathematical formulae of a physical theory are based upon sense-experience.

It is also understandable that when science speaks of a material property the quantitative aspects of such a property are particularly stressed, even to such an extent that the qualitative aspects are sometimes hardly noted. Yet, they are always present by the very fact that a scientific theory is always an *empirical* theory. The theory sets out with sense-experience and also finds its confirmation in sense-experience.[6]

This characteristic of science and the fundamental difference in attitude between the mathematician and the scientist who uses mathematics (see pp. 90 ff.) seems also to answer the question as to the degree of abstraction of modern science. Science belongs to the first degree. It is no *scientia media;* for the function of mathematics in science is entirely subordinate to sense-experience.

4. THE REDUCTION OF ONE QUALITY TO ANOTHER

Historical Importance of the Problem

There is still one important problem about the nature of qualities left to be discussed namely, the possibility of reducing one quality to another. It is a problem closely connected with Aristotelian physics. And it has much confused the understanding of the relations between science and the philosophy of nature, as was pointed out in Chapter II. It was shown there that one of the greatest difficulties in the revival of the Thomistic philosophy of nature was the tendency of modern science to deduce the properties of a chemical compound from the properties of the elements. Such a procedure seems to be in conflict with the spirit of hylomorphism, which claims that a chemical compound has a new form, different from the forms of the composing elements. Since a substantial form is characterized by a new set of prop-

---

[6]Cf. pp. 92 ff.

erties, it should be impossible to deduce that set from the respective sets characterizing the elements. Such a deduction seems to imply that the substantial form is only an accidental combination of the forms of the elements.

In discussing the concept of substance, it has already been stressed that this opposition between the spirit of modern science and that of hylomorphism is merely apparent. It develops from that sense of competition between science and the philosophy of nature, which has done so much harm to the right understanding of the relationship between them. The difficulty wholly disappears the moment the true meaning of the concepts "substance" and "substantial form" and of the problems with which these concepts are concerned is recognized.

Since the origin of the difficulties had to do not only with a wrong idea of "substantial form," but also with a wrong idea of "qualities," it is appropriate to discuss the problem again; this time, however, the discussion will be from another angle, namely, the reduction of qualities. This discussion is worthwhile because a good understanding of the problems connected with the reduction of one quality to another is of great help in clarifying the nature of a quality.

Aristotle's Idea of Qualitative Differences

The discussion should begin by recalling some of Aristotle's chemical ideas, for these are largely responsible for the difficulties.

According to Aristotle, each kind of matter is characterized by a different set of qualities. Well-known, for example, is the way in which he characterizes the four elements. The qualities of earth are dry and cold; of water, wet and cold; of air, wet and warm; of fire, dry and warm. Each element is characterized by its own specific set of qualities. Not all material qualities belong to each set. The same applies to the chemical compounds; each chemical compound has its own specific set of qualities.

A second important point in the Aristotelian approach to the problem of the qualitative differences between chemical substances is found in his rejection of Democritus' explanation of a chemical reaction. Such a reaction is not a juxaposition of unchanged atoms; it is "the becoming one of the changed reagents." The result of a chemical reaction is a new substance with a new substantial form and, therefore, with a new specific set of qualities.

From the assumptions of Aristotle, namely, that a specific set of qualities exists for each material substance and that every chemical reaction yields a new substance, it seems to follow that it is impossible to deduce the properties of a compound from the properties of the reacting elements. A chemical reaction creates new qualities. The qualities of the substance formed in the reaction did not exist in the substances out of which the new substance was formed. Consequently, the efforts of science to explain the qualities of a chemical compound by the qualities of the constituting elements seems entirely contrary to the Aristotelian doctrine of hylomorphism. However, this chain of thought has no conclusive force, as a careful analysis will show.

Aristotle Knew Reduction of Qualities

First of all, it should be noted that Artistotle himself was certainly not against the idea of reducing complex qualities to more elementary ones. His very reasoning in the deduction of the doctrine of the four elements proves that. Aristotle tried to discover the four elements by examining what different combinations of the elementary qualities were possible. Elementary qualities are known, according to Aristotle, by the sense of touch. However, not all qualities which correspond with the sense of touch are elementary. Fine and coarse, viscous and brittle, hard and soft, all correspond with the sense of touch, but according to Aristotle, they are derived from wet and dry. Only wet and dry are elementary and Artistotle indicates several reasons for believing that the other qualities can be reduced to wet and dry.[7]

It is hardly worth mentioning that the way in which this reduction is made is very primitive, but that is not important. Much more important is that Aristotle made an attempt to *reduce* qualities to certain elementary qualities. It proves at least that he himself did not think that such a reduction was in conflict with the philosophical principles as laid down in his doctrine of hylomorphism. Although this, of course, does not necessarily mean that the conflict does not exist—there are many philosophers who allow hidden inconsistencies in their system—the fact that Aristotle himself did not see any inconsistency gives food for thought.

However, only the conclusions of a philosophical analysis, proving that there is no inconsistency at all between hylomorphism and reduction of qualities, will be decisive.

---

[7]*De Gen. et Corr.* II 2, 329 b 33 - 330 a 12.

A Specific Set of Qualities Characterizes a Substance

In order to determine whether there exists an inconsistency between hylomorphism and the attempt to reduce qualities to more elementary ones, let us first consider the content of the doctrine of hylomorphism with regard to the relationship between a substance and the set of qualities characterizing such a substance. A substance as such can never be the object of immediate sense-experience. We admit the existence of substances in order to explain the existence of fixed patterns in matter, organization forms realized in individually existing things. Substances are known in our immediate sense-experience only by means of a fixed set of qualities, united in time and space.

It is, however, also possible that a fixed set of qualities may be the result of a fixed combination of substances, i.e. of an aggregate. This possibility is the basis of the problem now dealt with. When is a certain set of qualities the expression of the presence of just one substance? When does it indicate a combination of different substances, an aggregate?

The Supposed Difference Between a Substance and an Aggregate

The specific set of qualities characterizing an aggregate seems to differ from that characterizing a substance in that such a specific set will be itself a combination, namely, a combination of the sets of qualities of the composing substances. Well-known examples of such combinations are man-made things like houses and machines. They have what is called *formae artificiales,* artificial forms, which are responsible for the unity of the combination.

Since the set of qualities characterizing such a unity is nothing but a combination of the sets of qualities of the different parts, this set can be wholly reduced to the combining sets.

Thus the criterion for deciding between the unity of a combination of substances and that of *one* substance seems to be whether or not it is possible to understand the set of qualities characterizing that unity as a combination of the sets of qualities of the parts. This distinction dominated the general attitude of Aristotelian philosophers toward the problem of the difference between one substance and a combination of substances. Whenever an attempt was made to reduce the set of qualities of a certain thing to the sets of qualities of the parts, this very attempt seemed to prove that there was an underlying conviction that the unity of the thing involved was only an accidental unity. And since chemistry was nothing but an attempt to make such a reduction, it is quite understandable that Aristotelian philosophers distrusted the way chemistry worked. The fact that since its birth modern chemistry had been traditionally connected with a mechanistic philosophy only made things worse. It increased the suspicion that chemistry, since it was based on a wrong philosophy, was on a wrong tack and was trying to do the impossible.

Science Is Justified in Reducing Qualities

The Qualities of a New Substance Are Not Created. It is clear to anyone who understands modern chemistry and the way it works, that the inspiration of this science is not a wrong philosophy, but a spontaneous desire of the human mind to understand the phenomena of nature. The reduction of qualities of more complex matter to those of more elementary matter is just such a spontaneous desire. Since the opportunity has been taken several times in this work to show that the spontaneously presupposed principles of modern science are entirely correct from the viewpoint of the philosophy of nature, there appears to be no reason to distrust that desire of science. In order to prove that in this particular case also the spontaneous desire of science is correct, let us consider for a while the philosophical principle from which this desire stems. This philosophical principle is "the intelligibility of being." If it were really true that the qualities of a chemical compound could in no way be explained by the qualities of its elements, then it would follow that the qualities of the compounds originate in nothing. They would be entirely new in the strict sense of this word. They would be created *ex nihilo,* out of nothing.

Potential Existence of the Qualities of the New Substance. To avoid this difficulty, Aristotle said that the qualities of a compound were already present in the elements, but only in a potential way. This is, of course, correct philosophical language; for it expresses in a general way the fact that the qualities of the compound did not actually exist in its elements, as well as the fact that these qualities are closely related to the qualities of its elements.

Science, however, cannot confine itself to that general type of expression. As a matter of fact, it does not even speak about the necessity of a relationship between the qualities of elements and those of compounds. It simply presupposes that such a relationship exists whenever a chemical change occurs, and chemistry begins immediately to determine in what way the qualities of compounds are related to those of its elements. Whereas philosophy speaks of an existence in potency, it is the aim of science to determine this potential existence *in concreto*. This means that science wants to know how the actual qualities of the elements are able to be transformed into the qualities of a compound. In other words, science studies the actual qualities of the elements, not only in their actuality, but also insofar as they are potentially the qualities of a compound.

Let us consider a simple example in a field where insight is not difficult. It is clear that a circular object is in immediate potency to become elliptic. If we press a circle of moldable material, it will become an ellipse both on account of the relationship between a circle and an ellipse, and on account of the nature of elasticity, which is that the result of any pressure is communicated to all parts in definite proportion. To understand why a circle becomes an ellipse, of course, does not in the least imply that there is no essential difference between the form of an ellipse and that of a circle. Nor does it imply that the qualities of an ellipse do not differ from those of a circle.

Likewise, it does not follow from the simple fact that chemistry tries to establish a relationship between the qualities of elements and those of compounds that chemistry denies that a compound may be a new substance different from its elements. Chemistry does not even hint at that. It can be argued, of course, that this negative statement does not solve the original problem. That problem was how to distinguish between a set of qualities characterizing an aggregate and a set of qualities characterizing a substance. This problem is not yet solved, but at least we know now where not to search for its solution.

The Way of Reducing Qualities Is Decisive. So far it has been shown that the distinction between a substance and an aggregate cannot be based on the impossibility of reducing the qualities of a substance to those of its elements. The qualities of a new substance can be understood as resulting from the qualities of the substances out of which the new substance came into existence. Thus the decision as to what is the difference between the two kinds of unities, a substance or an aggregate, depends entirely upon the *way* in which the qualities of unities can be reduced to more elementary qualities. In Chapter IV, in order to explain the difference between a substance and an aggregate, a substance was said to possess a *natural* unity. This does not necessarily mean that no distinction can be made among its parts with their typical qualities. It simply means that these different parts, because of their nature, have a natural tendency to create the unities they form. The set of qualities, for example, which characterize sub-atomic particles are of such a kind that the act of forming atoms cannot be just one of the many accidental possibilities of these particles. The formation of atoms is, so to speak, the natural consequence of these qualities.

It should be noticed also that science is able to study most of the qualities of sub-atomic particles only insofar as these particles are parts of atoms and molecules. This characteristic of modern science marks a sharp difference between the modern mentality and that of the 19th century in dealing with such problems. The study of this difference in mentality will be of great help in solving the problem of the distinction between a substantial and an accidental unity insofar as the reduction of qualities is involved. So let us compare the mentality of both centuries before making an attempt to solve our problem.

The Attitude of Nineteenth Century Science Towards Elementary Qualities

As repeatedly stated, 19th century science was closely connected with a mechanistic philosophy; not because chemistry was actually able to explain the qualities of a chemical compound exhaustively with the help of the qualities of the elements, but because the partial results known were taken as a confirmation of the mechanistic view that molecules are only mechanical combinations of atoms. Atoms, in their turn, were supposed to be mechanical combinations of sub-atomic particles.

The philosophical difficulties of the mechanistic philosophy need not to be taken up again, nor the fact that the actual chemistry of the 19th century was not built upon a strict mechanistic plan. For our present purpose it is sufficient to note that the development of science in the 20th century has clearly shown that a mechanistic approach cannot solve the problems of matter. Such a mechanistic approach depends upon the possibility of determining the qualities of a particle wholly independent of the study of the greater units of which such a particle may be a part. The smallest particles are considered not only the *ultimate* substances, but also the *only* substances. They are, therefore, the only possessors of qualities. Greater units are nothing but accidental units, and their qualities are nothing but mechanical combinations of the qualities of their constituents. It should, therefore, be possible to get a knowledge of the original qualities entirely independent of the accidental combinations in which they take part.

The Attitude of Twentieth Century Science

The development of science in the 20th century has taken an entirely different course from that which the 19th century expected. An exclusively mechanical explanation of matter has proved to be unsatisfactory. Mechanical models of elementary particles, and combinations thereof, are still used. But these models are, in principle, considered inadequate. They may, and often actually do, illustrate certain properties of matter; but they make other properties entirely incomprehensible. As a result, the scientist nowadays uses mutually contradictory models. He is not too much embarrassed by their contradiction, for these models have an exclusively auxiliary purpose. They are not intended to be an adequate representation of reality. The only way to describe and to understand the structure of matter is by using mathematical formulae. The important point for the present discussion is that such formulae are based upon the behavior of *greater natural unities* than *the elementary particles*. The principles governing the behavior of matter are principles known only by the way in which nature itself builds its greater units.

In order to describe an atom, quantum mechanics does not start with electrons and protons and their supposed properties, such as size, shape, charge, velocity, and the like. Quantum mechanics starts with an analysis of the properties which an atomic structure as a whole reveals. These properties give the basic notions of the theory. One of the fathers of the development of science in this direction, Max Planck, expressed the new tendency in these words: "It is only then possible to get a useful description of the laws of nature, if a physical structure in its totality is considered."[8] In order to know what an electron is, one must first know what structure an electron can be a part of. The selective principles revealed by these structures make it possible to understand the properties of electrons.

---

[8]Max Planck: *Das Weltbild der neuen Physik,* Leipzig, [6]1938, p. 25.

The Real Difference Between a Substance and an Aggregate

The difference in attitude between the 19th and 20th century science towards the problem of elementary qualities indicates the way in which the problem of the difference between a substantial unity and an aggregate is to be solved. The characteristic qualities of both kinds of unities can be reduced to more elementary ones. The difficulty is to find the difference in the method of reduction. This difficulty can now be solved. In a substantial unity the elementary qualities can be known only after a study has been made of the whole. The elementary qualities belong to the parts of a substantial unity only insofar as these parts are parts of such a unity. So the properties of an electron can never be fully known unless the electron is studied as part of a greater unity, such as a nucleus, an atom, or a molecule.

The elementary properties belong to an electron only insofar as an electron has the capacity of entering into these greater natural unities. Hence the fixed pattern of these natural unities. They are not the result of an accidental combination of smaller units for which this combination is but an accident of their existence. No, the whole existence of an electron, with its elementary qualities, is attuned to the formation of these greater unities. In the case of an aggregate of several independent substances, the situation is different. There the combination is accidental. That means that we can understand the properties of constituents independently of their possible entrance into the aggregate. Aggregates are possible in an infinite variety. An electron and proton can form all kinds of accidental combinations, but only in one way can they form an atom of hydrogen or a neutron.

The Twofold Mutual Relationship of Matter

The conclusion to be drawn from the foregoing consideration is that reduction of qualities is not in conflict with the doctrine of hylomorphism. On the contrary, hylomorphism requires the existence of a relationship between the qualities of the different kinds of matter, the more elementary and the more complex ones. This problem has been approached in the beginning of this section with the help of the principle of intelligibility. At this point still another consideration deserves attention.

Hylomorphism also requires the reduction of qualities because of its fundamental principle that all matter is mutually related. This mutual relationship has a double character according to the fundamental non-simplicity in matter. Both *materia prima* and *forma sub-stantialis* play a part in this relationship.

The Part of Materia Prima. The relationship based upon the presence of materia prima in matter means that, in principle, all actually existing material things can become something else. The substantial form, actualizing primary matter as this or that kind of matter, can be replaced by another substantial form. Thus primary matter establishes a fundamental relationship in material substances. On account of primary matter, a particular material thing has a potency to become all other material things, but this is true only in a very fundamental sense. This way of expressing the mutual relationship of all matter disregards what may be called a certain hierarchy in matter.

The Part of Forma Substantialis. A particular material thing on account of its substantial form, i.e. on account of the way primary matter is actualized, is much more in potency to become one material thing than to become another. The primary matter of Na and Cl, for example, is much more in potency to become the compound NaCl than to become H_2O. And NaCl, in its turn, is much more in potency to become Na and Cl than H and O. This simple fact, of course, is not in conflict with the fundamental role played by primary matter. It stresses the fact that prime matter exists exclusively in an actualized form. And actualization means automatically that the pure potency of primary matter is determined in such a way that not all other material forms which, in principle, are possible are alike as to their actualization. Some are near to that actualization; others are far removed. The actualization of the latter can be reached only in a gradual way. Several phases must be passed through. This situation proves that all matter is also mutually related because of the different substantial forms, because the forms themselves are related.

Consequently, the specific sets of properties characterizing the different forms are related, too. This justifiies the attempt of science to reduce the specific sets of properties which characterize the different kinds of matter to certain elementary qualities. This procedure is not in any way in conflict with hylomorphism. On the contrary, it reveals in a concrete way the general principle that all substantial forms are related. Such a relation is possible only when the forms have common characteristics. The fact, therefore, that science tries to find the same fundamental qualities in all matter is entirely in accordance with hylomorphism.

5. CONCLUDING REMARKS

The discussion in the present chapter did not solve all problems about quality. It did not even touch on all the problems, such as, for instance, the famous problem of whether colors exist in sensation only, or in sensation and reality. This is, undoubtedly, an important problem, but not a problem of the philosophy of nature. It belongs to psychology. In the philosophy of nature only material quality in general comes up for discussion, not the specific nature of different material qualities. Hence this discussion has been confined to problems which have to do with the existence of qualities, and with the relation which material quality has with quantity and substance. All these problems are concerned with the general nature of quality.

A good deal of attention was paid to the problem of the reduction of qualities because of the fundamental misconceptions about this reduction. Such a discussion provided an opportunity for determining the place of this problem within the general doctrine of hylomorphism.

SUGGESTED READINGS

P. Hoenen, *Cosmologia*, Liber II.
John Locke, *Essay Concerning Human Understanding*, Bk. II, Chapter 8.

CHAPTER SEVEN

ACTIVITY IN MATTER

1. GENERAL OUTLINE OF PROBLEMS

Interaction, Determinism, and Specificity

In the preceding chapter material qualities have been discussed mainly in connection with the way these qualities characterize the different kinds of matter. In doing this, attention was focused on the way in which matter is known to us. Specific sets of qualities characterize specific differences in matter.

The function of qualities in matter, however, is not only to make matter observable and distinguishable; matter also acts upon matter by means of qualities. The fact, for instance, that matter affects our sense-organs is nothing but one of the activities of matter. Apart from that, there is in nature a continuous interaction between material things. And both action and reaction are specific. The way Na acts upon Cl is determined as much by the specific nature of Na as by that of Cl. This example illustrates, as a matter of fact, the three typical characteristics of all material activity. They are: determinism, specificity, and interaction. These three concepts are extremely useful for describing material activity. Both the practical and the scientific knowledge of the material world show that the way one material thing acts upon another is specific, always the same, and not only determined by the nature of the acting thing but also by that of the thing acted upon. Although the description of the behavior of matter by means of these three concepts is quite simple and quite true, still there are many difficult problems, old as well as new, connected with it. That makes a careful analysis of the exact meaning of these concepts necessary.

Determinism and Free Will

Some of the problems should first be mentioned so that the direction the analysis is to take may be known. In former times one of the most important problems was the analysis of the relationship between human and material activity. Well-known is the problem of man's free will. Many philosophers and scientists thought that the existence of a strict determinism in matter, combined with the fact that no human activity was possible without the use of material energy, necessarily led to the denial of the existence of free will, which for many reasons was supposed to be the main characteristic of human activity. The solution of this apparent contradiction was one of the greatest philosophical problems with which philosophers, and others, were concerned.

How can the existence of determinism in matter be reconciled with the existence of a free will? In the discussion of this problem practically no one doubted the existence of determinism in matter. The very existence of scientific laws made such a doubt impossible. Therefore the possibility of free will was denied.

A New Situation. Nowadays the situation is entirely different. Many scientists and philosophers are convinced that the development of science in recent years has shown that there is no strict determinism in matter. As a result they no longer see any objection to free will. Since there is no strict determinism in material activity, there is no longer any need to maintain determinism in human activity. There is in both activities an indeterminism, a kind of freedom, which in the case of human activity assumes the form of free will.

The Reasons for Discussing Free Will in the Philosophy of Nature. It is, of course, not the task of the philosophy of nature to discuss the problem of free will. However, since this problem, both in the past and in the present, is brought in close relationship with the problem of determinism in matter, this relationship must be discussed. This more or less traditional reason, however, is not the only one. There is another. Not for nothing have philosophers and scientists asked themselves whether or not the acceptance of determinism in matter is in conflict with free will. Human activity may have a spiritual aspect which lifts it above the level of purely material activity. It is only by means of material acts that this spiritual activity can express itself. So there is a real problem involved. How is free act possible if it has to use deterministic means?

The discussion of this question will serve still another purpose. In order to understand the meaning of a philosophical concept, it is often necessary to compare its meaning with that of another concept which expresses a certain contrast with the concept in which we are primarily interested. So the concept of determinism can be better understood when it is compared with that of free will.

The first part of this discussion then, will be an examination of the exact nature of determinism in matter. This immediately raises the problem of what the quantum theory has to say about it. Is it really true that the quantum theory has shown that determinism in matter has only an apparent existence?

The problems of determinism and free will are, however, not the only philosophic problems which are supposed to have a close relation with the quantum theory. The analysis of the quantum theory with respect to the problems of determinism and free will offers an opportunity to discuss briefly some of these other philosophic problems in order to illustrate again the distinction between philosophic and scientific problems. After this discussion we shall take up the matter of the relationship between activity in matter and human activity with respect to determinism and free will. Discussing the exact meaning of the concept of determinism and contrasting it with that of free will, will also provide an opportunity for clarifying the meaning of the concepts of *interaction* and *specificity*.

2. THE CLASSICAL IDEA OF DETERMINISM IN MATTER

Scientific Laws Presuppose Determinism and Specificity in Material Activity

The reason why generations of scientists and philosophers as far back as the Greeks have always accepted determinism in matter is obvious. The effort to establish strict and universal laws presupposes determinism. Therefore, it is more the *conviction* that it is possible to establish strict and universal laws than the actual establishment of those laws which shows that scientists presuppose determinism. It is because of the conviction that a certain kind of matter necessarily always behaves in the same way that it makes sense to search for universal laws.

If, for instance, sodium did not of necessity react with chlorine in a specific way, it would make no sense to perform experiments to examine the properties of sodium and chlorine. The inductive method presupposes, as has repeatedly been seen, the existence of a fixed order according to which individual representatives of a certain species always act in the same way under the same circumstances. Different circumstances may produce a different behavior, but this behavior is nothing but an expression of the same specific nature. For this reason variations in experimental circumstances which cause different concrete behavior enable us nevertheless to study the same underlying specific behavior because the latter is always the same. And this is exactly what the term "determinism" means. The behavior of anything with a certain nature is entirely determined by that nature. Given certain circumstances the thing must of necessity act as it does; it has no choice whatever about it. Therefore *deterministic* behavior implies *specific* behavior. It is the nature of the thing that forces it to act as it does. Consequently, specific differences in nature will express themselves in specific differences in activity. Hence the fact that material activity is not only deterministic, but also specific.

In view of these considerations it seems strange that certain scientists should claim that recent developments have proved that there is no strict determinism in matter. One suspects that there must be some misunderstanding about the term. That suspicion can be proved true. Listen to what scientists have to say about the way science looked upon the problem of determinism in the 19th century, and about certain developments in the field of science which have altered that outlook. The story is rather complicated, because there are many problems involved. The main difficulty is that these problems are partly scientific, partly philosophic, for some belong to what we earlier called the philosophical background of science. In what follows, more attention will be paid to the latter problems, but an effort will be made to elucidate the main points of the new insight into pure physics which have a bearing upon our problem.

The Nineteenth Century Conception of Determinism and Causality

Nineteenth century science was not only convinced that there was determinism in nature, but it also had a very definite idea about the way in which that determinism was given reality. The general concept "determinism" was closely related to a mechanistic idea about the structure of matter. This idea was that activity in matter was similar to that of a mechanical model. The concept of causality was narrowed to mean only the relationship between two successive situations of a mechanical model. Since the successive stages of any changing situation was regulated by fixed laws, causality was tantamont to determinism. Causality meant the *necessary succession* of the different phases of a mechanical model.

The Narrow Concept of Causality Is Not Tenable

It should be noted that the scientists of the 19th century implicitly used the concept of causality in a much broader sense than the meaning scientists and philosophers attached to it. That was inevitable. The human mind at work could not dispense with the broader sense; otherwise all scientific understanding and explanation would be impossible.

Even Hume and Kant, the most prominent of the philosophers who held the narrower meaning of causality, in their actual discussion of causality, could not abstain from using a much broader concept of it than was implied by their definitions. Hume, for example, tried to explain why the human mind always looked for causal relations in the sense of regular succession. This very attempt at explanation was nothing but an attempt to give a *cause* for human behavior. This implicit use of the concept *cause* certainly did not fit the definition of causal relation which Hume was trying to establish.

Kant's discussion of causality shows similar inconsistencies. Causality as one of the categories has, according to him, no meaning with respect to the world of the "things in themselves." In spite of his own doctrine of causality, Kant tells us that the "things in themselves" affect our sense-organs. He makes this statement in order to safeguard the material value of human knowledge. Such a statement, if it makes any sense at all, can only mean that there actually is a *causal* influence of the "things in themselves" upon our sense-organs. For *affecting* means causal influence.

These inconsistencies in the narrow concept of causality have been mentioned because they show clearly that the implicit use of the concept "causality" cannot be limited in an artificial way. Consequently, the implicit use scientists made of the concept "causality" was much broader than the meaning which the concept had in the doctrine of such philosophers as Kant, Hume, and their followers. The actual explanations given in the science of the 19th century clearly reveal the variety of meaning which the concept "causality" has. Explanations can be found which use the concepts *material* and *formal cause* (explanation of isomerism: same material in different structures); explanations are found in which the concept of *final cause* is used (the minimum principles in mechanics).[1] Therefore, science of the 19th

---

[1]Cf. Ch V, 3.

century can certainly not be cited as a conclusive proof of the correctness of the narrow idea of causality which was prevalent among most philosophers and philosophizing scientists. Such a narrow concept stemmed from the philosophical background against which all 19th century scientific theories were projected. This background was mechanistic; and as a result philosophic language, in which the concepts implicitly used in science were analyzed, was mechanistic, too.

The Rejection of Free Will

The close relation between and the practical identity of the concepts *causality* and *determinism* in the mind of the 19th century scientist was one of the reasons why the idea of *free will* was rejected. For free will was obviously an instance of causality, i.e. of necessary succession. This interpretation of causality excluded the possibility of a free human act being the result of an original source of activity. If human activity was causal, then it had to be the necessary result of a previous situation.

The Universe as One Mechanical Model. This conception of determinism in human activity was strengthened by another consideration. It has been mentioned that a mechanical model was the favorite form of physical explanation. This is understandable, because most of the scientific theories of the 19th century could use such a model successfully. This success was the main reason why scientists so easily accepted a mechanistic philosophic background for their science. According to this background, the whole universe was conceived as one big mechanical model. Each situation was a necessary result of a previous situation of the whole universe. A human action at a certain moment was, therefore, only a part of the activity of the whole universe in which all phases were connected by means of iron laws.

Famous is a passage of Laplace in which he stated that a mind, powerful enough to know both the situation of the universe at a certain moment in all its details and the causal laws governing the succession of situations, could predict the future and could also have a perfect knowledge of the whole past.[2]

It is clear that this conception of the universe was based upon an extrapolation of certain mechanical ideas far beyond any possible scientific means of confirmation. For even apart from the question as to whether the whole universe was governed by iron laws, it was

---

[2]Laplace, *Essai philosophique sur la probabilité, Oeuvres VII*, Paris, 1847, p. VI. Quoted in *From Atomos to Atom*, p. 164.

simply impossible to know the actual situation of the universe in all its details.

It was, however, the idea of scientists that such a knowledge was, in principle, *not* impossible. Science offered in isolated systems (such as, for instance, an astronomical system, or a mechanical device) examples which, on the whole, fulfilled the requirements of Laplace's universe. The laws governing the motions in these systems were sufficiently well known, and the situation at a certain moment could be determined with enough accuracy to predict the future behavior of the system.

So the rejection of free will was certainly not justified by the actually existing knowledge of the universe. But there were some physical ideas, which when combined with general mechanistic principles, make it understandable to us why the 19th century scientists rejected free will.

An Exact Knowledge of a Physical Situation Is Not Possible

The ideal of Laplace was based upon two conditions: first, a complete knowledge of the laws of a system, and, secondly, a complete knowledge of all the details of just one situation of that system. It is especially the last of the two conditions that merits our attention. How accurately can a certain situation be determined? This problem may be first discussed in the light of the knowledge possessed by 19th century science.

There are, of course, limitations to an absolute accuracy. First, no means of observation or measurement is absolutely accurate. This limitation, however, does not seem very essential for the purpose of *predicting* the future. For the checking of the accuracy of the prediction must be done by an equally inaccurate means of observation.

A second limitation lies in the fact that each observation of a measurement means a physical interaction between the observed system and the means of observation. A thermometer brought into a room to measure the temperature disturbs the temperature in that room ever so little. However, this limitation to accuracy seems practically negligible, because we can rather accurately calculate the degree of the disturbance and, if necessary, accordingly correct the result of the measurement.

A more fundamental limitation is that some physical systems are composed of parts which are so small that it is impossible to acquire the desired data about them. For example, the actual velocities and positions of the individual molecules of a gas cannot be measured. We are able to deduce from the results of certain experiments the size and weight of the different kinds of molecules, but we are not able to determine data which differ from individual to individual. The only thing that can be done is the determination of the average velocity and the average position of the individual molecules. These problems can be handled mathematically by the laws of statistics. Well-known, for example, is the kinetic gas theory. The observable behavior of a certain amount of gas, such as is expressed in the laws of Boyle, Gay-Lussac, etc., can be reduced to the average mechanical behavior of molecules, described in such mechanical quantities as velocity, position, mass, energy, etc.

The Older Quantum Theory

It was only natural that when scientists discovered sub-atomic particles, they should try to apply the same principles, as outlined in the previous section, to the structures made up of these sub-atomic particles. In this attempt they ran into serious difficulties. It gradually became clear that it was not possible to reduce the observable behavior of a multitude of sub-atomic particles to mechanical and electrodynamic quantities which describe the situation of the individual particles. In order to construct an atom-model in accordance with the observable behavior of atoms, N. Bohr was forced to add to the classical theory certain postulates which deviate considerably from the classical line of thought in physics. To mention only one instance, according to the classical theory, an electron moving around the nucleus constantly emits electromagnetic waves. Consequently, it gradually loses energy. One of the postulates of Bohr stated that an electron did not lose any energy so long as it moved within one of the stable orbits of an atom. Energy-emission in the form of electromagnetic waves took place only when an electron jumped from one orbit to another.

The postulates of Bohr were, however, theoretically speaking, not entirely arbitrary, i.e. introduced only to save the phenomena under consideration. They were in agreement with similar deviations from the classical theory introduced earlier in connection with other problems. Several of the deviations indicated just where the classical theory was inadequate. As a result, there was need for the formulation of a new theory to supersede that of classical mechanics and electrodynamics.

3. QUANTUM MECHANICS

The Uncertainty Principle

The new theory that superseded classical mechanics and electro-dynamics became known as quantum mechanics. Some of its features are very important for the problems under discussion in this chapter. First, the old dream of predicting the future of the universe had to be abandoned. For one of the two requirements for such a prediction, namely, the accurate knowledge of the situation at a certain moment, could never be met. According to quantum mechanics, it is impossible to determine exactly at the same time both the velocity and position of a particle. The exact determination of one excludes, in principle, the determination of the other.[3] Thus the attribution of an accurate velocity to a particle automatically removes the possibility of also attributing an accurate position. The fact that it is not even possible to *attribute* both accurate velocity and position to a particle indicates a very distinct difference from the classical theory. The classical theory considered the *measurement* of both velocity and position of an individual particle impossible only because nobody could figure out how to perform such a measurement. It was not impossible within the framework of the classical theory to attribute to all particles both an exact velocity and an exact position. Quantum mechanics, however, excludes, *in principle,* the very *attribution* of both quantities in an exact way.

There has been much philosophical discussion about the import of this "uncertainty principle." Some scientists and philosophers think that as a result of it, strict causality and strict determinism in nature must be denied.

This problem, which is the chief concern of this chapter, will be taken up again after some other so-called philosophical consequences of the quantum-theory have been discussed.

---

[3]The impossibility is expressed in the famous uncertainty principle of Heisenberg $\Delta p \cdot \Delta q = \dfrac{h}{2\pi}$, stating the relation between the uncertainty with which place (Δp) and that with which speed can be determined (Δq). It is easy to see that if Δp is zero, which means that place is fully determined, Δq is infinite (h, the so-called constant of Planck, has a finite value). This principle is also known as the principle of indeterminism.

Quantum Mechanics and Corpuscle Models

The first consequence of quantum mechanics is said to have been that once again the development of physics proved how inadequate the spontaneous philosophical convictions of mankind are sometimes. Spontaneous conviction says that a corpuscle must have a definite speed and a definite position; whereas quantum mechanics proves this conviction to be wrong and shows that it does not make sense to ascribe to a particle both definite speed and definite position. One must, therefore, never trust even the most obvious phenomena. It is always possible that subsequent scientific research will contradict what seems most obvious. "Heaven knows what seeming nonsense may not tomorrow be demonstrated truth."[4]

Now if it were true that quantum mechanics forces the acceptance of both the reality of corpuscles and of the impossibility of attributing to these corpuscles definite speed and position, then it must be agreed that nothing obvious can be trusted. However, it is entirely erroneous to think that quantum mechanics forces us to such an acceptance. The simple truth is that one of the suppositions on which the quantum theory is based is that the corpuscle model of electrons and other elementary particles is inadequate. The corpuscle model can only be used on certain occasions, but not on all. It covers only a part of the phenomena. Quantum mechanics as a mathematical theory, however, attempts to cover the whole field of phenomena. Accordingly, quantum mechanics implies the inadequacy of the corpuscle model. Therefore, it is wrong to say that quantum mechanics forces us to accept the existence of real particles which have no definite speed and position. To deny definite position and speed to a particle is tantamount to denying the adequacy of the corpuscle model.

Quantum Mechanics and the Objectivity of Human Knowledge

Still another so-called consequence of the quantum theory may be discussed briefly. Some positivistic thinkers have said that the quantum theory provides definite proof that human knowledge is subjective, not objective. Therefore, the old epistemological dispute between idealistic and realistic philosophies is supposed to have been solved by the development of science. If this were true, it would perfectly fit in with the old positivistic doctrine that the only method for solving problems is the method of positive science. However,

---

[4]A. N. Whitehead, *Science and the Modern World*, Cambridge, 1946, p. 143.

the quantum theory in the form of quantum mechanics says nothing about the old epistemological problem of the value of knowledge. This immediately becomes clear when one considers what the quantum theory says about the problem of the objectivity of human knowledge, or rather about the objectivity of human observation. For observation is the only problem which the quantum theory says anything about, and even that is said indirectly.

Quantum Mechanics and Observation. Let us first consider an illustration, which Heisenberg gave, of certain implications of the quantum theory regarding observation.[5] Suppose one wants to get some information about an electron at a certain moment. Such information can be obtained only with the help of certain physical means, such as, for example, light rays. The act of observation of the electron implies, therefore, an interaction between the electron and the light rays used. This interaction disturbs the situation of the electron. Such a disturbance in itself is, as has been seen, not specific to the quantum theory. Specific to the quantum theory is the claim that it is theoretically impossible to calculate exactly the degree of disturbance of, for example, the position of the electron under observation. That means that the actual information to be obtained is information about an electron whose position is altered by the very act of observation. We do not know where the electron was before we observed it.

Although the term "objective," has been used above, it should be clear that the problems involved have nothing to do with that which in philosophical circles is called the "objectivity of human knowledge." The quantum theory speaks exclusively of an interaction between the physical means of observation and the physical reality to be observed. It even supposes that this interaction is real in the physical sense of that term, for the quantum theory aims to give us a true knowledge of what happens in reality. It says that it is impossible to measure or to calculate the scope of the disturbance caused by the observation. Briefly, the very aim of the quantum theory is to give an *objective* knowledge of what happens when one tries to observe certain physical realities.

The Meaning of the Term "Objective." The main cause of the confusion is a misunderstanding of what is meant when the realist says that human knowledge is "objective." This does not mean that

---

[5] W. Heisenberg, *Die Physikalischen Prinzipien der Quantentheorie*, Leipzig, [3]1942, pp. 15ff.

human knowledge is *complete*. The realist simply wants to say that, in principle, the object of our knowledge is reality as it is.

This objective knowledge can, as a matter of fact, be quite incomplete or deficient because of several factors. One of these factors is the limitation of accurate observation resulting from the necessity of using physical means of observation. This limitation is a limitation of the completeness, not of the objectivity, of human knowledge.

A second cause of the confusion is, of course, the analogous use of the term "objective." It makes sense to speak of the impossibility of observing objects in the state in which they would be if they were not observed as a "lack of objective knowledge," but the term "objective" is then not used in the philosophic sense. Since the physical influence of the act of observation is considered an influence in the order of *reality,* it is clear that the philosophical and physical problems of objectivity are entirely different. The confusion shows again how necessary it is to distinguish between the philosophical and the physical levels of abstraction spoken of in Chapter III.

Regarding this distinction, it should be kept in mind that the quantum theory does not say anything explicit about the epistemological problem of objectivity. Therefore, the assertion that the quantum theory establishes nothing against the objectivity of human knowledge in a philosophic sense does not imply that the quantum theory explicitly proves the objectivity of human knowledge in a philosophic sense. This conclusion would also be wrong. When the quantum theory was said to aim at giving objective knowledge about reality, reference was made simply to that which any physical theory tries to do. The ultimate philosophic evaluation of the term *reality* is thereby not at stake. Physics takes that term in its unanalyzed sense, and no development of physics can contribute anything to the philosophic analysis of what the term *reality* means. As far as physics is concerned, such a contribution can be made only by a philosophical analysis of the epistemological presuppositions of any physical theory.

4. QUANTUM MECHANICS AND DETERMINISM

Identification of Causality and Determinism

It is time now to turn back to the main problem of this chapter, the problem of determinism in nature. The precise content of that which quantum mechanics teaches us regarding this problem has to be examined. It has already been mentioned that some scientists claim that old philosophical concepts, such as causality and determinism, should be reviewed, because quantum mechanics has shown that there is no strict causality and determinism in nature. Taking warning from past experience with other philosophical statements by scientists, it is very important to find out what physical things scientists have in mind when they make a philosophical statement. There usually exists a surprising physical discovery or theory behind any such statement which is worth studying from a philosophic point of view, also. Experience has shown, however, that the philosophic terms chosen to express the supposed philosophical consequence of the physical theory involved are usually not the most fortunate ones. The choice of terms is often based upon a too narrow meaning of the philosophic concepts involved.

This is exactly the case with the problem under discussion. The 19th century concept "causality" was identical with the concept "determinism." This in itself is an unwarranted limitation of the concept "causality," but it is not the only one, as shall be seen presently.

Identification of Causality and the Possibility of Prediction

The content of the concept "causality" was further reduced because it was tacitly assumed that causal relations existed only in the form of necessary successions of the different phases of a physical, i.e. a mechanical, system. The main importance of the existence of such a causal relation was that, in principle, it made the prediction of future events possible. For actual prediction two additional things were, of course, necessary. The nature of the causal relation in question must be known, and experimental methods to determine the different physical quantities characteristic of a certain situation must be available. In principle, however, causality was for many scientists tantamount to the possibility of prediction. The checking of a prediction was the main way of determining whether or not a supposed causal relation existed. Hence the identification between causal relation and the possibility of prediction. When a scientist, therefore, spoke of the existence of causality or determinism in nature, he had in mind a twofold physical program of investigation: first, to discover the ways in which succeeding situations in a physical system were connected, and, secondly, to improve the means of measuring and determining the different physical factors characteristic of such a situation.

Mechanical Models and the Possibility of Exact Prediction

The quantum theory was bound to destroy the belief in the possibility of carrying through such a physical program as has just been described. For one of the typical features of the quantum theory was precisely that it proved the theoretical impossibility of knowing exactly the different factors necessary for the complete knowledge of a certain physical situation. Consequently, the quantum theory destroyed the possibility of exact prediction.

It can be argued, of course, that this can never be sufficient reason to justify the statement that the quantum theory shows that there is no strict causality or no strict determinism in nature. The possibiliy of exact prediction is based upon two conditions, namely, upon the existence of causal relations between physical situations, and upon the assumption that exact knowledge of such a situation is possible. The denial of one condition does not necessarily deny the other.

This argument is perfectly sound. Yet it overlooks one point of importance. Quantum mechanics not only proved the impossibility of exact observation; it also proved that mechanical models are unsatisfactory for exemplifying all aspects of the physical universe. So *both* conditions for an exact prediction were involved. The reader may recall what was said on p. 224. Quantum mechanics not only claims that the *measurement* of both velocity and position at the same time is impossible, it also claims that it is theoretically impossible, within the framework of the quantum theory, to *attribute* exact values to both these quantities at any one time. In other words, the mechanical model is inadequate. It is precisely this inadequacy which seduces the scientist into speaking of the failure of the classical physical program which was based upon the belief in the existence of strict causality. This way of speaking is wrong, of course, but it is understandable in view of the assumption that causality is adequately exemplified by means of a mechanical model. The quantum theory destroyed the whole idea of a mechanical universe in which the macro-phenomena were nothing but the average result of the way the individual microphenomena were believed to be causally related.

Difference Between Classical and Quantum Statistics

The inadequacy of mechanical models also had a great influence upon the attitude scientists took toward statistics. This is another reason why scientists became concerned about the traditional doctrine of determinism.

Classical Statistics. Under the old statistical theory, probability was the expression of a lack of knowledge about the individual circumstances which determined the behavior of **an individual particle.** The scientist could not predict at what particular time an individual molecule would leave a liquid, because he did not know which molecule had an actual energy great enough to overcome the attraction-forces of the surface-molecules of the liquid. The scientist, however, was convinced that certain individual molecules were possessed of such energy that they were bound to leave the liquid. In view of his ignorance of individual circumstances, the scientist could predict only the *percentage* of the molecules which would leave the liquid. He could do so because he knew something about the *average* energy of the molecules and something about the probability of a certain number of molecules having a great enough energy to get them outside the liquid. The point to be stressed here is the fact that the average value of which the scientist spoke in classical statistic was considered an average value of individual values existing in reality.

Quantum Statistics. Now consider the way in which the modern theory speaks of statistics and average values. A good example is the disintegration of radioactive matter. This disintegration takes place according to a law which states that in a certain lapse of time one-half the amount of radioactive matter disintegrates. The time required for that one-half to disintegrate is called the "half-life" of the material. The "half-life" is specific for any particular material. For radium it is found to be 1600 years. For other radioactive materials "half-lives" vary between about 10^{-11} seconds to about 10^{10} years.

It is clear that the disintegration law is a statistical law. The law does not say anything about any individual atom; it states only that in a certain time half of the atoms will disintegrate. Nothing can be said about the fate of any one atom. The reason why one individual atom will disintegrate tomorrow, whereas another will not disintegrate until after some 1600 years is not known. And the reason why it is not known is, according to the quantum theory, not that we do not know the individual status of an atom, but that there is no such thing as a sharply defined status of an individual atom. It does not, therefore, make sense to attribute to certain individual atoms a definite status which predisposes them to disintegrate at a particular time.[6] Each atom has the same chance to disintegrate, and it seems that an individual atom has a certain "free choice"[7] as to the particular moment at which it shall disintegrate. It is not a completely "free choice," for the choice is limited by the statistical laws governing the behavior of all atoms. The atoms seem to be free within the limits of the laws of probability.

It is just this situation with respect to the behavior of individual atoms which has forced scientists to the conclusion that there is no strict causality or determinism in nature. There is still causality or determinism to a certain degree; witness the existence of laws governing the average behavior of the atoms. However, this is not a strict determinism, because it does not determine completely the behavior of individual atoms. As far as the individual atom is concerned, there seems to be a certain degree of freedom.

Different Use of the Term "Determinism"

Thus far the usage of the term "determinism" by scientists who speak of a lack of strict determinism in nature has been followed. This usage seems to reveal a contradiction with what has been said at the beginning of this chapter, where determinism was taken as one of the main characteristics of *all* material activity.

So the first question to be faced now is whether the term "determinism" as used by scientists has exactly the same meaning as given it at the beginning of this chapter. This is certainly not the case. The scientist uses the term "determinism" in close connection with the mechanistic conception of matter, a conception which, in its turn, is closely related to the belief that all physical problems can be solved by means of the use of mechanical models. When the mechanical model was proved to be inadequate, the scientist thought that he also had to abandon the idea that the course of events in nature was fully determined. When the scientist speaks of the absence or the partial absence of determinism, then he really means that mechanical models are inadequate.

---

[6]The interpretation given in the text prevails among contemporary scientists. For a deviating interpretation which states that the quantum theory gives an *incomplete* knowledge, see A. Einstein, *Reply to Criticisms* in *Albert Einstein; Philosopher-Scientist*. The Library of Living Philosophers, New York, 1951, pp. 667 ff.

[7]The term "free choice" is actually used in this connection by scientists. Cf. N. Bohr, *Atomtheorie und Naturbeschreibung*, Leipzig, 1931, p. 8; H. Kramers, *Grundlagen der Quantentheorie*, Leipzig, 1938, p. 6.

The important philosophical problem now is whether or not it still makes sense to speak of determinism with respect to material activity. Or is the only possible determinism the determinism that can be represented by a mechanical model? The difficulty in answering this question is that it is practically impossible to imagine anything other than a mechanical model. The human mind is bound to think in terms of mechanical models. It is for that very reason that science still uses them, even though different models may be of mutually contradictory characters (waves and particles).

Yet, the *philosophical* concept of determinism is much broader than that of a deterministic mechanical system. The scientist, with his desire for scientifically useful concepts, may have identified determinism with the way a mechanical system works. This identification is not a matter of necessity. So the philosophical question as to whether there is determinism in material activity cannot be answered by the fact that modern science has abandoned the idea of a deterministic universe in a mechanistic sense.

It is science itself that in its presuppositions provides an answer to the philosophical problem of determinism. For like its classical predecessor, modern science presupposes determinism in nature. That may seem strange after what has just been said of quantum mechanics, but it is nevertheless true. Quantuum mechanics, because it makes use of the laws of probability, also presupposes determinism. In order to prove this important point, consider for a while what the use of the laws of probability means when applied to the description of natural phenomena.[8]

The Laws of Probability Presuppose Determinism

It is clear that no laws of probability could be established at all if there were not at least some determinism in nature. This partial determinism, which causes a collection of individual events to obey the laws of probability, is not questioned. It seems, however, that the individual events covered by the laws of probability are "free," save for the general limitation that the collective behavior of such events must satisfy the laws of probability. Here is where the problem lies. The term "free" should not be understood in the sense that a radioactive atom has a free will and freely decides to disintegrate. Nobody seriously believes that atoms have free will.

---

[8]For the present we are not concerned with the use of the laws of probability as they apply to human behavior. Cf. p. 240.

The term "free" simply means that from the nature of the entity involved or from circumstances there flows no necessity to disintegrate at a *definite* moment.

It is necessary to analyze what this supposed absence of necessity would mean. It would mean that there is nothing which determines the exact moment of disintegration. "Nothing" means exactly *nothing*. Parmenides' warning should be recalled: "*Nothing* does not exist." Therefore, if "nothing" determines the individual behavior within the limits of the laws of probability, then there is no determination at all. Anything can be possible. The result would be complete chaos, of which no law of probability could give a description. In order to understand this conclusion more clearly, let us elaborate upon the problems connected with probability in greater detail.

It is often said that the moment at which an individual atom disintegrates is determined by chance. This statement avoids the dangerous use of the term "nothing." It also explains why the laws of probability are valid, for these laws are deliberately designed for the description of chance events happening at random. Yet the use of such terms as *chance, probability,* and *at random* does not imply the absence of determinism. In order to see this, a paragraph must be devoted to explaining each of these terms, wherein an effort will be made to establish the precise meaning of these concepts with the help of some appropriate examples. Thereafter the problem of the disintegration of atoms and the problem of determinism will be taken up again.

Chance

The first example may illustrate what is meant by "chance." The ignition of the gas mixture in the combustion chamber of an engine is not a chance effect, but the result of the structure of the engine. The spark is produced by a series of causes which differ from the series of causes that take care of the supply of gas. Both series of causes, however, are regulated by the structure of the engine. This structure can be considered as the formal cause, for it combines the two series of events in such a way that the spark ignites the gas mixture at the right time. Compare this situation with the casual ignition of a gas mixture by a casual spark, as sometimes happens in a plane or automobile accident. Note that in such an accident both the presence of the gas mixture and that of the spark are caused; two different series of causes are responsible for the presence of the gas and the spark at a particular moment and at a particular place, but there is no cause which regulated the meeting of both series. The meeting was by pure chance.

The term "chance" does not indicate that there is no determinism involved. For a spark of necessity starts an explosion of a gas mixture. The term "chance" simply expresses the absence of a cause *regulating the presence of the spark* in the gas mixture. Such a cause is not absent in an engine. The structure of the engine is designed to cause the presence of a spark exactly at the particular moment an appropriate gax mixture is present in the combustion chamber. Yet we are not too surprised when a plane crash results in a gas explosion. There are too many chances for sparks and a leaking gas tank at the same place at the same time. Therefore, there is a rather high probability that an explosion will take place.

Probability

The meaning of the term "probability" is closely related to that of chance. The term "chance" denies the presence of a cause regulating the meeting of two causal series as the normal effect of that cause. The term "probability" expresses something about the occurrence of such a chance meeting. In the absence of a cause regulating such a meeting, the fact that somewhere there is an explosive gas mixture does not imply that there is also a spark at the same spot. However, there is a *possibility* of the presence of a spark, for sparks do exist, and they have to be somewhere. They can, therefore, be at the place where an explosive gas mixture happens to be. This means that in principle the meeting of two causal series is possible. In the case of a plane crash, the circumstances are favorable for the presence of both an explosive gas mixture and sparks at the same time and place. Hence the rather high probability of an explosion. In view of the complexity of the circumstances and the factors involved, nobody can calculate this probability. The proportion between the circumstances and factors which will cause a spark and those which will not cause a spark cannot be known. The same applies to the causes of a leaking tank. Finally, what proportion of possible sparks will be in the neighborhood of the leaking tank also cannot be calculated. At best it can be imagined that the probability must be high, a fact which is confirmed by experience.

There are cases, however, in which we can calculate almost exactly the probability of something that happens by chance. For example, nobody can tell when a dice is thrown which side will come up. There are too many factors involved. However, only one of six sides will come up, and we know that the factors determining which side will come up do not have a preference for any one of the sides of the cube. So there exists a definite, although incomplete, knowledge of the causes which determine the result of a throw. This partial knowledge is not enough to predict the result of *any one* single throw, but it makes possible the prediction of the results of a great number of throws. Such a prediction is possible because it is known that each combination of factors determining the result of one single throw is an accidental combination. These factors do not operate together as the result of a "supervising" cause. There is no formal or structural cause which each time combines the factors to produce the results obtained according to the nature of that formal or structural cause. Therefore, when a great number of throws is made, two characteristics are bound to appear: first, an irregularity in the sequence of the results, because of the absence of a regular supervising and dominating cause; and, secondly, the respective scores for each side of the dice will be about equal. If this were not so, then there would be a preference for one side, and this is excluded by the fact that the sides are equal.

So probability is based upon a *partial knowledge* of the factors involved. It is this partial knowledge that makes it possible to use the laws of probability.

Random

Besides the term "chance" and "probability" there is still a third term, "random," used in connection with chance events. Random is, first of all, used with respect to human actions. A human action is said to be "random" when it is not guided by a specific purpose or not based upon a specific principle. For example, a decision is made at random when it is not based upon considerations specific to the problems involved. Therefore, "random" does not mean that the decision was based upon nothing at all. It means that there was no *appropriate* basis to decide the matter in question. If a judge, for example, made a decision simply by tossing a coin and not according to the law, then such a decision would unquestionably be based upon something. Nevertheless, it would be a "random" decision, because it was not determined by the principles upon which a judge should base his decisions.

The Term "at Random" in Science. The term "at random" seems to have a slightly different meaning when, in a scientific report, it is said that the samples which were tested were chosen "at random." Here "at random" seems to imply a specific *purpose,* namely, a reliable test. However, our definition is still valid. For in order to obtain a reliable result, the samples have to be chosen in such a way that they are representative of the things to be tested. In making this choice, any criterion that could possibly lead to a biased choice should be avoided. Thus "at random" means "no preference whatsoever." Any specific aim or specific principle which would lead to the selection of samples with special features must be carefully avoided. By "special feature" is meant any feature added to those which characterize the kind of material or objects which the sample represents. It is of interest to note that "at random" does *not* mean that the things tested should have no definite character; such a character is presupposed by speaking of "samples" of a certain kind of things.

Random Distribution. The example discussed above brings us close to the meaning of the term "random" when used in cases where no human action is involved. For example, "random" is used in such an expression as a "random distribution of the motions of the molecules in a certain amount of gas." This means that there is no special principle assumed according to which certain motions are favored above others. It does not mean that there are in this instance no principles at all assumed. "Random distribution" implies that the general principles, regulating the motions of the molecules of a gas, apply. Excluded are *special* principles, such as a principle which would cause all the molecules to flow in just one direction. Consequently, it is not correct to say that "at random" means complete disorder or chaos. There is an order in the motions of the molecules, namely, the order which the general principles express. These general principles apply wherever there is motion of molecules. The term "disorder" makes sense only with reference to a *special* order. The "disorder" of "random distribution" means that the motions of the molecules do not possess a special order, though this order is capable of existence.

"At Random" Includes Both Order and Disorder. Thus "at random" is a rather complicated concept. It includes, indeed, both order and disorder, though in different ways. Properly speaking, disorder as disorder does not exist in reality. Existing reality is ordered according to the principles or causes working in reality. Therefore, only order exists. To speak of disorder, as if disorder also existed, is correct only insofar as a certain order which we have in mind does not exist. If my desk, for example, is in disorder, which sometimes happens, then the term "disorder" means that a certain ordering principle, according to which the various things on a desk should be ordered, is not actually governing the order of things on my desk. The things are, therefore, ordered only according to the law of gravitation, according to the spatial and physical properties of my desk, etc.

Thus the term "disorder" is, as a matter of fact, always used with respect to a certain kind of order; it expresses the absence of a particular order and not the absence of *all* order. Likewise, the term "random," which includes "disorder," expresses no complete disorder or chaos, but the absence of a certain type of order. The use of the term "at random," in such an expression as that an event happened at random, does not, therefore, imply that the event was not determined. It indicates only that this event was not determined by the cause whose presence was excluded by the term "at random." It is, therefore, not correct to speak of three sorts of events: those dependent upon free will, those dependent upon determinism in nature, and those happening at random. Random events do not form a third category alongside the two other. As has been shown, events in both other categories can be "at random." A human action is said to be taken "at random" when it is not taken in accordance with a certain principle that ought to determine that action.

Outside the field of human activity it is, of course, nonsense to speak of a principle that *ought* to determine activities. Therefore, in instances of material activity the term "at random" refers only to a principle that perhaps *could* have been present, but which, as a matter of fact, was not. In both human and non-human activity, events are entirely determined by the actually working principles and causes.

Classical Science and Random-Distribution

When science, classical as well as modern, uses the term "random," it presupposes exactly what has been said above. This is immediately clear as it applies to all classical instances. If the term "random" in the phrase "random-distribution of the motions of molecules" meant absolute disorder and absence of determinism, then science would not be able to say anything about these motions. Science, however, does say a lot about them because all the laws governing the motions of molecules are supposed to be valid. With respect to these laws there is no disorder at all. The term "random-distribution" expresses the fact that there is no principle assumed which would give all the molecules just one direction or speed. Therefore, the random-distribution is entirely determined by the way the laws of motion work in the absence of a special principle of order.

The same is true of the throwing of dice. It is assumed in that problem that there is a random-distribution of the different factors which determine the result of a single throw. So "random-distribution" means simply the absence of a *special* principle or cause, not the absence of *all principles* or causes. Therefore, random-distribution implies determinism.

Quantum Mechanics and Random-Distribution

The crucial problem now is whether or not what has been said holds true of quantum mechanics. When this new branch of science speaks, for example, of the disintegration of a sample of radioactive material as being entirely "at random" within the laws of probability, is determinism also presupposed? According to the way some scientists speak of it, one would conclude that the situation of quantum mechanics is entirely different from that of classical physics. The term "at random" in quantum mechanics seems to express a kind of third possibility along with "free choice" and "determinism." However, what *scientists* say is not conclusive, for their philosophical terminology is not always correct. Conclusive are the presuppositions of science. Therefore we are interested in the philosophical convictions implicitly present in the methods which quantum mechanics uses in handling its problems. The discussion will be confined to the problem of the disintegration of radioactive material.

The Data. Let us first restate the different data which are of importance for a correct view of the problem offered by radioactive disintegration.

First of all, the behavior of a sample of a certain radioactive material is always the same. It may not be possible to predict the disintegration of an individual atom, but the behavior of all atoms together can be predicted because this behavior is subject to a fixed law. Secondly, the reason why the behavior of an individual atom cannot be predicted is definitely known. The data necessary for making such a prediction cannot be learned, because of the disturbance of the situation caused by the act of observation itself. The exact degree of this disturbance cannot be calculated because of the discontinuity that exists in nature, a fact expressed in the constant of Planck.

Analysis. When the implications of these fundamental data are studied, it becomes clear that determinism in the philosophical sense of this term is presupposed by quantum mechanics, notwithstanding the fact that scientists say that the disintegration of individual atoms is not "determined," but occurs "at random." Let us first analyze the physical reason that explains the impossibility of predicting a single event.[9] The reason is that the data available are not sufficient for making such a prediction. Any attempt to learn these data can never yield satisfactory results because of the fact that a disturbance of the data under observation is *bound* to occur by the very act of the observation. A *necessary* interaction takes place between the physical means of observation and the physical reality under observation. The assumption of such a necessary interaction is tantamount to the assumption that there is determinism in matter.

The fact that the result of the interaction is not exactly known does not in the least weaken this conclusion of the necessity of the interaction. For it is assumed that the laws of probability can be applied to the interaction, and this means that there is a random distribution of the disturbances.[10] Such an assumption, as has been seen, can be based only upon the knowledge that there is no reason at all why the disturbances should have but *one* definite tendency. They are *bound* to reveal every possible value. Here again necessity is involved in the process of interaction. This necessity is simply that which is called "determinism" in the philosophical sense of the word.

"Random" Is No Alternative for "Determinism" or "Free Will." Let us now approach the philosophic problem of determinism in

[9]Cf. p. 226.

[10]The laws of probability in this case differ somewhat from the laws which are valid for a classical example, but that is not important. What is important is that the distintegration process is governed by laws of probability.

nature from a different angle. Suppose for a moment that the disintegration of individual atoms was not entirely determined, but to a certain extent "free." "Free" means here, of course, not "free" in the human sense; it only indicates a certain lack of determinism. An atom cannot do just anything; its possible behavior is, up to a certain point, determined by its nature and its situation. A radioactive atom is bound to disintegrate in a definite way, but the exact moment of disintegration is not exactly determined. In order to avoid the term "free choice," scientists prefer to say that the exact moment of disintegration is chosen "at random."

The content of the concept "at random" is intended to exclude both "free choice" and "determinism." But a random-event is also said to be wholly governed by the laws of probability. Consequently the sum total of all random-events yields a law. One is bound to ask how that is possible if the moment of individual disintegration is entirely "at random" in the scientists' use of this term. For in that sense "at random" can only mean that "nothing" determines the exact moment. So we are right back at the point where the discussion of the terms "chance," "probability," and "at random," started. If "at random" is meant to exclude both "determinism" and "free choice," then there is no determination at all. Consequently, if nothing determines the exact moment, then it could be *any* moment. And if it could be *any* moment, then all atoms could disintegrate at precisely the same moment. That moment could be now; it could be in the future. To put it briefly, if the exact moment of disintegration is not determined, then there can be no definite "half-life" law. There cannot, in fact, be any law at all. The disintegration of radioactive material would have to be lawless. Hence a physical science of radioactivity would be impossible. However, the very fact that there are certain laws according to which the whole acts indicates that the behavior of the parts is also determined.

Thus the phrase "random-distribution" has in quantum mechanics exactly the same fundamental meaning as in other branches of sciences. It denies that there is a particular order of a certain type; but random distribution itself represents an order, and it is this order that makes it possible to use the laws of probability.[11] Certainly no indeterminism

---

[11]Because of the fact that free will is a principle which establishes order, the laws of probability can, within certain limits, be applied to human behavior. This possibility does not imply that the will is not free. It simply indicates the presence of a determining principle of behavior, and does not say anything about the manner of determination.

is meant, at least not if this term is taken in its real sense, namely, that nothing at all determines individual events.

The Reason for the Confusion Lies in Erroneous Philosophical Concepts

The reason why scientists are inclined to make use of the term "indeterminism" is not difficult to discover. The term is meant to express the impossibility of conceiving a mechanical model, the classical example of determinism, to understand the phenomena of radioactivity. However, the *philosophical* term *determinism,* correctly understood, does not in any way imply that a mechanical model is possible or imaginable. Philosophically speaking, the term *determinism* means only that a thing, of necessity, behaves as it does in accordance with its given nature. The origin of the whole trouble is, of course, the philosophically incorrect use of the term determinism in the 19th century. The term had too much of a physical sense, so that its proper philosophical meaning remained more or less in the dark. It is understandable that when the development of science showed that determinism in the wrong classical physical sense did not exist, scientists started to speak of indeterminism. Yet, the term is extremely unfortunate and not at all suited for physical purposes, for the term in itself has only a philosophical meaning. Even those scientists who were very careful in speaking of indeterminism and who tried to limit the term to its physical sense, could not avoid getting involved in philosophical problems. They spoke, for example, of free choice as a characteristic of elementary particles, a statement which immediately put their discussion outside the limits of science. This must necessarily happen because the terms "determinism" and "indeterminism" are not scientific terms; their original meaning is philosophical. Only in philosophy does it make sense to discuss determinism. Science is concerned with determinism only insofar as its methods presuppose determinism in nature. But science does not have at its disposal the concepts necessary for discussing the philosophical problems involved in determinism.

5. DETERMINISM AND FREE WILL

Quantum Mechanics and Arguments for Free Will

The conclusion that there is determinism in nature naturally leads to another problem; namely, that of the existence of free will.

How can free will be reconciled with determinism in nature? This is an old problem which was thoroughly discussed in the time of classical physics, and rediscussed on an apparently new basis after the development of quantum mechanics. Whereas, according to many philosophers and scientists, classical physics could not be reconciled with the existence of free will, quantum mechanics, with what is called "indeterminism in matter," is supposed to have opened up a new perspective for viewing the problem of free will. Two kinds of arguments are used. Sometimes it is said that the classical conception that the course of a material event was entirely determined, cannot any longer be considered true. Individual events are only partly determined by nature itself, and there is, therefore, room for a further determination, and this determination can be the result of free will.

This argument, although it is wrong, certainly is more to the point than another that is based upon the strange notion that the nature of free will consists in the impossibility of predicting its actions. This latter argument will be discussed first, and then will be taken up the argument based upon the supposed existence of indeterminism in nature.

Possibility of Prediction and Free Will. The argument for the possibility of free will based upon the impossibility of exact prediction usually takes the following line. Before the development of quantum mechanics the scientist thought that exact prediction of all events was, in principle, possible. Such a prediction, however, is in conflict with the general idea of free will. This idea was identified with the conviction that the outcome of no one's free choice can be predicted. Quantum mechanics now has shown that absolute prediction is impossible; therefore, the feeling that no one can predict the outcome of a free choice is justified.

It was said that this argument is not to the point, because it does not even touch the real problem. Characteristic of a free choice is not that its results cannot be predicted. It can even be argued that, as a rule, the result of a *real* free choice can be quite well predicted. For example, the decision a man of character will make in certain circumstances can be known, because such a man will be guided only by what is right. The only thing that has to be known is what he considers right in the given circumstances. It is, on the other hand, often difficult to predict what decision a man who is subject to all kinds of influences will take, because not all these influences, nor the way he will respond to them, are known. So the more a man is really free, the more his decisions will show a definite course, and, consequently, the more predictable they will be. Since the impossibility of prediction has no immediate connection with the existence of free will, there is no need to elaborate the present argument any further—the argument is beyond the question.

The Argument Based Upon Indeterminism. The argument for free will, based upon the fact that quantum mechanics is supposed to have proved a fundamental indeterminism in nature, has the merit that it deals with something that belongs to the essence of free will. For the argument attributes to free will the property of final determination of that which is not fully determined by the laws of nature. Now the essence of free will is undoubtedly its power of determining one's own behavior. So the argument involves essential problems. The question is, however, whether the argument is correct. The answer to this depends largely upon the answer to another question, namely, is it true that quantum mechanics has proved that there is no strict determinism in nature? The answer was given in the previous section, when it was made clear that quantum mechanics presupposes determinism in nature. The only reason for a belief to the contrary was based upon a misunderstanding of the term "determinism." Thus quantum mechanics has contributed nothing to the solution of the problem of free will insofar as philosophy is concerned. Philosophically speaking, our day still faces the same problem that the 19th century faced, the problem of how the existence of free will can be reconciled with the existence of determinism in matter. The only thing quantum mechanics has contributed to the problem of free will lies more or less in the psychological field. It has changed the intellectual climate, which was not very favorable for the unprejudiced discussion of the problem of free will, for one that is favorable.

The Psychological Effect of Quantum Mechanics

The appearance of the quantum theory has destroyed quite a few traditional convictions of scientists. Some of the convictions were purely scientific, i.e. entirely within the realm of science; some did not belong to science, but belonged to that philosophical background which has traditionally been associated with science. One of these traditional convictions was that causality was identical with the necessary succession of the different phases of a mechanical system. The immediate result of this identification of causality and mechanical determinism was the exclusion of free will, because free will was supposed to be a source of activity not subject to the principle of causality. An event without cause was considered impossible. Another result of this narrow conception of causality was that the whole universe came to be conceived of as one mechanical system. Causal laws were held to be universally valid, and since causality was supposed to be a mechanical association, the whole universe had to be just one vast mechanical system.

The merit of the quantum theory, as it related to all these problems, was that, by attacking some of the physical principles of current science, it revived the discussion of those philosophical problems, rightly or wrongly, connected with these principles. For it was a typical feature of quantum mechanics that it did not so much destroy classical principles as it brought to light the unwarranted generalization of these principles in physics. Now, if classical science generalized too much within its own field, it was clear that generalization outside the field of physics really could not be trusted. This is the main contribution of quantum theory to the solution of the problem of free will. It changed the mental attitude of scientists and made them more careful in the extrapolation of physical principles outside the field of physics. This new attitude makes a philosophical discussion of the problem of free will a great deal easier.[12]

The Philosophical Problem of Free Will

Let us now return to the philosophical problem of free will. It is, of course, not the task of this work to prove the existence of free will, nor to analyze its nature. So the discussion will be limited to the question whether free will is possible even if all material activity takes place according to strictly deterministic laws. The question is justified; for whatever the nature of free will, it is quite clear that a free will can produce effects only through the medium of matter. This means that the activity of free will is to be realized in and by virtue of material activities. If the latter are, therefore, deterministic, how then can the will be free? Is not the functioning of free will entirely determined by the deterministic necessity of the material activities? The problem is difficult but not unsolvable.

---

[12]As pointed out previously, it must be said that scientists have also attempted to use the data of quantum mechanics for the solution of all kinds of philosophical problems. The danger of confusing degrees of abstraction always exists, and what has been won on one side is usually lost on another.

In working out the solution, it is necessary first to attempt to state as precisely as possible the difference between determinism and freedom with respect to human actions. What precisely is meant by saying that material activity is deterministic?

Determinism

The guiding principle in answering this question as to the essence of both determinism and freedom is as follows: Every being acts by necessity according to its nature. This general principle holds good for both human and non-human beings. The difference is that with non-human beings nature works, as it were, blindly. Given certain circumstances, the results follow by necessity. The activity is wholly determined by the nature and the actual situation. There is no *self*-determination in the sense that a material being, confronted with the possibilities of its nature and the given circumstances, is able to decide upon the course to be followed. There can be no self-*determination* because there is no self-*knowledge*. This complete lack of self-determination means that the determination of the activity depends entirely upon the given nature of the thing acting and the situation in which it acts. There is no choice save determinism. No material being can determine its own future, because it has no command of its own activity. Causal relationships in *matter* are, therefore, identical with deterministic relationships.

Determinism and Interaction

The deterministic character of material activity also explains another typical feature of that activity, namely, the fact that all material activity is essentially *inter*activity. If one material being acts upon another, then the latter necessarily reacts by virtue of its own nature. The circumstances have changed; therefore, it must act according to these changed circumstances. Its action in turn will change the circumstances of the "original" agent. Hence interactivity is a necessary result of deterministic activity.

The Essence of Free Will

With human beings the situation is entirely different. One of the characteristics of human nature is that it does not completely determine the individuality of its individual bearers. Each human person builds within the limits of human nature his own being, his own personality. This is possible because of the knowledge man has of what a human being is and what the ends are towards which his life can be directed. His free will enables him to direct his life toward that particular end toward which he believes his life should be directed. This end is not necessarily the same for other persons.[13] Free will is, therefore, the faculty of self-determination based upon self-knowledge. It is of importance to note that self-determination implies causality. Hence it is a serious misunderstanding to locate free human actions outside the field of causality merely because a type of causality which is different from that of a deterministic cause is met with. This point must be stressed, because many a philosopher wants to limit the term causality to deterministic causes only. This attitude is an unfortunate survival of the 19th century approach to the problem of causality.

It can be argued, of course, that anybody is free to determine his own terminology, but this is only partly true. A philosophical terminology should never distort reality nor unnecessarily violate general usage. General usage justly considers a human being as the cause of his free actions. By using the term "cause" with respect to both human and material activity, the fact is stressed that both activities have so much in common that the one cannot be understood independently from the other. As a matter of fact, even within the realm of science human causal influence plays an important role. For the typical feature of an experiment is that the phenomenon under observation is subject to circumstances which the experimenter has consciously created. The particular circumstances of the experiment are due to the causal influence of the experimenter. Therefore, if any one desires to reserve the term "cause" to material activity alone, then he will need a new term to express the common element in human and material activity. And even if this new term avoided the *word* "causality," it would not take away the close connection which the human mind always sees between material causality and "causality in general." For the causality of free will differs only analogously from that of a material thing, just as the finality of both differs analogously.[14]

---

[13]We abstract from the problem of moral freedom.
[14]See pp. 170 f.

Limitation of Free Will

It is clear that the faculty of self-determination which is called free will is not unlimited with respect to its freedom. This freedom is limited, first, by the limited possibilities of human nature in general, and secondly, by the individual realization of human nature in a particular person. To become an artist may be possible for human beings in general, but not for me, given my individual capacities.

The limitations mentioned here are closely connected with the fact that matter enters into the composition of man. And the exact problem is whether or not this bond with matter makes human freedom entirely illusory. For a human body is made up of matter, and this matter has its own physical and chemical nature. Therefore, if absolute determinism in matter exists, does it not then follow that the course of events in a human body is entirely determined, so that no influence of free will can alter it? If the answer to this question is "yes," then free will can only be an illusion. The implication is that a man *thinks* that *he* determines his own actions, but this determination is in its turn entirely determined by forces beyond his control. The ends that were apparently freely chosen are the necessary result of certain material forces in him. The problem is clear: Does the limitation of free will by the material structure of the body go so far as to eliminate freedom entirely? Formerly most scientists did not hesitate to say that it did. Nowadays, however, after the development of quantum mechanics, most of them think that determinism in matter is not absolute. Thus they believe that free will is possible. Quantum mechanics, however, does not authorize this belief in the absence of an absolute determinism. So the question as to whether or not determinism in matter eliminates free will is still unanswered.

Determinism Alone Does Not Exclude Free Will

In the discussion of the problem of free will and determinism, it is necessary to realize that the *main* reason why scientists formerly had difficulty with the problem of free will was not so much because of the theory of determinism in matter. It was rather the corollary that the whole universe must be conceived as *one mechanical* system. This conception leaves no place for such a thing as free will. If, however, both the qualifications of the universe, namely, that it must be *one* system and that it is a *mechanical* system, are dropped—neither of these being the necessary consequences of classical science—then the difficulty can easily be solved. First, if the idea that the universe is just *one* system is dropped, then there can be *several* more or less mutually independent systems which will naturally interact, though only in an accidental way. This means that the interaction is not entirely dominated by *one* structural principle which regulates the activities of all systems as if these were only parts of a whole.

Secondly, if all existing material beings are not necessarily mechanical systems, then there is the possibilty that not all these beings will act in essentially the same way.

Let us now consider more in detail what the elimination of both these unnecessary qualifications of the universe means with respect to free will.

The Universe Is Not a Substantial Unity

The absence of one regulating structural principle in the universe, the absence of a kind of universal substantial form, to use an Aristotelian expression, has important consequences. Several mutually independent systems can exist. In each system, if it is a purely material system, determinism exists. As a consequence, the future of such a system is entirely determined by the nature and the situation of that system, provided no external cause, i.e. no cause from outside the system, intrudes. Such an intrusion would not, of course, suspend determinism. For the effect of that external cause upon the system would be deterministic, for the simple reason that any reaction of the system is deterministic. But the future of the system would not be **entirely determined by its nature and situation.**

The possibility of the intrusion of an external cause makes it perfectly clear that the essence of determinism is *not* that the future of a certain system in which determinism exists should always be fully determined. It could be fully determined only if no external causes existed. So the essence of determinism is that all the activity of a system be a necessary result of the nature and the situation of that system. Determininism does not say, however, that all circumstances of a certain situation are themselves the result of deterministic causes. Thus the effect of an external cause can be deterministic in a given system, whereas the external cause does not *necessarily* have to belong to a deterministic system. A human hand, regulating the speed of an engine, for example, undoubtedly has a deterministic effect on that engine. Yet this does not imply that the human hand itself belongs to a deterministic system. This leads to the all-important conclusion that there can be complete determininism in material systems without there being any necessity of determinism in the universe as a whole.

It can be argued, of course, that if all existing systems were deterministic, then all possible external causes would also be deterministic. In other words, any cause that is external with respect to a certain system is supposed to belong to a deterministic system. Its intrusion into another system would be a necessary result of the determininistic activity of its own system. Therefore, if only purely material and, therefore, deterministic systems existed in the universe, then all interactions between these systems would be deterministic too.

This brings up the second problem, namely whether or not all existing systems in the material universe are deterministic systems.

The answer must be negative, because human beings have free will and are, therefore, not deterministic systems. Only if one arbitrarily limited all causality to deterministic causality would the conclusion follow that all external causes acting upon deterministic systems must themselves be deterministic. Causality is, however, a broader concept than determinism. Free beings can be active in the universe and intrude into the deterministic systems which exist there. This simple answer settles the question as to whether the universe as a whole should be considered deterministic. There are human beings in that universe and, therefore, the total universe is not deterministic. In the universe, both deterministic and free beings exist. Therefore, the universe is not just *one* substantial unity.

Free Will and Determinism in One Being

The greatest difficulty involved in the acceptance of the idea that both freedom and determinism can at the same time exist in the universe does not lie in the fact that human beings dwell among deterministic material systems. Deterministic and free beings can exist together in the same universe. The real difficulty is in the nature of human beings themselves. The material components which form the human body obey exactly the same laws as does all other matter. At least, that is the generally accepted opinion among scientists, based upon very plausible, if not conclusive, experimental evidence. If all material activity outside the human body is entirely deterministic, how is it possible that these same physical and chemical laws in a human body do not result in making human action deterministic? How can human beings have a free will, if all actions of that free will are the actions of a deterministic human body?

The answer to this question is that a human being is more than just a human body, i. e. more than a chemico-physical system. Such a system undoubtedly exists, and science can study it. However, by studying this system science comes upon a cause which, from the point of view of science, seems to be external. This seemingly external cause constantly intrudes upon and regulates the chemico-physical system. The regulation takes place, of course, in such a way that physico-chemical laws are not violated.

The determinism included in these laws is never disregarded, just as the hand regulating an engine always respects the deterministic laws which govern the functions of the engine. The engine does not cease to be a deterministic system because there is a regulating hand from outside. The way the hand works means that the engine *plus* the hand is not a deterministic system. But the engine itself remains what it is—a deterministic system.

In the human body the situation is, of course, different. That which, considered from the one-sided view of science, seems to be an external cause, is, as a matter of fact, an internal cause which belongs to the nature of the system itself. Free will is, in reality, a source of activity flowing directly from the spiritual organization principle of the human body, a principle of a higher order than that of purely material organization forms. Because it is a principle of higher order, the way in which it regulates human activity by means of free will gives science the impression that an external cause is continually intruding into the material system. The strange thing about that external cause is that it does not seem to belong to any material system. However, this latter conclusion is only partly correct because the cause is undoubtedly present in a material system, though not in a purely material way. It belongs to a material system, but by its very presence it lifts the status of a human body to a higher order than that which a purely material system possesses. Briefly, it makes a human body a human being.

Physical science can never study a human being in all his aspects for the simple reason that it can examine only his physical aspects. These aspects seem to be entirely deterministic, and they are indeed so. On the other hand, science also notices a continuous activity of an apparently external cause in the physico-chemical system. It notices the effects of this cause without being able to determine its true character. The functioning of this cause clearly shows, however, that the physico-chemical system of a human body is not only a physico-chemical system. There are continuous intrusions originating neither in the physico-chemical system of the human body nor in the physical environment of that body.

So it is possible that the physico-chemical system of a human body is entirely deterministic, whereas existing reality as a whole, namely, the human being, is not deterministic.

Free Will and Conservation of Energy

It is clear that the very fact of the existence of determinism in matter also limits the freedom of the will. The discussion of the forms in which these limitations express themselves lies, however, outside the scope of this book. Only one problem, which always arises when free will is under discussion, will be mentioned: namely, the problem of the conservation of energy.

It has been said that the existence of free will is incompatible with the laws of the conservation of energy. Free will would be a kind of creative source of activity in matter, and so would increase the total energy. Since there is experimental evidence that human actions are also subject to the law of the conservation of energy, free will would seem to be impossible.

The error in this argument is quite obvious for anyone who has some understanding of the nature of free will. Free will is not a creative source of *physical* energy. It is simply a principle within a material body which directs its energy. All free-will actions, insofar as these actions are realized in matter, are subject to material laws. Therefore, if an act of free will needs physical energy, then that energy had to be produced according to physical laws. There can be no doubt about that.

It can be argued, however, that directing energy also takes energy. It may be that the energy the hand needs to regulate an engine is negligible with respect to the energy needed for the operation of the engine itself, but nevertheless the hand needs energy. So does the free will. Where does this directing energy come from? The answer is quite simple. Not that it is simple to know how free will operates in directing muscles for instance, but it is clear that if there is energy needed for such a process this energy must be supplied by physical and chemical reactions. This necessity, however, makes the action of free will not an exclusively deterministic process. It shows only that there is a partial determinism.

This discussion of free will and determinism may be concluded with one remark of a more or less terminological character. It is customary to speak of the "determinism of nature" or the "determinism of matter." This way of speaking is dangerous because it suggests that nature as a whole or all matter together is just *one* deterministic system. That is not true. Human beings undoubtedly belong to nature and to the material world. This very fact limits determinism in nature and in matter. The presence in the material world of human beings with their free will lifts the material world as a whole above the level of pure determinism.

6. CONCLUSION

The discussion in the present chapter has dealt mainly with the consequences which quantum mechanics is supposed to have for the problems of causality, determinism, and free will. It has been seen that these supposed consequences do not exist. The erroneous idea that these exist stems from too narrow, and therefore wrong, definitions of causality, determinism, and free will. These erroneous definitions are the result of an understandable, but nevertheless unfortunate, desire to treat philosophical definitions as if they were identical with scientific definitions. It is unfortunate that philosophical definitions are analogous and, as a consequence, very general and not immediately helpful in solving concrete scientific problems, but this does not give the scientist the right to ignore the philosophical character of the definitions involved. The result can only be misunderstanding and confusion. Neither philosophy nor science gains anything by such an attitude of scientists.

The fact that material activity is a deterministic causality is important for the knowledge of the *general* nature of matter, but it does not solve any *specific* scientific problem. It does not yield any scientic law. Scientific laws presuppose deterministic causality in material phenomena, but the specific content of these laws is not in the least determined by that presupposition. If a scientist, nevertheless, tries to use the concepts of causality and determinism to arrive at a specific scientific law, his attempt will be a failure. And what is still worse, he will lose sight of the philosophical importance of the concepts involved. What then is the reason that scientists speak so often about determinism and causality? The reason is that deterministic causality is constantly in the mind of the scientist, prescisely because of the fact that it is a presupposition of every scientific law. This makes it understandable why the scientist desires to discuss causality. It is also understandable why he desires to treat this concept as if it were a scientific concept, why he tries to give it a specific content within the body of science. For that is the only way he can handle it as a scientist. Hence the fact that the 19th century scientist tied up the concept of causality with that of the way a mechanical system works.

On the other hand, the general philosophical character of the concept of causality was so obvious that the philosophical problems connected with causality could not be separated from it. This explains why the 19th century scientist discussed the problem of free will in terms borrowed from those which were useful in his description of a mechanical system. Hence the supposition that quantum mechanics, which is essentially a scientific theory and as such is an improvement upon classical mechanics, ought to be of great importance for the philosophical discussion of the problems of causality, determinism, and free will. In reality, however, the contribution of quantum mechanics to these problems was only incidental.

SUGGESTED READINGS

David Hume, *A Treatise of Human Nature*, Bk. I, Part III.

P. Henry Van Laer, *Philosophico-Scientific Problems*, Pittsburgh, 1953, Chapters V and VI.

Henry Margenau, *The Nature of Physical Reality*, New York, 1950, Chapters 17-19.

N. Bohr, *Discussion with Einstein on Epistemological Problems in Atomic Physics*, in *Albert Einstein: Philosopher-Scientist*, New York, 1951.

L. de Broglie, *La physique quantique restera-t-elle indeterministe?*, Paris, 1953.

CHAPTER EIGHT

EPILOGUE

Now that the end of the discussion of the philosophy of nature has been reached, it is worthwhile to view in retrospect some of the main problems which again and again came up for discussion or which implicitly were in other problems.

Such a problem, for instance, was the relationship between the philosophy of nature and science. In the first three chapters, where the discussion chiefly centered around this problem, several formulae were proposed in order to illustrate from different angles the relationship between science and the philosophy of nature. It was said that the philosophy of nature has the task of discussing the general or generic nature of matter, whereas science examines the specific nature of each particular kind of matter or material phenomenon. This formula has some merit insofar as it clearly points out that both the philosophy of nature and science deal with the essence of matter. But it does not escape the fate of all philosophical formulae, namely, that it provokes at least as many misunderstandings as it makes clarifications. One of these misunderstandings is that the terms *specific* and *generic* suggest the idea that science and the philosophy of nature work on the same level of abstraction, whereas these levels are actually different. Science does not start at the point where the general considerations of the philosophy of nature end. Nor does the philosophy of nature summarize in a general way the specific results of science. Science and the philosophy of nature both go their separate ways in complete autonomy. They abstract essentially different aspects from pre-scientific knowledge.

And this leads to a second formula which we have used to describe the difference between science and the philosophy of nature. The philosophy of nature analyzes the primary aspects of pre-scientific knowledge, i.e. those aspects which are present in the content of any experience and which reveal, therefore, the basic character of matter. Science, on the other hand, examines those aspects which differ specifically from experience to experience and which can be analyzed by experimental methods only.

Closely related to this formula is another which assigns to the philosophy of nature the task of examining the presuppositions of science insofar as these presuppositions deal with the general nature of matter and of material phenomena. Many times when a philosophical analysis was attacked in the name of science, this third formula proved very useful because it enabled a check to be made of the genuineness of the primary aspects upon which a philosophical analysis was based.

Again and again the conclusion was reached that the so-called philosophical consequences of science did not exist; they were based upon a misunderstanding of certain terms or upon a confusion between science itself and the philosophical background against which the scientist unconsciously projected his science.

The fact that science itself never leads to philosophical consequences confirms the ideas developed in Chapter III about the differences in degrees of abstraction existing between science and the philosophy of nature. Both *scientiae* work on a different level; consequently, their results do not interfere with one another.

This difference in degrees of abstraction does not mean that the philosophy of nature and science have no relationships at all. For the philosophy of nature studies those aspects of material being which science implicitly presupposes. This fundamental truth was expressed by saying that an implicit philosophical view of matter is incarnated in the basic methods of science. So scientific knowledge is at the same time complete and incomplete. It is *complete* because the specific knowledge of matter implicitly contains a philosophical knowledge of matter. The latter knowledge always remains implicit on the scientific level of abstraction, because every attempt to make it explicit requires a transgression of the very methods of science. In this sense, scientific knowledge is essentially *incomplete*. In this sense, scientific knowledge needs to be completed by a philosophical reflection.

Such a philosophical reflection has been attempted in the preceding chapters on the basis of an Aristotelian philosophy of nature. The interesting result has been that this philosophy has proved to be extremely well fitted for the philosophical needs of modern science. Modern science needs a philosophical concept of matter that can explain the radical changes which occur in matter, changes so radical that no material entity has a permanent existence. On the other hand, all changes take place according to definite patterns. These facts lead to the same concept of matter as Aristotle developed in his hylomorphistic doctrine.

An effort was also made in this study to point out how other basic views on matter, which are revealed by the way science works, are shared by Aristotle's philosophy of nature. It again confirms the possibility of developing a satisfactory philosophy of nature on the basis of our primary knowledge of matter. Otherwise Aristotle could not have developed his philosophy, long before modern science was born.

In conclusion, one important point must be stressed. It was said that scientific knowledge is at the same time complete and incomplete. It is incomplete because of the fact that the philosophical outlook on matter is only implicit. So the conclusion may seem obvious that a combination of philosophical and scientific knowledge gives a *complete* knowledge of material reality. This conclusion, however, does not follow. It is true that philosophy attempts to make explicit what is implicit only in science, but that attempt will never fully succeed. For philosophy has to work with analogous concepts, i.e. with concepts which can be used beyond the field for which they were originally devised. But that use is essentially limited. In an analogous concept something more is present than can be conceptualized. As a result, philosophical knowledge always points beyond what is known explicitly. It is forever striving to make explicit what in scientific and other knowledge remains entirely implicit. But that effort is essentially a motion towards an act which it will never reach. Philosophy is a desire for wisdom, never wisdom.

INDEX OF NAMES

INDEX OF SUBJECT MATTER